Second Edition

UT CLASSROOM TRAINING BOOK

Includes Guided Wave Method

Written for ASNT by:

Paul T. Marks
NDT Training Center

The American Society
for Nondestructive Testing

Second Edition
first printing 02/15
second printing 04/16 with corrections
third printing 06/18 with corrections
fourth printing 01/20
fifth printing 08/21 with corrections
ebook 08/21

Errata, if available for this printing, may be obtained from ASNT's website, asnt.org. Ebooks contain all corrections and updates, including the latest errata.

ISBN: 978-1-57117-345-4 (print)
ISBN: 978-1-57117-349-2 (ebook)

Printed in the United States of America

Published by:
The American Society for Nondestructive Testing Inc.
1711 Arlingate Lane
Columbus, OH 43228-0518
asnt.org

Edited by: Bob Conklin, Educational Materials Editor
Assisted by: Cynthia M. Leeman, Educational Materials Supervisor
Joy Grimm, Production Manager
Tim Jones, Senior Manager of Publications

ASNT Mission Statement:
ASNT exists to create a safer world by advancing scientific, engineering, and technical knowledge in the field of nondestructive testing.

ASNT *Code of Ethics*:
The ASNT *Code of Ethics* was developed to provide members of the Society with broad ethical statements to guide their professional lives. In spirit and in word, each ASNT member is responsible for knowing and adhering to the values and standards set forth in the Society's Code. More information, as well as the complete version of the *Code of Ethics*, can be found on ASNT's website, asnt.org.

Acknowledgments

The American Society for Nondestructive Testing, Inc. is grateful for the volunteer contributions, technical expertise, knowledge, and dedication of the following individuals who assisted with this edition of the Ultrasonic Testing Student and Instructor Packages, which include the Student/Lecture Guides and Instructor PowerPoint™ Presentation in addition to the Classroom Training Book:

Yoseph Bar-Cohen – Jet Propulsion Laboratory
Carter L. Bohn – Fish & Associates, Inc.
John Brunk
James B. Elder III – Savannah River National Laboratory
Nat Y. Faransso – KBR
Philip E. Fish – Fish & Associates, Inc.
Jerry Fulin – Fugro Consultants, Inc.
Vladimir Genis – Drexel University
Antonio Giorgi, Jr. – Ellwood City Forge Company
Xuefei Guan – Siemens
William Hardy – Fish & Associates, Inc.
Donald E. Harvey – Harvey NDE Services, LLC
Danny L. Keck – BP America
Donald D. Locke – HELLIER
David A. Mandina – Mandina's Inspection Services, Inc.
Thomas E. McConomy – ATI Allvac
Scott D. Miller
Ronald T. Nisbet – QualSpec
Robert F. Plumstead
Robert L. Saunders – Ellwood City Forge Company
Curtis Schroeder – Fish & Associates, Inc.
Ronald M. Schuna – Kakivik Asset Management, LLC
Krutik Dilip Shah – DK Shah NDT Training Institute
Gilbert Torres, Jr. – Apex NDT Training Services
Phillip W. Trach – Laboratory Testing, Inc.
Robert J. Woodward – Industrial Process Group

The Publications Review Committee includes:

Glenn M. Light, Chair – Southwest Research Institute
Martin T. Anderson – Alaska Technical Training
Joseph L. Mackin – Reel Group

Foreword

Purpose

The American Society for Nondestructive Testing, Inc. (ASNT) has prepared this series of Personnel Training Publications to provide an overview in a classroom setting of a given nondestructive testing method. Each classroom training book in the series is organized to follow the body of knowledge found in *ANSI/ASNT CP-105: ASNT Standard Topical Outlines for Qualification of Nondestructive Testing Personnel* (2011). Level I and Level II candidates should use this classroom training book as a preparation tool for nondestructive testing certification. Note, however, that an ASNT NDT Level I or Level II may be expected to know additional information based on industry or employer requirements.

Supplementary Material

Although the classroom training book may be purchased and read as a standalone product, it is intended to be used in conjunction with the Lecture Guide and PowerPoint presentation for instructors and Student Guide for students. These guides contain a condensed version of the material in the classroom training book and quiz questions per chapter (lesson) for review purposes.

Additional Information

The ultrasonic testing method includes two specific techniques: phased array and time of flight diffraction. Each technique provides information in specific material testing applications that conventional ultrasonic testing may not be able to provide in the same test situation. In *Recommended Practice No. SNT-TC-1A: Personnel Qualification and Certification in Nondestructive Testing* (2011), guided wave is considered a method in its own right and is treated as such in this classroom training book.

Changes to This Edition

The second edition builds on the first edition written by Paul T. Marks of the NDT Training & Testing Center based in Houston, TX. Changes to this edition are as follows:

New chapters are included on phased array, time of flight diffraction, and guided wave. *Note:* Chapter 10 from the first edition on transducer characteristics has been eliminated due to its covering advanced material not found in the Level I and II topical outlines of *CP-105* (2011). All questions in the Student/Lecture guides are now multiple-choice with four unique answers to more closely match ASNT exam format.

Contents

LEVEL >I

1

Introduction to Ultrasonic Testing

Introduction

The complexity and expense of today's machines, equipment, and tools dictate fabrication and testing procedures that ensure maximum reliability. To achieve this reliability, test specifications are set and test results must meet established criteria. Of the number of nondestructive testing procedures available, ultrasonic testing is one of the most widely used. The test method is regularly used to measure the thickness or to examine the internal structure of a material for possible discontinuities, such as voids and cracks.

The purpose of this classroom training book is to provide the fundamental knowledge of ultrasonic testing required by quality assurance and test personnel to enable them to:

- ascertain that the proper test technique, or combination of techniques, is used to ensure the quality of the finished product;
- interpret, evaluate, and make a sound decision as to the results of the test; and
- recognize those areas exhibiting doubtful test results that require either retesting or assistance in interpretation and testing.

Definition of Ultrasonics

Ultrasonics is the study and application of sound waves having frequencies higher than the human ear can hear. Traditionally, ultrasound begins at 20 000 cycles per second (20 kHz). In comparison, the frequencies used for testing materials are significantly higher.

Ultrasonic testing frequencies commonly range from 50 000 cycles per second (50 kHz) to 25 000 000 cycles per second (25 MHz). Applications have been developed that use frequencies in the range of 400 MHz for testing laminated materials.

As a nondestructive testing method, ultrasonic testing uses ultrasonic waves to test materials without destroying them.

History of Ultrasonic Testing

For centuries, objects were tested by hitting them with a mallet and listening for a difference in tonal quality. Around 1900, railroad workers tested rails using a combination of liquid penetrant and resonance testing. Objects were tested by applying kerosene to the object and covering it with a coat of whiting. Then the object was struck with a mallet. In areas where the whiting looked wet, the object was assumed to be cracked. In the early 1940s, Floyd Firestone developed the first pulse-echo instrument for detecting deep-seated discontinuities. The establishment of basic standards and the first practical immersion testing system are credited to William Hitt and Donald Erdman.

John William Strutt (Lord Rayleigh) was the first to describe fundamental principles of sound in a treatise published in 1870. In 1880, Pierre and Jacques Curie were the first to demonstrate the piezoelectric effect and in 1881 Gabriel Lippman extended their discoveries. The generation and detection of sound wave frequencies required for discontinuity detection as we know it today was made possible by the work of the Curie brothers and Lippman.

In the early 1970s, many advances were made in the technology related to nondestructive testing equipment that created an increased ability to detect ever smaller discontinuities. The development of fracture mechanics assisted inspectors in determining a critical discontinuity size for various components. This allowed inspectors to set thresholds or sensitivity levels, which allowed for rejection of discontinuities of a given size (or greater) — relabeled defects or flaws — while enabling smaller detected discontinuities to continue in service when it could be established that they would not grow to a critical size. These needs led to the use of ultrasonic testing as both a detection method as well as an evaluation tool.

Ultrasonic testing is used to test a variety of both metallic and nonmetallic products, such as welds, forgings, castings, sheet, tubing, plastics (both fiber reinforced and unreinforced), and ceramics. Since ultrasonic testing is capable of economically revealing subsurface discontinuities (variations in material composition) in a variety of dissimilar materials, it is one of the most effective tools available to quality assurance personnel.

In recent years, a shift has been created in the interpretation of data. The integration of software into the collection of data has made for advancements in how the data is displayed or even saved for later interpretation and evaluation.

Basic Math Review

Most of the math required to understand the physics of ultrasound involves fairly simple equations. Math helps the technician understand the principles of ultrasound in terms of velocity, distance, and angles. The following is an example of how the principles and the supporting math are used to explain the characteristics of ultrasound.

Acoustic Formulas

Sound is produced by the mechanical vibration of particles in a material. When a sound wave travels in a material, the particles in the material vibrate around a fixed point at the same frequency as the sound wave. The particles do not travel with the wave but only react to the energy of

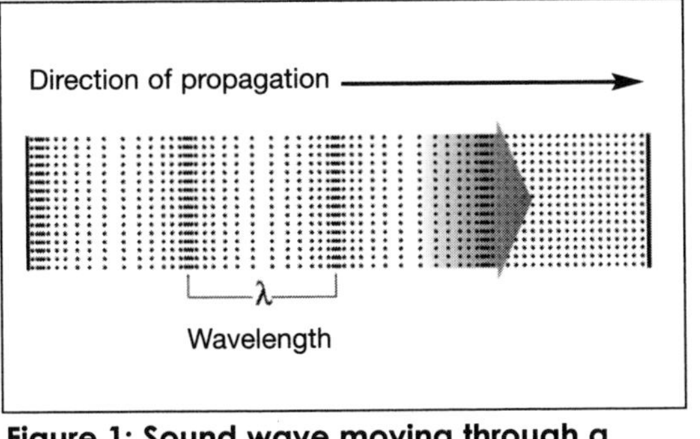

Figure 1: Sound wave moving through a material.

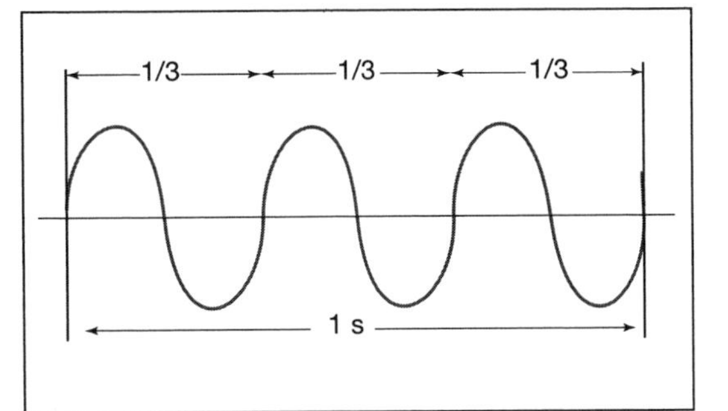

Figure 2: Length of sound wave from trough to trough. Three periods per second equals three cycles per second, or 3 Hz.

the wave. It is the energy of the wave that moves through the material. This concept is illustrated in Figure 1.

If the length of a particular sound wave is measured from trough to trough, or from crest to crest, the distance is always the same, as shown in Figure 2. This distance is known as the wavelength. The time it takes for the wave to travel a distance of one complete wavelength is the same amount of time it takes for the source to execute one complete vibration.

The velocity of sound V is given by Equation 1:

(Eq. 1) $$V = \lambda \times f$$

where

λ = the wavelength of the wave (most often expressed in millimeters)

V = the velocity of sound in the material being tested (most often expressed in kilometers per second)

f = the frequency of the wave (most often expressed in megahertz)

By performing a few simple algebraic manipulations to this formula, we can get the formula for wavelength (λ) and frequency (f) as shown in Equations 2 and 3.

(Eq. 2) $$\lambda = V / f$$

(Eq. 3) $$f = V / \lambda$$

The propagation of ultrasonic waves depends primarily upon material density and elasticity, and the wave mode. Table 1 shows typical sound velocities for materials that may be seen when performing ultrasonic inspections.

Table 1: Nominal material sound velocities.

MATERIAL	LONGITUDINAL WAVES		SHEAR WAVES	
	V_L = 10^3 in./s	V_L = m/s	V_S = 10^3 in./s	V_S = m/s
AIR	13	330	-----	-----
ALUMINUM, GALVANIZED	246	6250	122	3100
BARIUM TITANATE	217	5500	-----	-----
BERYLLIUM	504	12 800	343	8710
BRASS (NAVAL)	174	4430	83	2120
BRONZE (P-5%)	139	3530	88	2230
CAST IRON	177	4500	94	2400
COPPER	183	4660	89	2260
GLYCERINE	76	1920	-----	-----
LEAD, PURE	85	2160	28	0700
MAGNESIUM, AM 35	228	5790	122	3100
MOLYBDENUM	248	6290	132	3350
NICKEL	222	5630	117	2960
PLASTIC (ACRYLIC RESIN-PLEXIGLASS)	105	2670	44	1120
POLYETHYLENE	60	1530	-----	-----
QUARTZ, FUSE	233	5930	148	3750
SILVER	142	3600	63	1590
STEEL	230	5850	127	3230
STAINLESS 302	223	5660	123	3120
STAINLESS 410	291	7390	118	2990
TIN	131	3320	66	1670
TITANIUM (T1 150A)	240	6100	123	3120
TUNGSTEN	204	5180	113	2870
WATER	59	1490	-----	-----
ZINC	164	4170	95	2410

Note: Values are approximate and may vary depending on the source of data; multipying a number *N* by $10^3 = N \times 1000$.

Order of Mathematical Operations

A useful acronym for remembering the order of mathematical operations is PEMDAS, which stands for parentheses, exponents, multiplication, division, addition, and subtraction.

- **Parenthesis** – groupings of numbers and/or variables using ( ) or [ ]. If parentheses are enclosed in other parenthesis, simplify the inside sets first and then move outward.
- **Exponents** – are performed next (unless inside parentheses). If the formula contains multiple exponents, these are performed from left to right. Examples include x^2, 2^3 and 10^4.
- **Multiplication and division** – when outside of parentheses, multiplication and division are of equal importance and performed from left to right.
- **Addition and subtraction** when outside of parentheses, addition and subtraction are of equal importance and performed from left to right.

Trigonometry

As shown in Figure 3, the right triangle is an essential part of the shear wave formulas you will be using to calculate the location of discontinuities. These formulations are based on sound path distance. Snell's law is used to calculate incident and refracted angles using the velocities of two dissimilar materials and is another reason to be familiar with trigonometry. Here is a brief overview of trigonometry based on the relationship of angles and sides as it relates to shear wave testing.

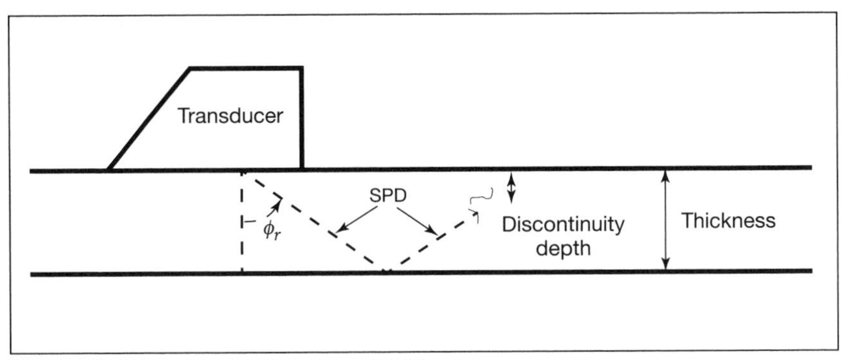

Figure 3: Sound-path distance (SPD).

Right Triangles

Refer to Figure 4 as you review the following:

1. All triangles are made up of three angles and three corresponding sides.
2. The sum of the three angles totals 180°.
3. In a right triangle, one angle is equal to 90° and, as a result, the sum of the other two angles must total 90°.
4. The length of a side is directly proportional to its corresponding angle; the greater the angle, the greater the length of its corresponding side.

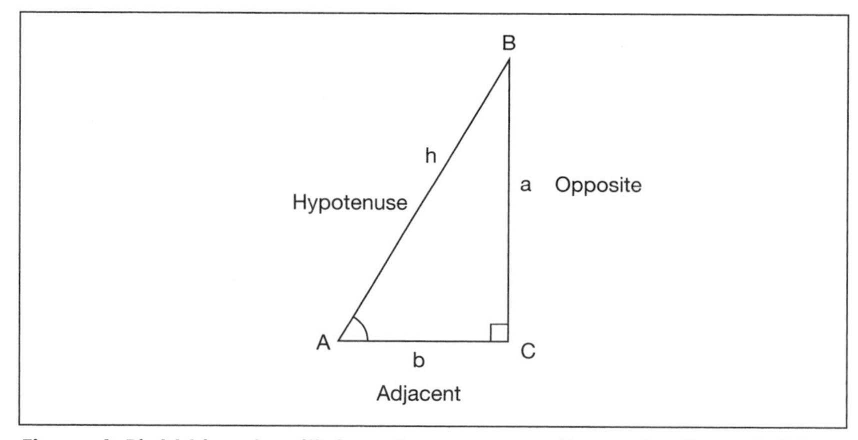

Figure 4: Right triangle with hypotenuse, opposite, and adjacent sides for angle A.

5. The side opposite the 90° angle is therefore the longest side and named the hypotenuse.
6. A side directly across from an angle is its opposite side.
7. A side that makes up an angle but is not the hypotenuse is called its adjacent side.

Sine, Cosine, and Tangent

The *sine, cosine,* and *tangent* of an angle are the ratios of the length of one side to the length of a related side as described below. The acronym SOH-CAH-TOA is a useful mnemonic device for these ratios.

S = O/H
C =A/H
T = O/A

where

S = sine (sin)
C = cosine (cos)
T = tangent (tan)
A = adjacent side (next to the angle but not the hypotenuse)
O = opposite side
H = hypotenuse (longest side)

Introducing Decibels

In most engineering-related problems, logarithmic scales rather than linear scales are used to compare two quantities. In various parts of this book, decibels (dB) are presented as an indication of a particular gain. The standard definition of decibel is a *logarithmic unit* that indicates the ratio of a physical quantity relative to a specified or implied reference level. For example, in ultrasonics, pressure ratios and intensity ratios are measured in decibels. Two formulas are used for calculating ratios in decibels.

The formula for calculating the ratio of *intensities* in decibels is:

(Eq. 4) $$\text{ratio in decibels (dB)} = 10\log_{10}\frac{J_1}{J_2}$$

where J_1 and J_2 are acoustic (ultrasonic) intensities. A similar formula is used for calculating the ratio of energies or powers in decibels.

In many NDT applications, the ratio of acoustic (ultrasonic) pressures is of interest. Since the intensity is proportional to the square of the acoustic pressure, the formula for calculating *pressure ratios* in decibels is:

(Eq. 5) $$\text{ratio in decibels (dB)} = 20\log_{10}\frac{p_1}{p_2}$$

where p_1 and p_2 are acoustic (ultrasonic) pressures. A similar formula is used for calculating the ratio of voltages and currents in decibels.

Here is an example of calculating the ratios of acoustic pressures in decibels. For example, if the ratio of acoustic pressures is 2, this would correspond to:

(Eq. 6) $$\begin{aligned}\text{ratio in decibels (dB)} &= 20\log_{10}\frac{p_1}{p_2}\\ &= 20\log_{10}2 = 6\text{ dB}\end{aligned}$$

If the ratio of acoustic pressures is 10, this would correspond to:

(Eq. 7) $$\begin{aligned}\text{ratio in decibels (dB)} &= 20\log_{10}\frac{p_1}{p_2}\\ &= 20\log_{10}10 = 20\text{ dB}\end{aligned}$$

Qualification

It is imperative that personnel responsible for ultrasonic testing are trained and highly qualified with a technical understanding of the test equipment and materials, the test object and the test procedures.

The American Society for Nondestructive Testing (ASNT) publishes guidelines for training and qualifying nondestructive testing personnel in *Recommended Practice No. SNT-TC-1A: Personnel Qualification and Certification in Nondestructive Testing.* This publication describes the responsibilities of nondestructive testing personnel in terms of certification levels.

Levels of Qualification

There are three basic levels of qualification applied to nondestructive testing personnel used by companies that follow *SNT-TC-1A*: Level I, Level II, and Level III.

An individual in the process of becoming qualified or certified in Level I ultrasonic testing is considered a trainee. A trainee does not independently conduct tests or interpret, evaluate, or report test results of any nondestructive testing method. A trainee works under the direct guidance of certified individuals.

Level I Responsibilities

Level I personnel are qualified to:

1. Perform specific calibrations, nondestructive tests, and evaluations for determining the acceptance or rejection of tested objects in accordance with specific written instructions.
2. Record test results. Normally, the Level I does not have the authority to sign off on the acceptance and completion of the nondestructive test unless specifically trained to do so with clearly written instructions.
3. Perform nondestructive testing job activities in accordance with written instructions or direct supervision from a Level II or Level III technician.

Level II Responsibilities

Level II personnel should be thoroughly familiar with the scope and limitations of each method for which the individual is certified. Level II personnel are qualified to:

1. Set up and calibrate equipment.
2. Interpret and evaluate results with respect to applicable codes, standards, and specifications.
3. Organize and report the results of nondestructive tests.
4. Exercise assigned responsibility for on-the-job training and guidance of Level I and trainee personnel.

Level III Responsibilities

Level III personnel are responsible for nondestructive testing operations to which they are assigned and for which they are certified. A Level III should be generally familiar with appropriate nondestructive testing methods other than those for which he or she is specifically certified, as demonstrated by passing an ASNT Level III Basic examination. In the methods for which he or she is certified, the Level III should be capable of training and examining Level I and Level II personnel for certification in those methods.

Level III personnel are qualified to:

1. Develop, qualify, and approve procedures.
2. Establish and approve nondestructive testing methods and techniques to be used by Level I and II personnel.
3. Interpret and evaluate test results in terms of applicable codes, standards, specifications, and procedures.

4. Assist in establishing acceptance criteria where none is available, based on a practical background in applicable materials, fabrication, and product technology.

Challenges

The major challenge facing nondestructive testing personnel is to learn all that can possibly be learned during the qualification process. After becoming certified, another challenge involves developing the mindset that there is something else to learn each time the nondestructive testing method is used. There is no substitute for knowledge and nondestructive testing personnel must be demanding of themselves. The work performed in the nondestructive testing field deserves the very best because of the direct consequence of either protecting or endangering life.

Certification

It is important to understand the difference between two terms that are often confused within the field of nondestructive testing: *qualification* and *certification*. Qualification is a process that should take place before a person can become certified.

According to *SNT-TC-1A*, the qualification process for any nondestructive testing method should involve:

1. Formal training in the fundamental principles and applications of the method.
2. Experience in the application of the method under the guidance of a certified individual (on-the-job training).
3. Demonstrated ability to pass written and practical (hands-on) tests that prove comprehensive understanding of the method and ability to perform actual tests by use of the specific nondestructive testing method.
4. The ability to pass a vision test for visual acuity and color perception.

The actual certification of a person in nondestructive testing to a Level I, Level II, or Level III is a written testament that the individual has been properly qualified. It should contain:

- the name of the individual being certified,
- identification of the method and level of certification, and
- the date and the name of the person issuing the certification.

Certification is meant to document the actual qualification of the individual.

Correct qualification and certification are extremely important because the process of testing performed by certified nondestructive testing personnel has a direct impact on the health and safety of every person who will work on, in, or in proximity to the assemblies being tested. Poor work performed by unqualified personnel can cost lives.

Modern fabrication and manufacturing projects challenge the strength and endurance of joining techniques, such as welding, and the materials of construction. Preventive maintenance activities also present a challenge to nondestructive testing personnel.

The industries that depend on nondestructive testing cannot tolerate testing personnel who are not thoroughly qualified. Too much depends on the judgments made in the work performed every day.

Employee Certification

Training

Training involves an organized program developed to provide test personnel with the knowledge and skill necessary for qualification in a specific area. This is typically performed in a classroom setting where the principles and techniques of the particular test method are reviewed. Online training is also available. The length of training required is stated in the employer's written practice.

Experience

Experience includes work activities accomplished in a particular test method under the supervision of a qualified and/or certified individual. This includes time spent setting up tests, performing calibrations and specific tests, and other related activities. Time spent in organized training programs does not count as experience. The length of experience required is stated in the employer's written practice.

Examination

Level I and Level II personnel are given written general and specific examinations, a practical examination, and a visual examination. The general examination covers the basic principles of the applicable method. The specific examination includes the procedures, equipment, and techniques that the employee will be required to perform in their job assignment. The practical (hands-on) examination allows employees to demonstrate their ability to operate the appropriate test equipment and to perform tests using that equipment in accordance with appropriate specifications. Level III personnel must pass written basic, method, and specific examinations. Testing requirements are stated in the employer's written practice.

Certification

Certification of nondestructive testing personnel is the responsibility of the employer. Personnel may be certified when they have completed the initial training, experience, and examination requirements described in the employer's written practice. The length of certification is also stated in the employer's written practice. All applicants must have documentation that states their qualifications according to the requirements of the written practice before certifications are issued.

Basic Principles of Acoustics

Nature of Sound Waves

When a tuning fork is struck, it vibrates and produces sound waves by compressing the air. These waves travel through air to the ear of the listener, as shown in Figure 1. The tuning fork vibrations soon die out and no longer produce waves.

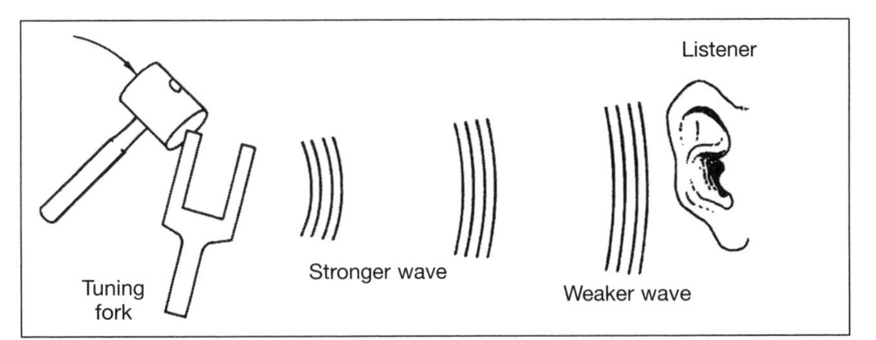

Figure 1: Sound-wave generation.

Similarly, in ultrasonic testing a short pulse of electrical current excites a transducer (crystal) that vibrates, as did the tuning fork. The sound beam from the transducer then travels through a couplant, which may be water or oil, to the front surface of the test object. Figure 2 shows

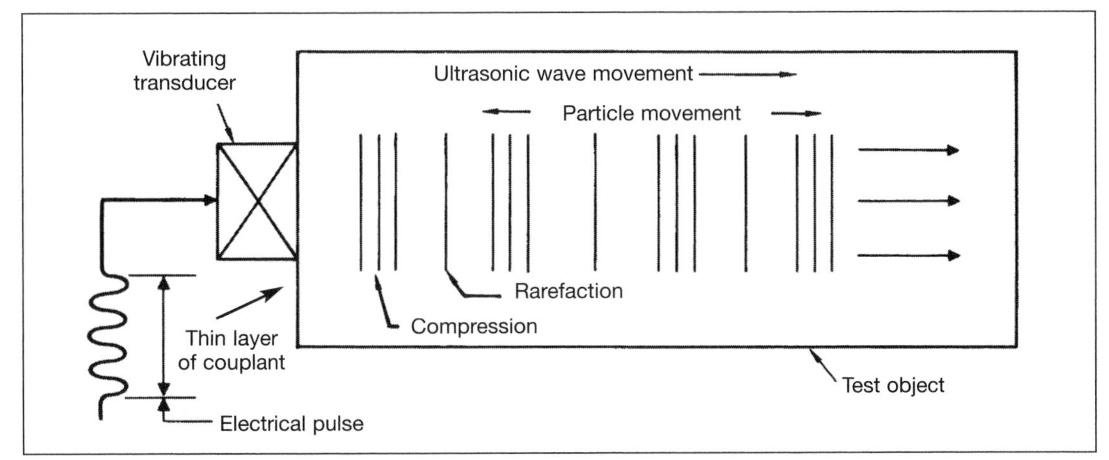

Figure 2: Ultrasonic wave generation.

the transducer in contact with the test object and the sound-beam pulses traveling through the test object.

Modes of Sound-Wave Generation

In general, all types of sound waves travel through solid matter. As a matter of fact, a solid is a much better carrier of sound energy than air because of its rigidity and density. Even a liquid, due to its greater density, is a more efficient carrier of sonic energy than air.

The sound waves used in ultrasonic testing are differentiated mainly by the type of vibrational motion set off within the particle structures that lie within the path of a given wave form. Two basic forms include:

- **Longitudinal waves** – also known as *compression waves*, where the particles of the matter vibrate back and forth in the same direction as the motion of the sound wave.
- **Shear waves** – also known as *transverse waves*, where the particles vibrate back and forth in a direction that is at right angles to the motion of the wave.

It is also possible to produce sound waves that travel along the free boundary (surface) of a solid. These are referred to as *surface waves* (or *rayleigh waves*) because they penetrate the material to a depth of about one wavelength and cause an undulating movement along the surface, much like a wave caused by a pebble dropped into a pond. A fourth wave mode is the *lamb wave*, also known as *plate wave*.

Propagation of Sound Energy

All materials are made of atoms linked by electromagnetic forces. Solid test objects usually have dense atomic structures compared to liquid and air, and also have degrees of resiliency that allow vibratory movement of the particles within a certain range.

Imagine a lattice where balls (atoms) are interconnected by springs (electromagnetic forces), as was shown in Figure 1 of Chapter 1. If the side of this lattice is struck, the first column of atoms exerts a force on the second column, which in turn exerts a force on the third column, and so on, in sequence. After each column of atoms is forced to move, it rebounds back in the other direction. This particle motion produces a wave movement in the direction away from the point where the energy was introduced. In the case shown in Figure 3, the particle movement is back and forth in a direction parallel to the direction of the energy traveling within the solid. As a sound wave, this type of motion is known as the *longitudinal-wave* (or *compression-wave) mode.*

Comparison of Wave Modes

Longitudinal-Wave Mode

Figure 4 shows two transducers generating ultrasonic waves in the same test object. Note that the transducer on the left is producing longitudinal waves. The back and forth vibration of particles, parallel to the direction of the wave, promotes efficient energy transfer. Longitudinal waves can

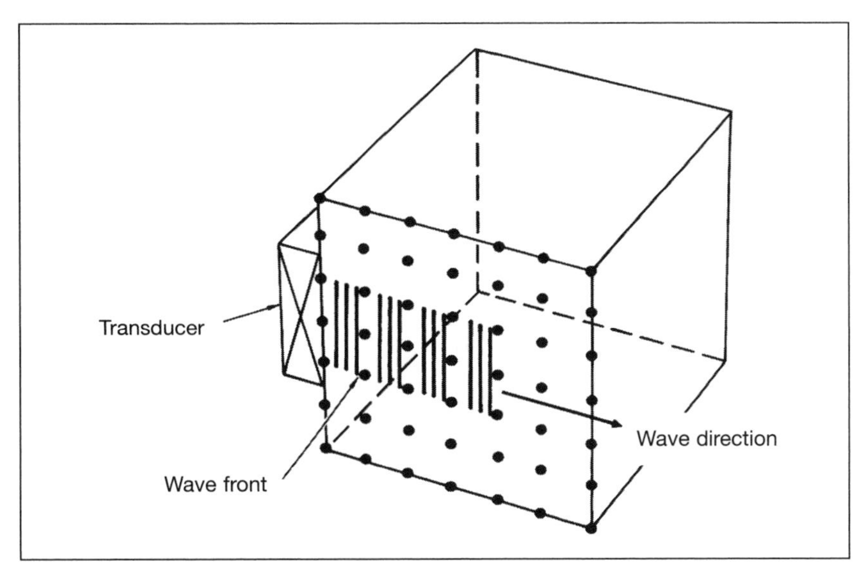

Figure 3: Longitudinal-wave mode.

be transmitted through solids, liquids and even gases, such as air. This is not true of the other modes of sound energy. Shear, surface, and plate waves can be transmitted only within a solid material.

Shear-Wave Mode

In Figure 4, the transducer on the right is producing a different kind of wave. This is called a *shear wave* because the direction of particle movement is at right angles to the direction of wave movement, otherwise referred to as the *direction of propagation*. The velocity of shear waves through a material is about half that of longitudinal waves. Note also that the right-hand transducer is mounted on a plastic wedge so that

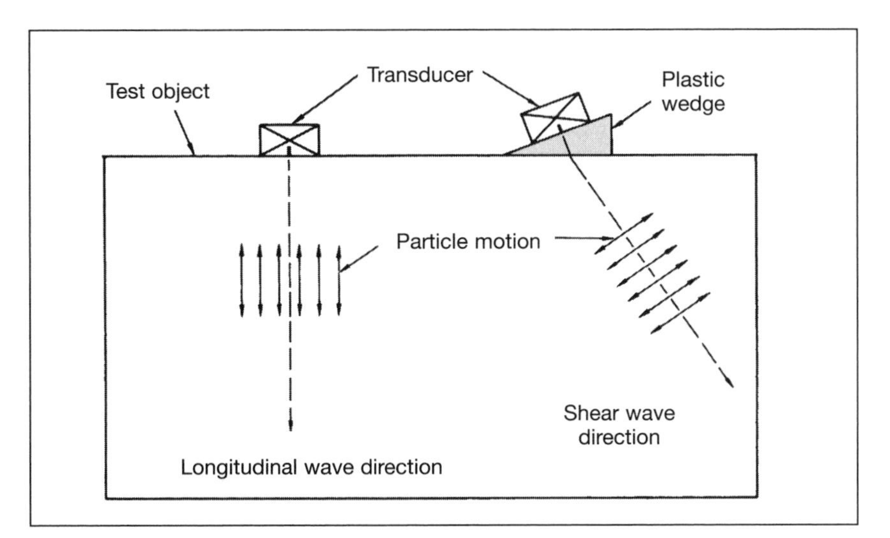

Figure 4: Longitudinal- and shear-wave modes compared.

the ultrasonic waves generated by the crystal enter the material at a specific angle. This specific angle, plus the velocity of the wave within the material, determines the angle of sound propagation.

Confusion may be encountered when angle-beam transducers, designed to produce a specific refracted angle in one kind of material, are applied to other materials with different acoustic velocities. A transducer designed to produce a shear wave beam at 45° in steel, for example, will produce a shear-wave beam at 43° in aluminum or 30° in copper.

Rayleigh-Wave Mode

A third type of wave is confined to a thin layer of particles on the free boundary of a solid material. Rayleigh waves travel over the surface of a solid and bear a rough resemblance to waves produced by a pebble dropped onto the surface of a pond. They were named for John William Strutt (Lord Rayleigh) because of his research on earthquakes and his identification of the rolling wave as the principal component of the energy waves that travel along the surface of the Earth.

Rayleigh waves, otherwise known as *surface waves*, are used extensively in ultrasonic testing applications. They travel at a velocity of 116 330 in. (295 478 cm) per second in steel compared to the shear-wave velocity of 127 000 in. (322 580 cm) per second. Thus, rayleigh waves travel in steel at 91.6% the velocity of shear waves, or 8.4% less. As shown in Figure 5, when a transducer is mounted on a steeply angled plastic wedge, the longitudinal beam in the wedge strikes the test surface at a high angle, producing a surface wave in the test object. As shown, a surface wave can travel around a curve.

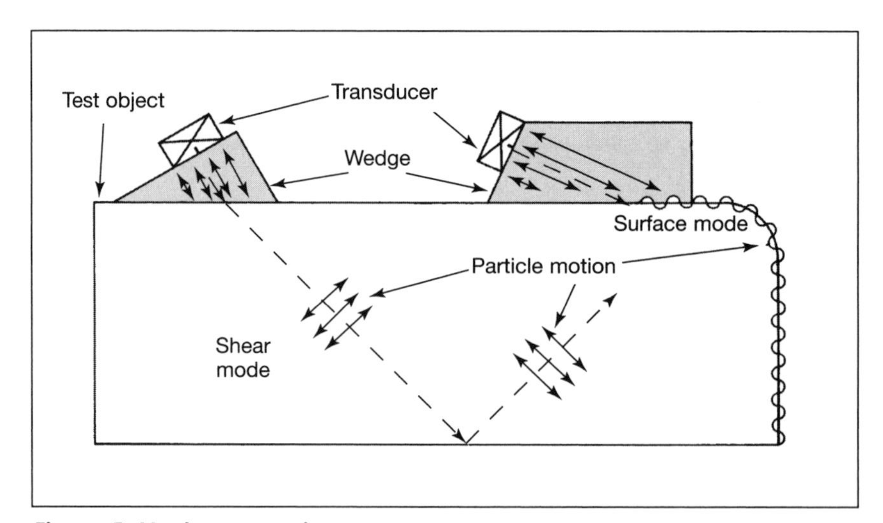

Figure 5: Mode conversion.

Reflection of the surface wave occurs only at a sharp corner or at a discontinuity. Figure 6 illustrates the elliptical particle motion within a rayleigh wave beam.

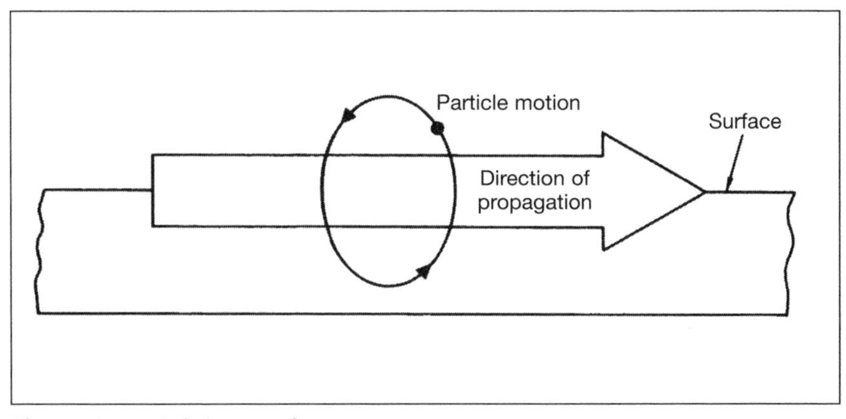

Figure 6: Rayleigh or surface waves.

Lamb Waves

If a surface wave is introduced into a material that has a thickness equal to three wavelengths or less of the ultrasound, a different kind of wave results. The material begins to vibrate as a plate because the wave encompasses the entire thickness of the material. When this occurs, the normal rules for wave velocity cease to apply. The velocity is no longer solely dependent on the type of material and the type of wave. Instead, a wave velocity is produced that is influenced by the frequency of the wave, in addition to the angle of incidence and the type of material. The theory describing lamb waves was developed by Horace Lamb in 1916, thus the name.

Lamb Wave Types

There are two general types of lamb (or plate) waves depending on the way the particles in the material move as the wave moves along the plate: symmetrical and asymmetrical. Both types are shown in Figure 7.

Lamb Wave Modes

Each type of lamb wave has an infinite number of modes that the wave may attain. These modes are dependent on three factors:

- Frequency of the wave.
- Angle of incidence.
- Type of material.

Lamb wave modes are differentiated by the manner in which the particles in the material are moving. Figure 7 illustrates the first mode, whereas Figure 8 illustrates the second and third modes.

The ability of lamb waves to flow in thin plates makes them applicable to a wide variety of problems requiring the detection of subsurface discontinuities. Mode 1 (Figure 7) does not reveal subsurface discontinuities because the energy is contained close to the surface of the medium, as with rayleigh waves. Where it is desirable that energy travels a considerable distance along the plate, or where detection of subsurface discontinuities is required, adjustments in applied frequency produce

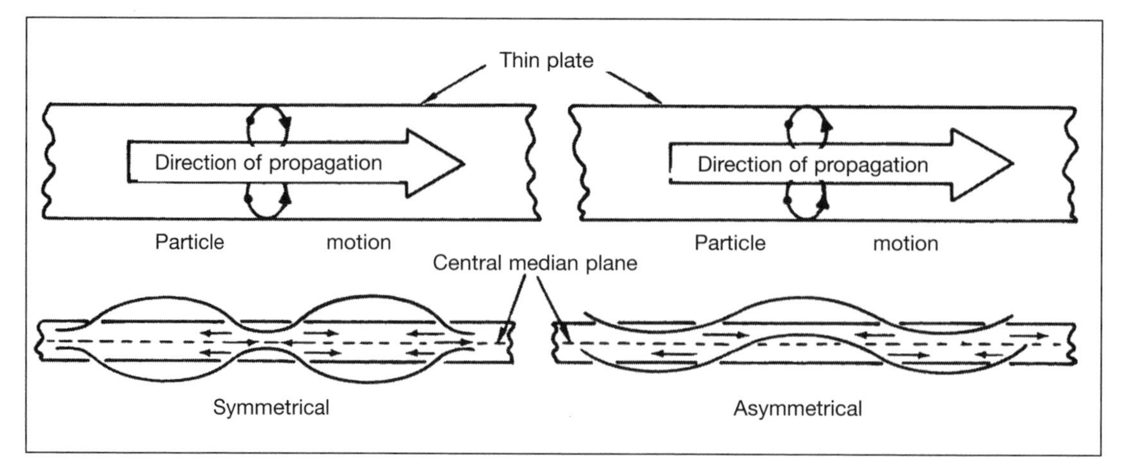

Figure 7: Symmetrical and asymmetrical lamb waves: mode 1.

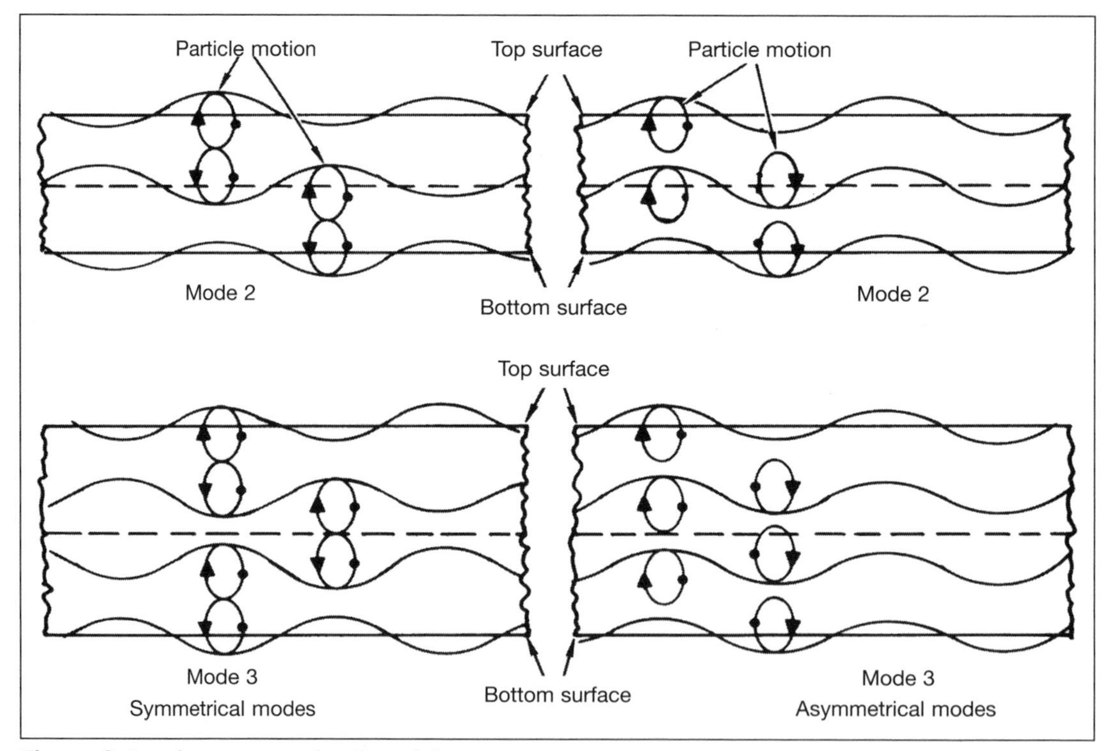

Figure 8: Lamb wave modes 2 and 3.

velocities near that of the longitudinal mode. These modes are useful for immersion testing of thin-walled tubing and plates for internal discontinuities or grain size determinations and testing of welds in thin plates and tubes.

Table 1 lists the modes produced by various incident angles when transmitting a 5 MHz ultrasonic beam into a 0.05 in. (1.3 mm) thick aluminum plate.

Table 1: Lamb-wave modes in aluminum.

Incident Angle	Mode Produced
33°	First asymmetrical
31°	First symmetrical
25.6°	Second asymmetrical
19.6°	Second symmetrical
14.7°	Third asymmetrical
12.6°	Third symmetrical
7.8°	Fourth symmetrical

Wave Reflection at a Boundary

Ultrasonic waves are analogous to light waves in the sense that they may be reflected, focused, and refracted. The high-frequency particle vibrations of sound waves are propagated in homogeneous solid objects in the same manner as a directed light beam passes through clear air. Sound beams are reflected (partially or totally) at any surface acting as a boundary between the object and a gas, liquid, or another type of solid. As with sonar, ultrasonic pulses reflect from discontinuities and enable detection and location of the interface.

Attenuation of Sound Waves

High-frequency ultrasonic waves passing through a material are reduced in power, or attenuated, by several mechanisms including reflection and scattering of the beams at the grain boundaries within the material and friction losses. Reflection and scattering losses are proportional to the grain volume in the material and the wavelength of the beam. Scattering losses are greatest where the wavelength is less than one third of the grain size. As the frequency is lowered and the wavelength becomes greater than the grain size, attenuation is caused partly by damping of the wave. In the case of damping, wave energy is lost through heat caused by friction of the vibrating particles.

Acoustical Impedance

Acoustical impedance is the resistance of a medium to the passage of sound waves. The impedance Z of any material may be computed by multiplying the density of the material ρ by the velocity of sound V through the material:

(Eq. 1) $$Z = \rho V$$

Air has a very low impedance to ultrasonic waves because it is low in density (ρ) and slow in velocity (V). The impedance of water is higher than the impedance of air. Solids, such as aluminum and steel, have even higher impedances.

Impedance Ratio

When a transducer is used to transmit an ultrasonic wave into a material, only part of the wave energy is transmitted; the rest is reflected from the surface of the material. Also, some amount of ultrasonic energy is reflected at the interface between two different materials as a sound beam passes from one to the other. How much of the sound beam is reflected depends on a factor called *acoustical impedance ratio*.

The acoustical impedance ratio between two materials is simply the acoustical impedance of one material divided by the acoustical impedance of the other material. When an ultrasonic beam passes from material A into material B, the impedance ratio is the impedance of the second material divided by the impedance of the first material. The higher the ratio, the more of the original energy will be reflected.

Since air has very small impedance, the impedance ratio between air and any liquid or solid material is very high; therefore, most, if not all, of the sound beam is reflected at the interface between air and any other material.

A high impedance ratio is often called *impedance mismatch*. For example, the impedance ratio for air-to-metal is about 115 000:1 (virtually 100% reflection); however, the impedance ratio for a liquid-to-metal interface is lower. For instance, the acoustic impedance values of water and steel are 0.148 and 4.616, respectively, making the impedance ratio about 31:1.

Reflection

Ultrasonic testing does not give direct information about the exact nature of the discontinuity. This is deduced from several factors, the most important being knowledge of the test object's material and construction. Ultrasonic waves are reflected from both the discontinuity and the back surface of the test object as echoes. The echo from the discontinuity is received before the back-surface reflection is received. These reflections may then be picked up by a second or, in many cases, by the same transducer, as shown in Figure 9.

The figure shows a situation where the time required for the sound beam to travel through the test object to the discontinuity and back is only two-thirds of the time required for the sound beam to reach the back surface and return. This time differential indicates that the discontinuity is located two-thirds of the distance to the back surface.

The distance that the sound beam travels to a reflecting surface can be measured on the display screen of the ultrasonic instrument, as shown in Figure 10. The initial pulse and the echo from the front surface of the test object produce the first two sharp indications that rise from the baseline of the instrument display screen. The distance between these two indications is proportional to the distance between the transducer and the front surface.

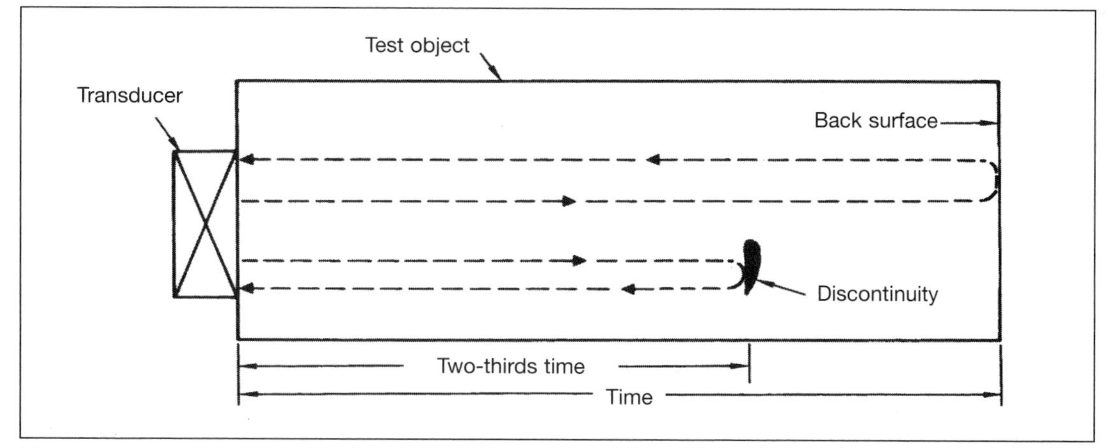

Figure 9: Sound-beam reflection.

Reflection Coefficient

Reflection (R) may be calculated by using the following formula for the intensity reflection coefficient:

(Eq. 2)
$$R = \frac{(Z_2 - Z_1)^2}{(Z_2 + Z_1)^2}$$

where Z_1 is the impedance value of the first material and Z_2 that of the second. Inserting the above values, a value of 88% reflection at the water-to-steel interface is obtained:

(Eq. 3)
$$R = \frac{(4.616 - 0.148)^2}{(4.616 + 0.148)^2} = \frac{4.468^2}{4.764^2} = \frac{19.963}{22.696} = 0.88$$

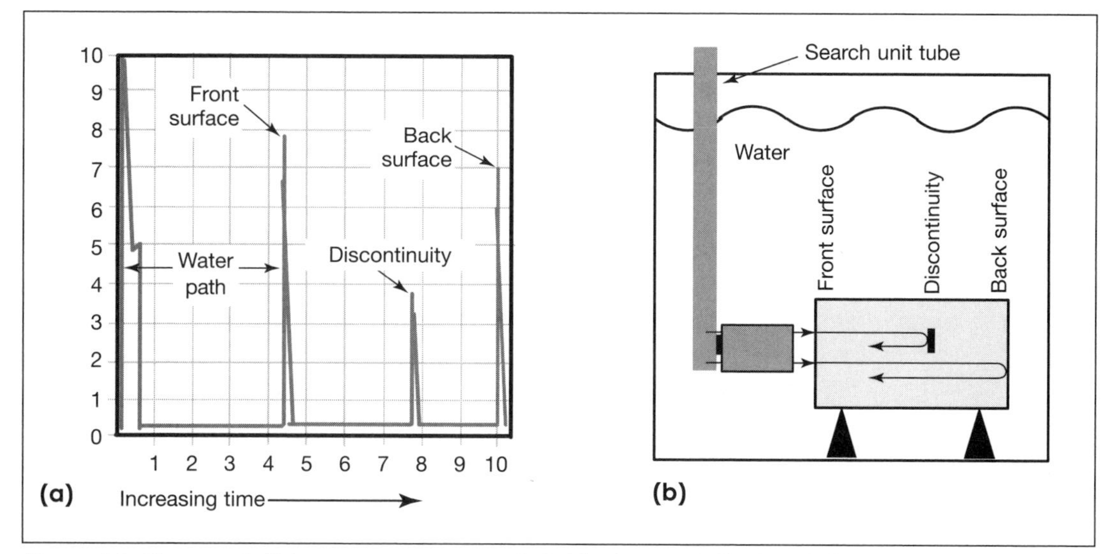

Figure 10: Time and distance measurement: (a) instrument display; (b) immersion tank.

The ability of ultrasound to detect features during testing is a function of the changes in acoustic impedance at interfaces. A related formula is used to calculate the pressure reflection coefficient (*R*) as follows:

(Eq. 4) $$R = \frac{(Z_2 - Z_1)}{(Z_2 + Z_1)}$$

An example of calculating the pressure reflection coefficient for water-to-air and water-to-steel interfaces would provide additional useful information about the reflection property of various materials. When students are asked which reflection coefficient is greater, water-to-air or water-to-steel, most students, if not all, intuitively answer water-to-steel. First, let's calculate the acoustical impedance of stainless steel (this data can be taken from a velocity and acoustical impedance table, such as Table 2 or 3). The unit for acoustical impedance is the *rayl.* We will use approximate data for the sake of illustration. The longitudinal sound velocity in stainless steel is about:

(Eq. 5) $$V_s = 5800 \text{ m/s}$$

The density of this material is:

(Eq. 6) $$\rho_s = 7800 \text{ kg/m}^3$$

Thus, the acoustical impedance of stainless steel is:

(Eq. 7) $$\begin{aligned} Z_s &= V_s \cdot \rho_s \\ &= 5800 \text{ m/s} \cdot 7800 \text{ kg/m}^3 \\ &= 45 \cdot 10^6 \text{ kg/m}^2 \cdot \text{s} \\ &= 45 \cdot 10^6 \text{ rayl} \\ &= 45 \text{ Mrayl} \end{aligned}$$

Using similar calculations, we find that the acoustical impedance of water is $Z_W = 1.5$ Mrayl and the acoustical impedance of air is $Z_A = 330$ rayl.

The pressure reflection coefficient for steel-to-water (or water-to-steel) interface is:

(Eq. 8) $$R = \frac{(Z_s - Z_w)}{(Z_s + Z_w)} = \frac{45 - 1.5}{45 + 1.5} = 0.935$$

Pressure reflection coefficient for water-to-air interface is:

(Eq. 9)
$$R = \frac{(Z_w - Z_A)}{(Z_w + Z_A)} = \frac{1\ 500\ 000 - 330}{1\ 500\ 000 + 330} = 0.999$$

The calculations above clearly indicate that the reflection of ultrasound wave by air bubbles in water is stronger that the reflection in water from steel. This provides an additional explanation why the use of ultrasound gel is necessary in contact testing.

Refraction and Mode Conversion

Refraction and mode conversion of the ultrasonic beam as it passes at an angle from one material to another is comparable to the refraction of light beams when passing from one medium to another.

Figure 11 shows a transducer inducing a longitudinal wave into water. The water transmits the beam to the test object. When the longitudinal sound beam is incident to the surface of the test object in the perpendicular direction, the beam is transmitted into the second medium as a 100% longitudinal beam and no refraction occurs.

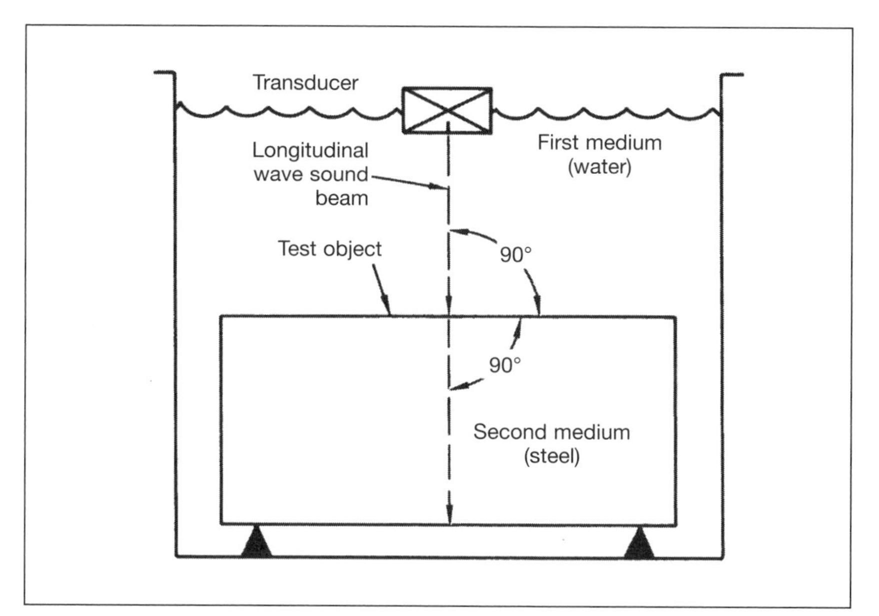

Figure 11: Normal (perpendicular) incident beam.

Mixed Mode Conversion

As shown in Figure 12, as the incident angle is changed from the initial 90° position, refraction and mode conversion occur. The original longitudinal beam is transmitted in the second medium as varying percentages of both longitudinal and shear wave beams. As shown, the refracted angle for the longitudinal wave beam is four times the incident angle and the shear wave beam angle is a little more than twice the incident angle. If the incident angle is rotated farther, the refraction angles of the longitudinal wave and the shear wave increase. The value of each refracted beam varies in the test object as the angle of incidence in the first medium is changed.

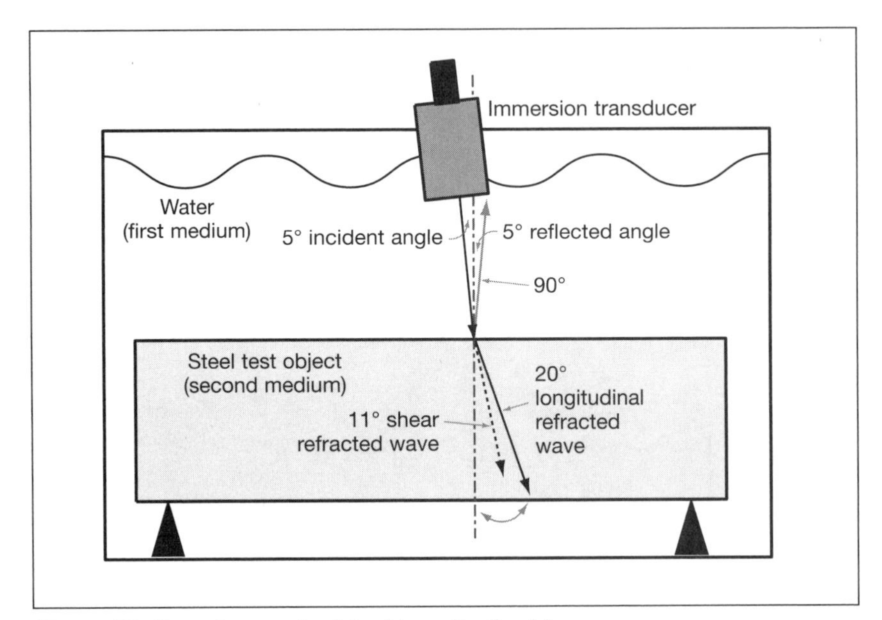

Figure 12: Five-degree incident longitudinal beam.

Refraction and mode conversion occur because the speed of the longitudinal wave changes when the beam enters the second medium. The velocity of the shear wave is about half that of the longitudinal wave, so the change in angle is approximately one-half as much. As the incident angle is rotated farther, the refracted angle of each wave mode increases until the longitudinal wave reaches a refraction angle of 90°. This point can be calculated by use of Snell's law. It is identified as the first critical angle, which refers to the incident angle that produces 90° refraction of the longitudinal wave.

Snell's Law and Critical Angles

In angle-beam testing, when the ultrasonic velocities in the liquid (used in immersion testing) or the wedge material (used in contact testing) are different from the ultrasonic velocity in the test object, the longitudinal beam passing through the wedge or couplant is refracted when the sound beam enters the test object. Incident or refracted angles may be computed by an equation known as *Snell's law*.

Snell's Law Calculations

Snell's law states that the sine of the angle of incidence in the first medium is to the sine of the angle of refraction in the second medium as the velocity of sound in the first medium is to the velocity of sound in the second medium. Mathematically, Snell's law is expressed as:

(Eq. 10) $$\frac{\sin\theta_I}{\sin\theta_R} = \frac{V_I}{V_R}$$

where

θ_I = the incident angle from normal (perpendicular) of the beam in the liquid or wedge

θ_R = the angle of the refracted beam in the test material

V_I = the velocity of incident beam in the liquid or wedge

V_R = the velocity of refracted beam in the test object

The calculations for determining angles of incidence or refraction require trigonometric tables. The sine (sin) ratios are given in decimal fractions. Velocities are often given in centimeters per microsecond (cm/µs). To convert from units of cm/µs to units of (cm/s) × 10^5, move the decimal one place to the right. Multiply in./s by 2.54 to obtain cm/s. Snell's law can be used to determine angular relationships between media for both longitudinal and shear waves.

Typical Problem-Solving Method

Figure 13 shows a contact transducer mounted at an incident angle of 35° 30′ on a plastic wedge. The angle of the refracted beam may be calculated with the formula for Snell's law because the incident angle and the velocity of the sound beam in the first and second medium are known. In this case, only shear waves are produced in the steel, as the incident angle is in the region between the first and second critical angles.

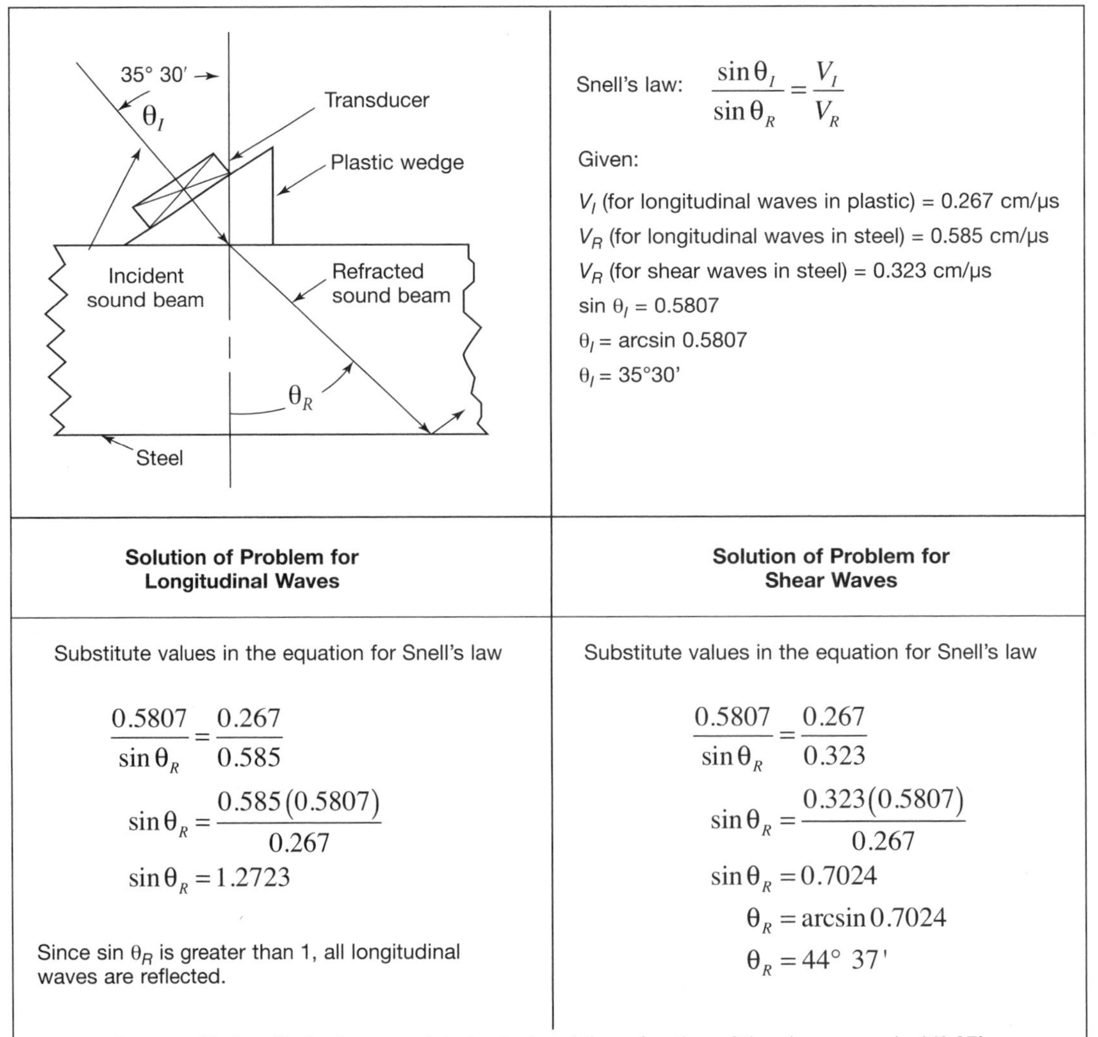

Figure 13: Calculation of refracted angle for longitudinal waves and shear waves.

Critical Angles of Refraction

Sound beams passing through a medium such as water or plastic are refracted when entering a second medium at an incident angle. For small incident beam angles, sound beams are refracted and subjected to mode conversion, resulting in a combination of shear and longitudinal waves. The region between normal (perpendicular) incidence and the first critical angle is not as useful for ultrasonic testing as is the region beyond the first critical angle where only shear waves are produced because the presence of two beams results in confusing signals.

First Critical Angle

As the angle of incidence is increased, the first critical angle is reached when the refracted longitudinal beam angle reaches 90°. At this point, only shear waves exist in the second medium. When selecting a contact shear wave angle-beam transducer, or when adjusting an immersed transducer at an incident angle to produce shear waves, two conditions are considered:

1. The refracted longitudinal wave must be totally reflected (its angle of refraction must be 90° or greater) so that the penetrating beam is limited to shear waves only.
2. The refracted shear wave must enter the test object in accordance with the requirements of the test standard.

With the immersion technique, the first critical angle is calculated to ensure that the sound beam enters the test material at the desired angle.

Second Critical Angle

As the incident angle is increased farther, the second critical angle is reached when the refracted shear beam angle reaches 90°. At this point, all shear waves are reflected and, in the case of contact testing with the test object in an air medium, surface waves are produced. In immersion testing, the liquid medium dampens the production of surface waves to a large degree. However, surface waves have been produced in experimental tests on immersed test objects.

Calculation of Critical Angles

If the sound beam velocities for the incident wave (V_I) and for the refracted wave (V_R) are known, either critical angle may be calculated with Snell's law using the sine of 90°. (*Note:* sin (90°) = 1.) Thus, to compute the first critical angle in the case of a contact transducer mounted on a plastic wedge for testing steel, Eq. 11 should be used.

(Eq. 11)

$$\frac{\sin\theta_I}{\sin\theta_R} = \frac{V_I}{V_R\,(\textit{longitudinal wave})}$$

$$\frac{\sin\theta_I}{\sin 90^\circ} = \frac{0.267\ \text{cm}/\mu\text{s}}{0.585\ \text{cm}/\mu\text{s}} = \frac{\sin\theta_I}{1} = 0.45641$$

Divide V_R into V_I = 0.45641 = 27° 9′ for first critical angle. If the second critical angle is desired, V_R is the sound beam velocity for a shear wave in steel: 0.323 cm/µs. V_R is again divided into V_I = 0.82662 = 55° 45′ for the second critical angle.

Table 2 lists longitudinal- and shear-wave velocities for selected materials. Table 3 lists approximate critical angles for the same test materials when water versus a plastic wedge is used as the first medium.

Note that in this case uranium does not have a second critical angle. This is because the shear wave velocity in uranium is less than the longitudinal wave velocity in plastic. Essentially, this means that the incident angle would have to be greater than 90° to obtain a 90° refraction of the beam in uranium. An incident angle greater than 90° is physically impossible.

Table 2: Longitudinal- and shear-wave velocities in selected materials.

Test Material	Velocity (in./µs)		Velocity (cm/µs)	
	Longitudinal	Shear	Longitudinal	Shear
Aluminum 17ST	0.246	0.122	0.625	0.310
Beryllium	0.5	0.343	1.280	0.871
Stainless 302	0.223	0.123	0.566	0.312
Steel	0.23	0.127	0.585	0.323
Tungsten	0.204	0.113	0.518	0.287
Uranium	0.133	0.076	0.338	0.193

Table 3: Critical angles in contact testing for selected materials when first medium is water (H_2O) versus plastic.

Test Material	H_2O V = 0.059 in./µs (0.149 cm/µs)		Plastic V = 0.105 in./µs (0.267 cm/µs)	
	First Critical Angle	Second Critical Angle	First Critical Angle	Second Critical Angle
Aluminum 17ST	14°	29°	25°	59°
Beryllium	7°	10°	12°	18°
Stainless 302	15°	29°	28°	59°
Steel	15°	27°	27°	56°
Tungsten	17°	31°	31°	68°
Uranium	26°	51°	52°	–

Equipment

Introduction

This chapter covers the more commonly used ultrasonic testing equipment. Manufacturers' manuals, in most cases, provide operation and maintenance instructions for the units, a review of theory, and other more specific information. In the event of conflicting information, manufacturers' recommendations supersede this chapter.

Figure 1 depicts training in the use of a portable ultrasonic discontinuity detector. This type of unit and others that are more elaborate are discussed in this chapter.

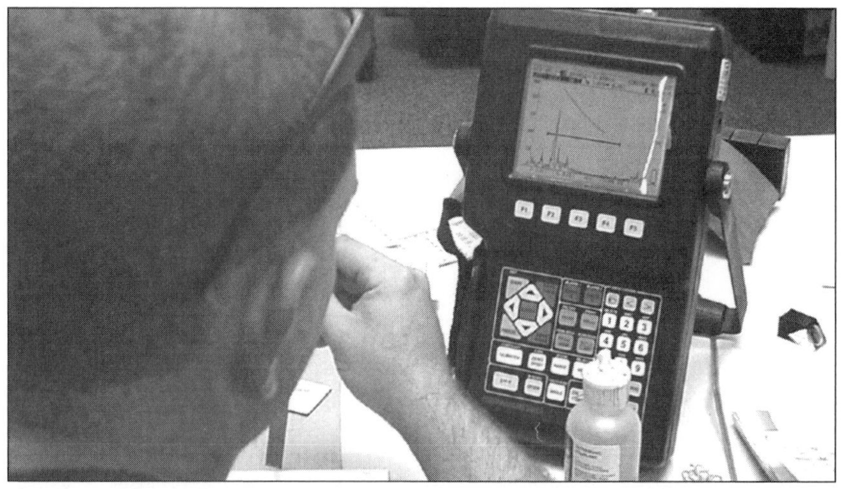

Figure 1: Ultrasonic testing trainee using a discontinuity (flaw) detector.

Pulse-Echo Instrumentation

Ultrasonic testing systems are referred to as being one of three types: A-scan, B-scan, or C-scan. Each term relates to the format that is displayed on the screen of the ultrasonic instrument used for a given test. Whether A-, B-, or C-scan, they are, for the most part, dependent on the same basic electronic components. Typical ultrasonic instruments are designed to produce outgoing electronic pulses and to amplify returning echoes from test materials. The essential differences lie in how the incoming information is represented on a display.

A-Scan Equipment

The *A-scan* system is a signal presentation method that displays the returned signals from the test material on the display screen, as shown in Figure 2. The horizontal baseline on the screen indicates elapsed time (from left to right). The vertical deflection shows signal amplitudes that allow the technician to gage the relative size of the reflector.

In Figure 3, a signal results when the transducer is coupled to a 1 in. (25.4 mm) thick mild steel test block. In Figure 4, a signal is produced when the same transducer is placed on a 0.75 in. (19 mm) test block made of the same material. Notice that the back-surface reflections have changed positions. The signal from the 0.75 in. (19 mm) reflector is closer to the left side of the display screen and accurately represents the change in distance between the two reflecting surfaces.

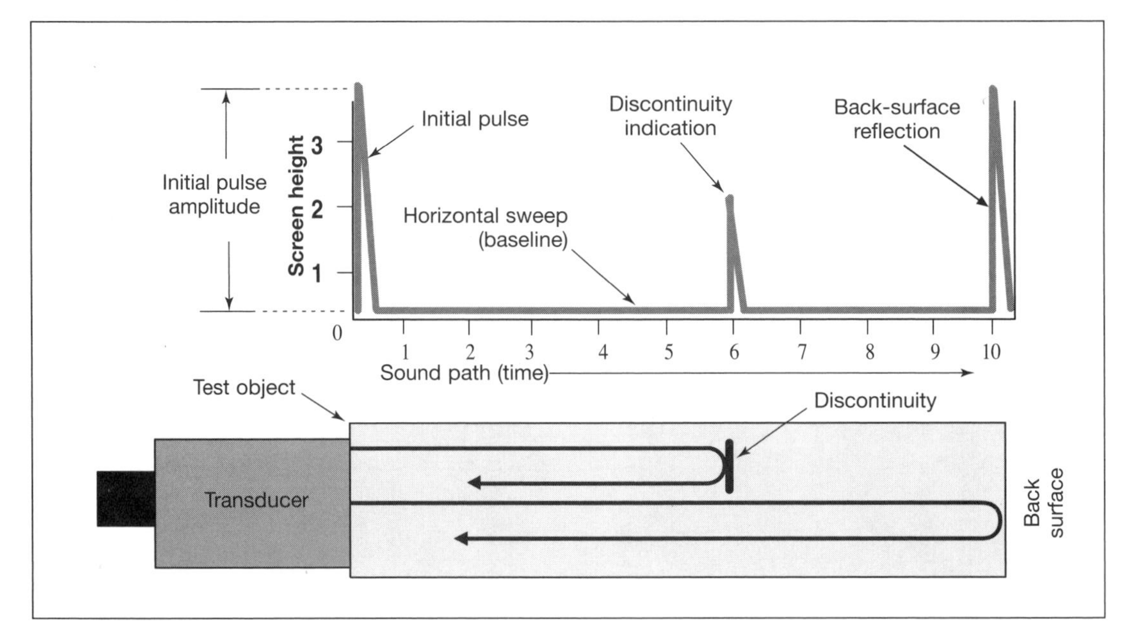

Figure 2: A-scan presentation.

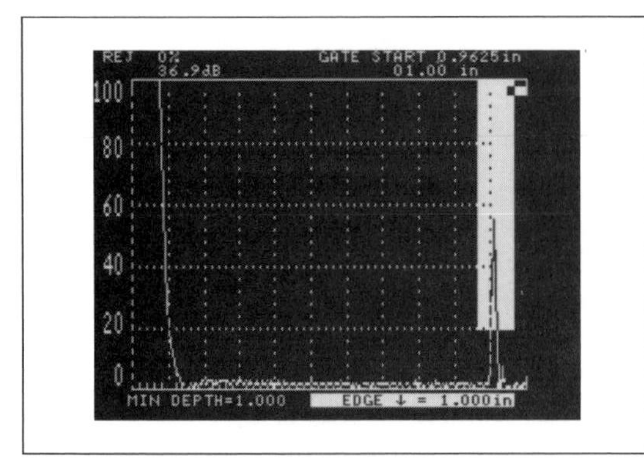

Figure 3: Resulting signal when a transducer is coupled to a 1 in. (25.4 mm) thick mild steel test block.

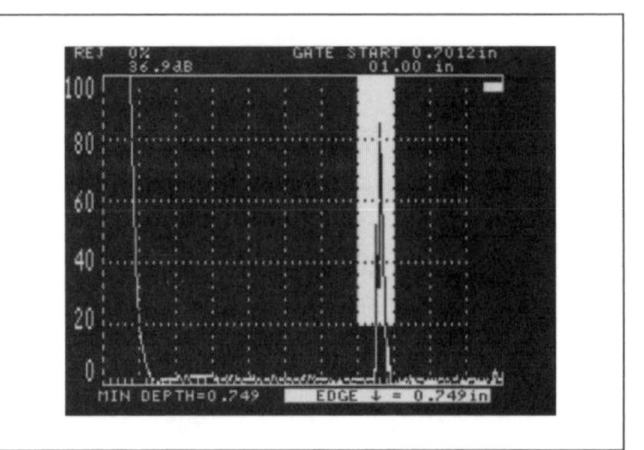

Figure 4: Signal as produced when the same transducer shown in Figure 3 is placed on a 0.75 in. (19 mm) test block made of the same material.

Also notice that the amplitude of the more distant reflector in Figure 3 is less than that of the reflector at 0.75 in. (19 mm) in Figure 4. The increased distance to the more distant surface causes a reduction in amplitude of that signal due to the attenuation of sound energy.

Distance and amplitude information gathered by use of A-scan applications enable the ultrasonic technician to view objective evidence of the conditions encountered within the test object.

B-Scan Equipment

A *B-scan* representation produces a two-dimensional view of the cross-sectional plane through the test object. It is typically used in applications such as corrosion monitoring and lamination detection in metals and composites. The B-scan display produces a view of the test material that looks as if it were cut through and turned on its side. This shows in cross-section whatever internal reflectors or opposite surface conditions exist.

Figures 5 and 6 show a B-scan produced by the same instrument used for the A-scans shown in Figures 3 and 4. Manufacturers of most discontinuity detectors provide a B-scan component to users who want the benefit of using the same unit for A- and B-scan applications.

Figure 6 represents the four steps of the 1 in. (25.4 mm) step wedge shown in Figure 5, with 0.75, 0.5, and 0.25 in. (19, 13, and 6 mm) steps displayed as a percentage of 1 in. (25.4 mm).

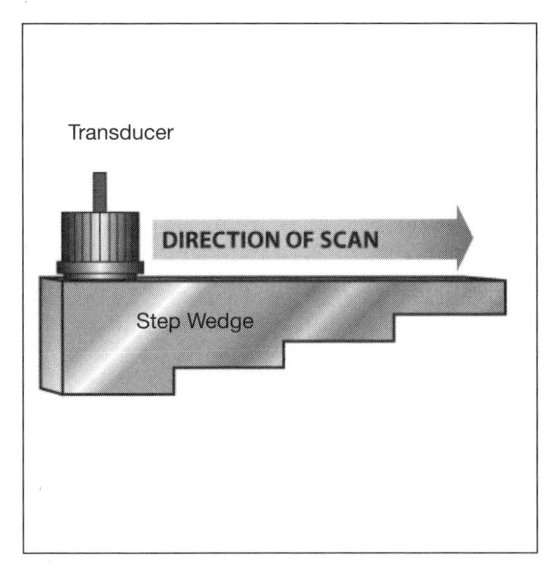

Figure 5: B-scan representation of the four steps of a 1 in. (25.4 mm) step wedge.

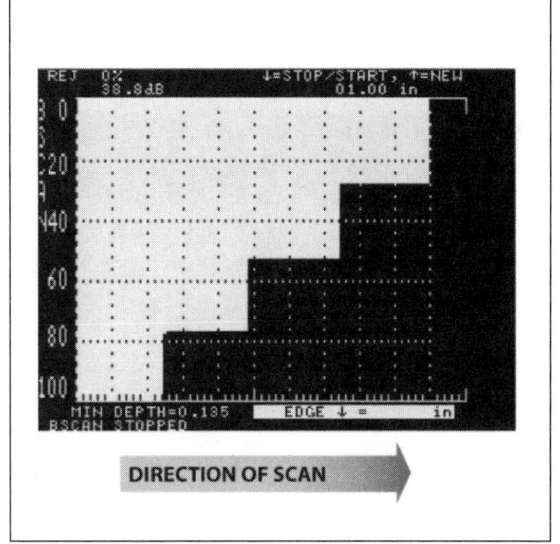

Figure 6: B-scan representation of a manual scan.

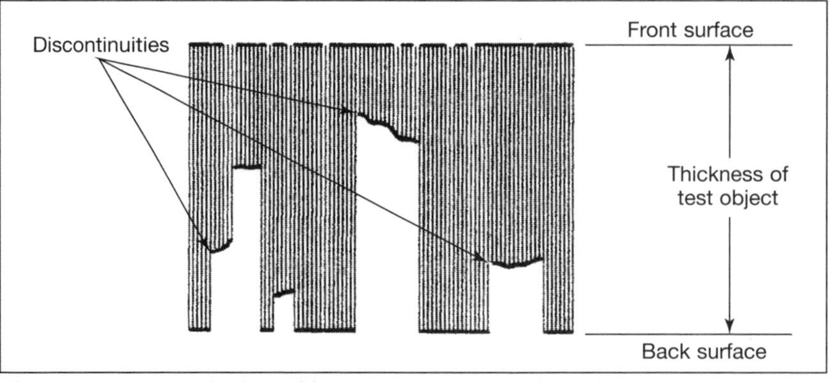

Figure 7: B-scan display of internal discontinuities lying under the scanning path of an ultrasonic transducer.

B-scan equipment provides opportunities for real-time visualization of the material condition as it is tested. Figure 7 illustrates a B-scan of internal discontinuities lying under the scanning path of an ultrasonic transducer.

C-Scan Equipment

Another common display of ultrasonic testing data uses a plan view (as though looking down on the test object) called a *C-scan*. In this approach, the transducer is scanned in a regular pattern over an area of interest, usually using an automatic mechanical positioning device. The received signals are converted to variations in color or grayscale density.

Created from A-scan data, the plan view of the test object is generated using signal criteria based on pulse height and time of arrival to determine color or grayscale density at each X-Y location. This is similar to the floor plan of a house in that the vertical and horizontal directions represent the area over which the transducer was scanned.

The resulting patterns correlate with the size and shape of the reflecting surfaces within the test object and, like X-ray images, are intuitively easy to interpret. Figure 8 represents a C-scan of a test object. The images show the shapes and plan positions of the reflectors.

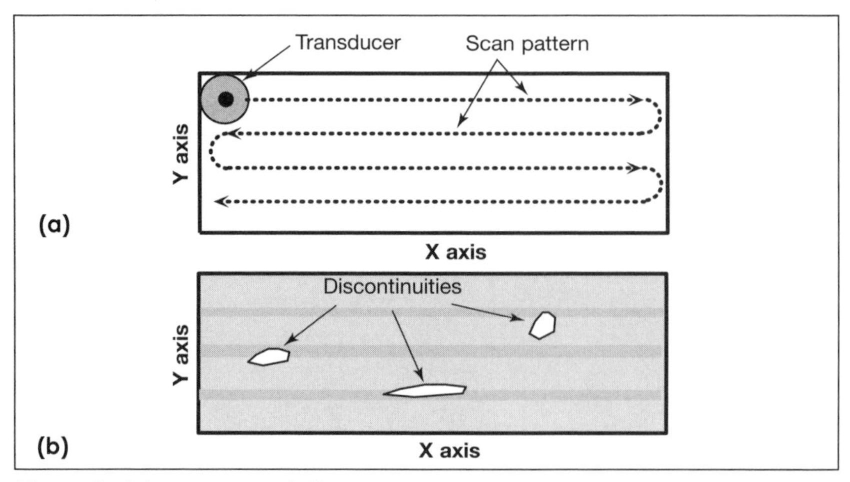

Figure 8: C-scan presentation.

The major advantage of a C-scan is the understandable display of information related to reflector shape and position that is not as readily interpreted when looking at an A-scan or B-scan display.

Pulse-Echo Instrumentation Electronics

All makes of pulse-echo equipment have similar electronic circuitry and provide basic common functions. Names of the various circuits vary from one instrument to another according to the manufacturer; however, each unit must provide certain essentials. The block diagram in Figure 9 illustrates these.

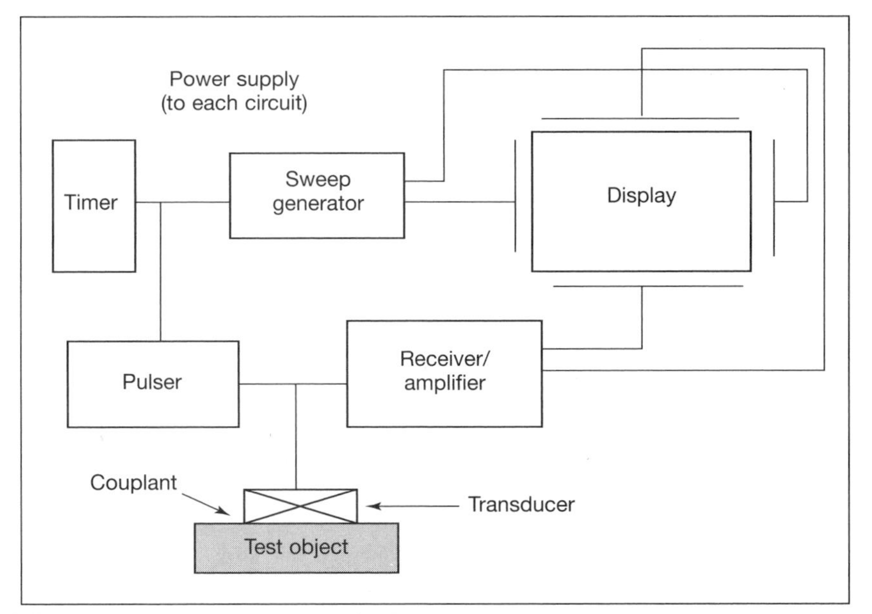

Figure 9: Pulse-echo system features.

Power Supply

The power supply is usually controlled by an on/off switch and a fuse. After the power is turned on, certain time-delay devices protect circuit elements during instrument warmup. Circuits for supplying current for all basic functions of the instrument constitute the power supply. Electrical power is served from line supply or, as in the case of portables, a battery contained in the unit.

Transducer

A transducer is a device that converts energy from one form to another. The ultrasonic transducer consists of a thin piezoelectric disk, sometimes called an *element* or *crystal*, and its holder. The disk converts electrical energy to ultrasonic energy and introduces vibrations into the test object. It also receives reflected ultrasonic vibrations from within the test object and converts them into electrical signals for amplification and display. (An in-depth review of transducers is presented in Chapter 4.)

Pulser/Receiver

The pulser, or pulse generator, is the source of short high-energy bursts of electrical energy (triggered by the timer) that are applied to the transducer. Return pulses from the test object are received by the transducer, sent to the receiver, amplified, and routed to the display unit.

Display and Timer

Ultrasonic displays, whether modern digital flat-panel screens or older analog cathode-ray tubes (CRTs), are integrated with a sweep generator and the controls required to provide a visual image of the signals received from the test object. The timer is the source of all timing signals to the pulser and is sometimes referred to as the *rate generator* or *clock*.

Control Functions

Controls are provided for the various circuits of the instrument, such as power supply, pulser, receiver, timer, and display. The nomenclature used in the following descriptions may vary from one type of unit to another. Figure 10 illustrates a typical instrument display.

Instrument Gain Controls

Instrument gain controls connect to the amplifier and permit adjustment of the amount of amplification that incoming signals from the transducer receive before being displayed on a screen.

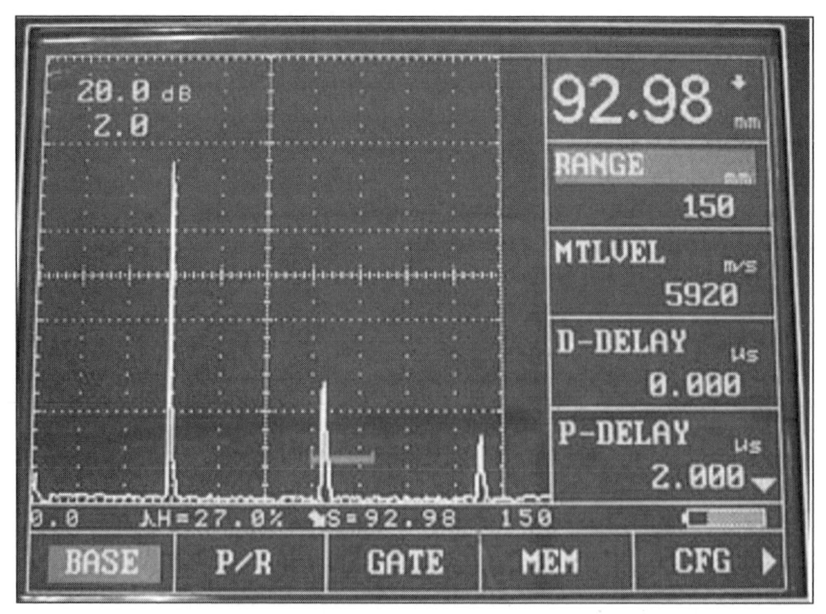

Figure 10: LCD display of an ultrasonic test.

Probe Mode Control

This control determines if the instrument will drive and display the activity of one transducer or two. In single probe mode, the instrument sends and receives short bursts of electrical energy through a coaxial cable to a single transducer.

In dual probe mode, the instrument directs outbound electrical bursts through the coaxial connector toward one transducer tasked for sending ultrasonic waves into the test object. Inbound signals are received by a separate transducer connected to the other coaxial connector. This setup is referred to as a *through-transmission* or *dual-probe test*, where the sending transducer is isolated from the receiving transducer.

Range and Delay Controls

These controls allow adjustment of the display along the horizontal axis. This display axis usually shows the time, distance, or depth of ultrasonic travel in the test object. Fine range controls are sometimes called *material calibration* or *material velocity controls*, depending on the manufacturer. These controls allow the technician to perform a basic part of the standardization/calibration of the instrument.

Range controls allow for the precise screen placement of signals from known reference distances within standardization blocks. By use of these controls, as well as the delay control, signals from known distances are placed in their correct position on the display screen. This enables the screen to represent the appropriate distance that allows for complete through-dimension testing. By use of standardization blocks made of material similar to that of the test object, the instrument screen can be set to represent 1, 5, 10 in. (25.4, 127, 254 mm) or more of sound travel within a test object.

Instrumentation

Modern ultrasonic instruments use push-button keypads or computer commands to make menu selections. The keypads and computer menus allow for the adjustment of all functions required for the standardization of the instrument in preparation for an ultrasonic test.

Figure 11 provides a chart of various functions used by technicians for an ultrasonic test of a setup.

On/Off Control

The on/off control admits (or stops) the flow of power to the unit's components, enabling (or stopping) operation.

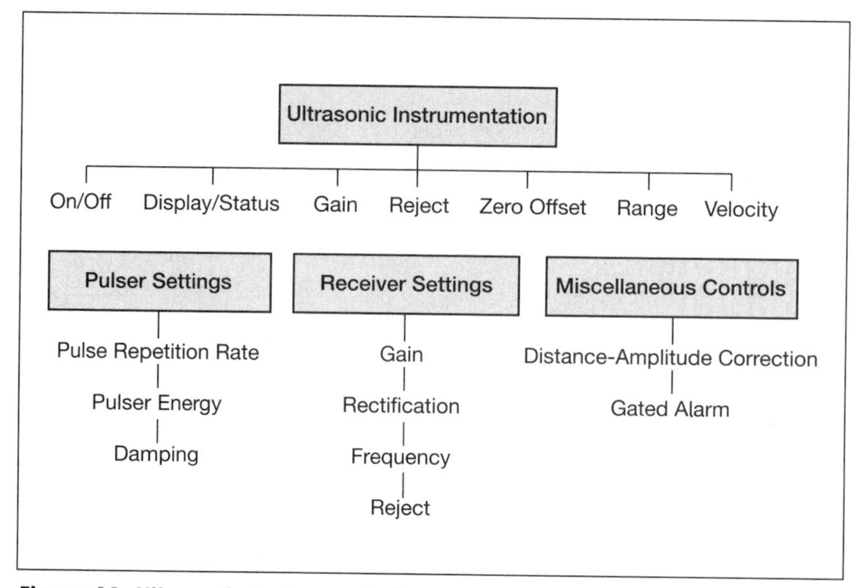

Figure 11: Ultrasonic instrumentation.

Display/Status Control

The display/status control allows the technician to switch between views of the display screen. For example, the screen could display the A-scan, the instrument settings, or a combination of both on a so-called *split screen*, as shown in Figure 12(a).

Figure 12(b) shows what the technician sees after pressing the display/status control a second time.

Gain Control

The gain key controls the amplifier circuit. It does not have any influence over outbound pulses but has everything to do with signals returning from the test material.

The gain, or system sensitivity, in modern ultrasonic instruments may exceed 100 dB and is adjustable in increments as small as 0.1 dB.

Reject Control

The purpose of the reject control is to eliminate unwanted low-level A-scan signals. It is particularly useful in the inspection of coarse-grained castings. This control also works on the amplifier circuit.

Zero Offset Control

The zero offset control compensates for sound transmission delays associated with the transducer, cable, and couplant. This is a subtracted time measurement to compensate for the difference between the time data as follows:

1. **Electric zero:** Point in time when the pulser fires the initial pulse to the transducer.

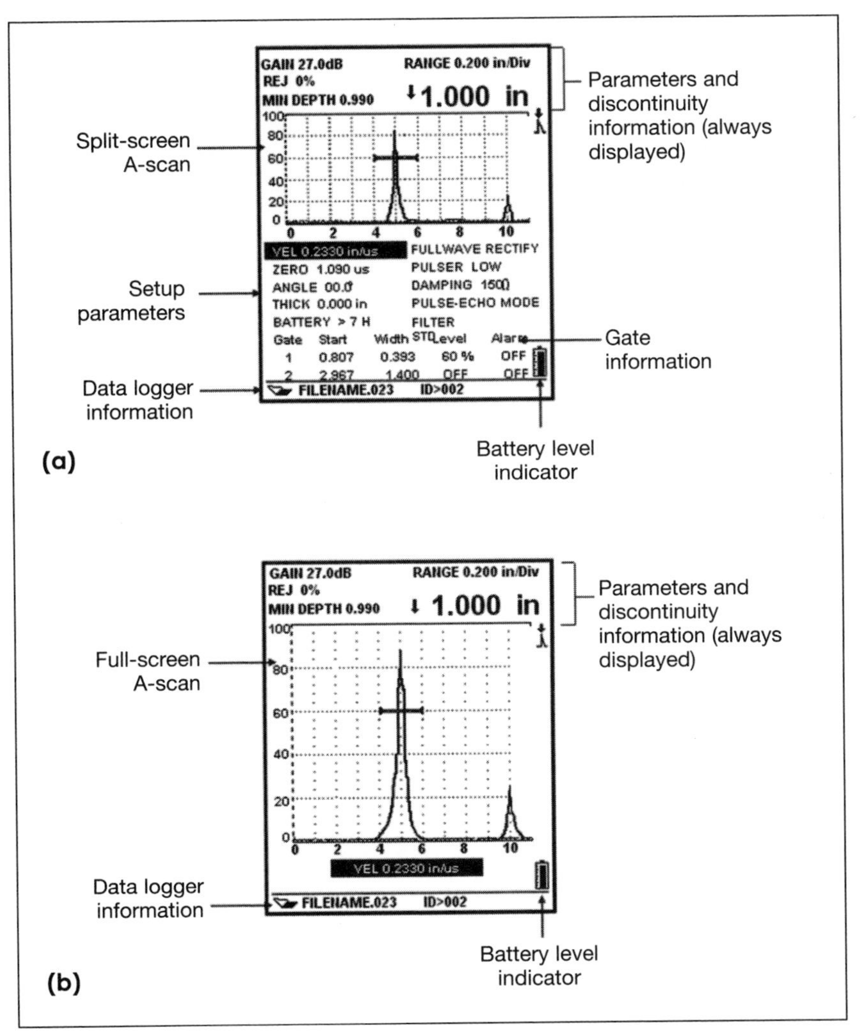

Figure 12: Mode displays: (a) split-screen mode displays A-scan and setup parameters simultaneously; (b) full-screen mode provides a large view of the A-scan for increased resolution.

2. **Acoustic zero:** Point in time when the sound wave enters the test object.

Range Control

The range control enables the technician to set the visible A-scan screen range. Generally, the range should be set so the echo from the thickest material will be displayed on the screen. Typically, the range control allows toggling through preset range values and also permits fine-tuning of the range setting.

Velocity Control

The velocity control adjusts the instrument settings to match the speed of sound in the test object. Velocity variables related to material density and elasticity, material temperature, and mode (for example, longitudinal wave versus shear wave) affect the sound velocity within a given material. This control allows the technician to adjust the ultrasonic instrument based on the chosen mode of transmission, as well as the true velocity of that mode within the test object.

Pulser Settings

As mentioned, the gain controls the amplifier circuit to boost incoming signals from the material. Several other controls provided in most ultrasonic instruments work to modify the pulses of energy or the display. These are referred to as *pulser settings* and include the following controls.

Rectification Control

This control adjusts the display signal on the screen. As shown in Figure 13, it adjusts the waveform display rectification among four selections:

- Full-wave rectify.
- Half-wave (+) rectify.
- Half-wave (–) rectify.
- Radio-frequency waveform (unrectified).

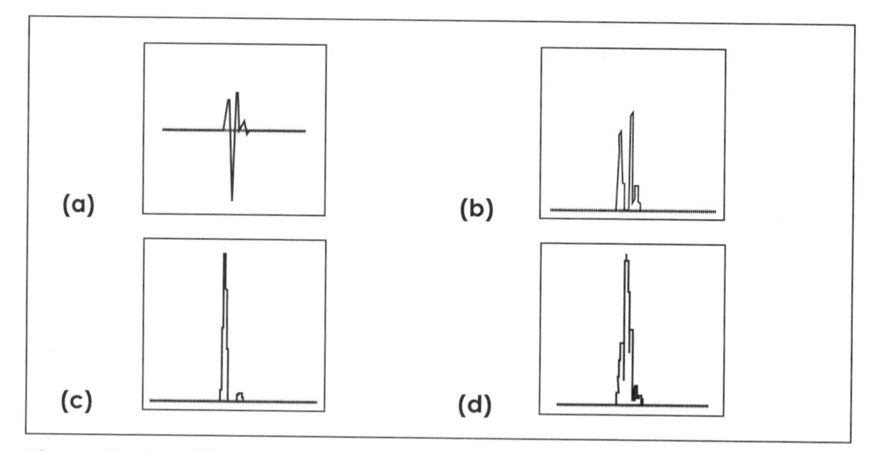

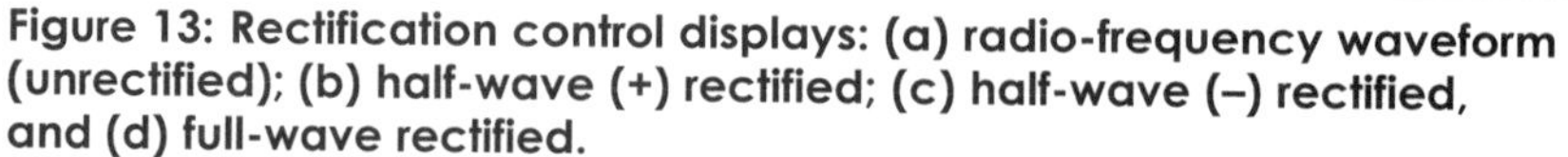

Figure 13: Rectification control displays: (a) radio-frequency waveform (unrectified); (b) half-wave (+) rectified; (c) half-wave (–) rectified, and (d) full-wave rectified.

Pulser Energy Control

The pulse of energy transmitted into the test object begins as an electrical impulse of low (100 V), medium (200 V), or high (400 V) voltage. The low-voltage pulse produces better resolution, while higher voltages produce greater penetrating power.

Damping Control

This control allows the technician to optimize waveform shape for high-resolution measurements and for a particular transducer selection. The pulse duration is shortened or lengthened by its use. Typically, there are three setting options:

- 50 ohms (Ω) for better near-surface resolution.
- 150 ohms (Ω) as a medium setting.
- 400 ohms (Ω) for improved penetration.

Frequency Control

The frequency control allows for selection of a frequency setting that produces the desired screen presentation for the particular transducer chosen for the test application. Available frequencies are expressed in megahertz and typically include 1, 2.25, 5, 10, and sometimes 15 MHz.

Other Features

Instruments with additional controls are available, as follows.

Distance-Amplitude Correction

Distance-amplitude correction (DAC), also referred to as *time-corrected gain* (TCG) or *time-varied gain*, compensates for a drop in amplitude of signals reflected from discontinuities deep within the test object due to attenuation.

Gated Alarm

Gated units enable automatic alarms when discontinuities are detected. This is implemented by setting up specific gated or zoned areas within the test object. Signals appearing within these gates may be programmed to automatically set off visual or audible alarms. These signals may also be passed to recorders and external control devices. Gated alarm units usually have three controls:

1. **Gate start or delay:** The gate start or delay control is used for adjustment of the location of the leading edge of the gate on the display screen.
2. **Gate length or width:** The gate length or width control is used for adjustment of the length of the gate or the location of the gate trailing edge.
3. **Gate alarm level or sensitivity:** The alarm level or gate level control is used for adjustment of the gate vertical threshold to turn on signal lights or to activate an alarm relay.

Calibration

The first step in any ultrasonic test is to calibrate the instrument system to ensure proper performance. A predictable and reproducible response to known reflectors of different sizes and depths within the calibration standard must be demonstrated before any actual application to the test object can begin.

The calibration process amounts to an adjustment of the test system to the characteristic velocity and attenuation factor of material to be tested. Ideally, the calibration standard should be made of the same material as the test object and should have been processed (including heat-treating) identically to the test object. Furthermore, the calibration standard, sometimes called a *calibration block*, should be adjusted to conform to the same temperature as that expected during the actual test.

Essentially, the calibration process is all about adjusting the ultrasonic test system so that it is capable of displaying signals from reflectors of known distance and size from the calibration standard. A properly calibrated test system will display linearity. That is, a reflector at a depth of 1 in. (25.4 mm) will cause a signal on the instrument display that can be easily read as being 1 in. (25.4 mm) deep.

The response of the instrument must be proportional to the size of the reflector, such that the technician will be readily able to see the difference between a signal from a reflector of 0.1 in. (2.54 mm) diameter versus one that is 0.125 in. (3.2 mm) in diameter. These and other details of calibration procedures are addressed in Chapter 7.

Basic Instrument Standardizing

A term less often used, but inherently more correct than calibrating, is *standardizing*. Standardizing the testing system involves the adjustment of the equipment controls so that the technician can be sure that the instrument will detect the discontinuities that the test is expected to find. Standardizing the test system consists of setting up the instrument system exactly as it is to be used in the test and adjusting the controls to give an adequate response to discontinuities of known size and depth in reference standards. The size and depth of the discontinuities are typically defined in a test specification.

Calibration Blocks

In ultrasonic testing, all discontinuity indications are compared to indications received from a reference standard. The reference standard may be any one of many reference blocks or sets of blocks specified for a given test.

Ultrasonic standard reference blocks, often called *calibration blocks*, are used in ultrasonic testing to standardize the ultrasonic equipment and to evaluate the discontinuity indication received from the test object. Standardizing does two things:

- It verifies that the instrument/transducer combination is performing with a proportional response.

- It establishes a sensitivity or gain setting at which all discontinuities of a specified size or larger will be detected.

Indications of discontinuities within the test object are compared with the indication from an artificial discontinuity of known size and at the same depth in a standard reference block of the same material.

Standard test blocks are made from carefully selected test stock that meets predetermined standards of sound attenuation, grain size, and heat-treatment. Discontinuities are represented by carefully drilled flat-bottom holes. Calibration blocks are made and tested to ensure that the only discontinuity present is the one that was added intentionally.

Area-Amplitude Blocks

Area-amplitude blocks provide a means of checking the linearity of the output of the test system; that is, they confirm that the amplitude (height) of the indication on the display screen increases in proportion to the increase in size of the discontinuity. Similar area-amplitude reference blocks are made from 2 in. (51 mm) diameter round stock.

The Alcoa™ Series A set consists of eight area-amplitude blocks, each 3-3/4 in. (95 mm) long and 1-15/16 in. (49 mm) square. A 3/4 in. (19 mm) deep flat-bottom hole is drilled in the bottom center of each block. The hole diameters are 1/64 in. (0.4 mm) in the Number 1 block through 8/64 in. (3.2 mm) in the Number 8 block, as shown in Figure 14. As implied, the block numbers refer to the flat-bottom hole diameter (in fractions). For example, a Number 3 block has a 3/64 in. (1.2 mm) diameter flat-bottom hole. (*Note:* Imperial rather than SI are the primary units for measurements of these blocks.)

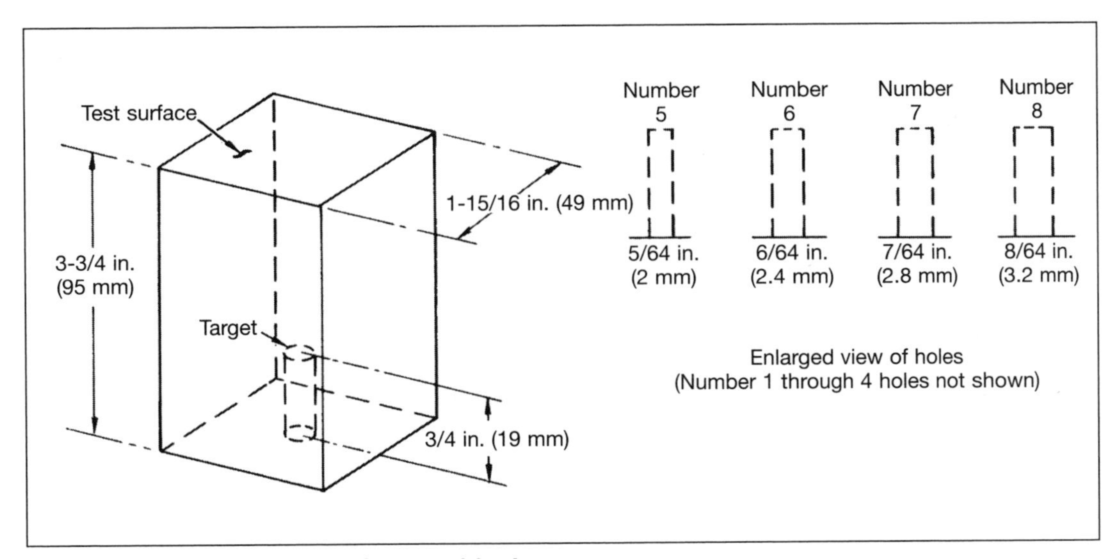

Figure 14: Area-amplitude reference blocks.

Distance-Amplitude Blocks

Distance-amplitude blocks serve as a reference by which the size of discontinuities at varying depths within the test material may be evaluated. They also serve as a reference for setting or standardizing the sensitivity or gain of the test system so that the system displays readable indications for all discontinuities of a given size and over; however, they will not flood the screen with indications of smaller discontinuities that are of no interest.

The set of Alcoa™ Series B distance-amplitude blocks consists of 19 cylindrical blocks 1-15/16 in. (49 mm) in diameter, all with 3/4 in. (19 mm) deep flat-bottom holes of the same diameter drilled in the center at one end. These blocks are of different lengths to provide metal distances of 1/16 in. (1.6 mm) to 5-3/4 in. (146 mm) from the test surface to the flat-bottome hole. Sets with 3/64 in. (1.2 mm), 5/64 in. (2 mm) or 8/64 in. (3.2 mm) diameter holes are available. The metal distances in each set are:

- 1/16 in. (1.6 mm),
- 7/64 in. (2.8 mm) through 1 in. (25.4 mm) in 1/8 in. (3.2 mm) increments, and
- 1-1/4 in. (32 mm) through 5-3/4 in. (146 mm) in 1/2 in. (13 mm) increments.

A set of Alcoa™ Series B blocks is shown in Figure 15.

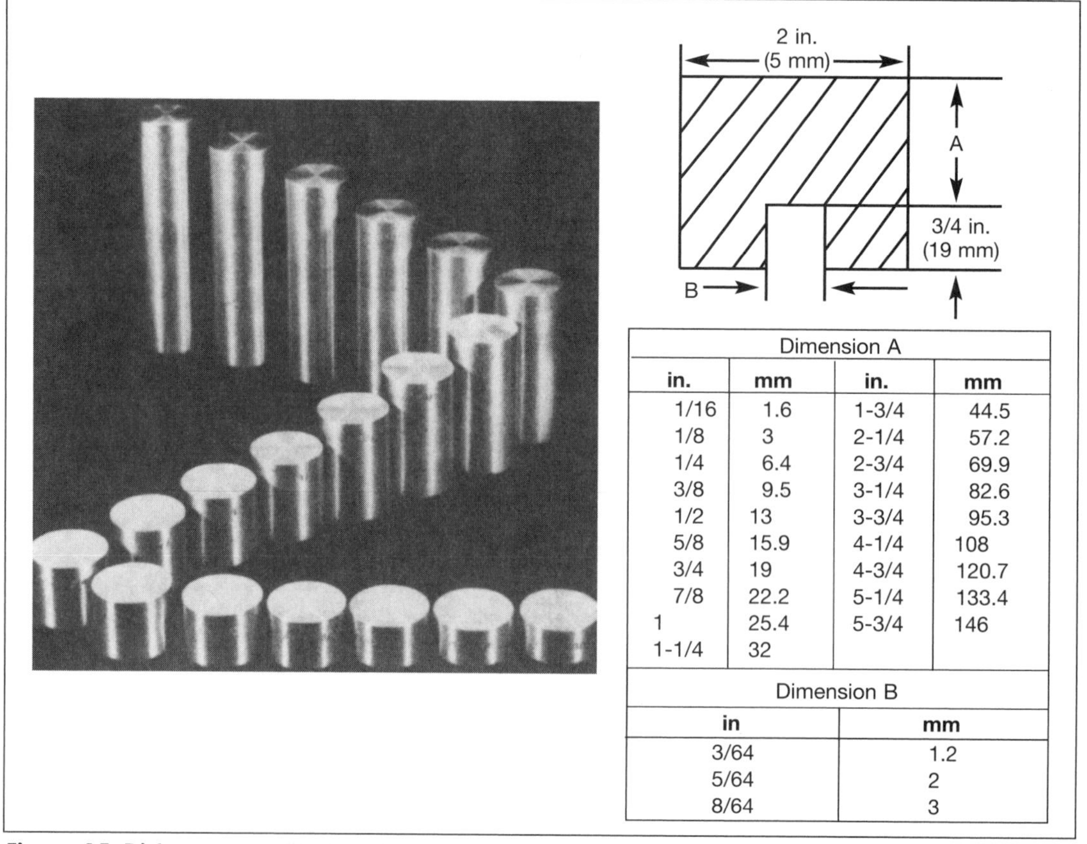

Dimension A			
in.	mm	in.	mm
1/16	1.6	1-3/4	44.5
1/8	3	2-1/4	57.2
1/4	6.4	2-3/4	69.9
3/8	9.5	3-1/4	82.6
1/2	13	3-3/4	95.3
5/8	15.9	4-1/4	108
3/4	19	4-3/4	120.7
7/8	22.2	5-1/4	133.4
1	25.4	5-3/4	146
1-1/4	32		

Dimension B	
in	mm
3/64	1.2
5/64	2
8/64	3

Figure 15: Distance-amplitude reference blocks.

On instruments so equipped, distance-amplitude blocks are used to set the sensitivity time control or *distance-amplitude correction* (DAC) so that a discontinuity of a given size will produce an indication of the same amplitude on the display screen, regardless of its distance from the front surface.

It is important that the test block material be the same as or similar to that of the test object. Alloy content, heat-treatment, and the degree of hot- or cold-working from forging and rolling — all affect the acoustical properties of the material. If test blocks of identical material are not available, they must be similar in sound attenuation, velocity, and impedance.

ASTM Calibration Blocks

Figure 16 shows an ASTM calibration block set. ASTM blocks can be combined into various sets of area-amplitude and distance-amplitude blocks. The ASTM basic set consists of 1-15/16 in. (49 mm) diameter blocks, each with a 5/64 in. (2 mm) deep flat-bottom hole drilled in the center of the bottom surface. One block has a 3/64 in. (1.2 mm) diameter hole at a 3 in. (76 mm) metal distance. Seven blocks have 5/64 in. (2 mm) diameter holes at metal distances of 0.125, 0.25, 0.5, 0.75, 1.5, 3, and 6 in. (3.2, 6, 13, 19, 38, 76, and 152 mm). The remaining blocks have 8/64 in. (3.2 mm) diameter holes at 3 in. (76 mm) and 6 in. (152 mm) metal distances. The three blocks with a 3 in. (76 mm) metal distance and hole diameters of 3/64, 5/64, and 8/64 in. (1.2, 2, and 3.2 mm) form an area-amplitude set. The set with the 5/64 in. (2 mm) diameter holes provides a distance-amplitude set.

Figure 16: ASTM calibration block set.

In addition to the basic set, ASTM lists five more area-amplitude standard reference blocks and 80 more distance-amplitude blocks. Each ASTM block is identified by a code, using the same system as that used for the Alcoa™ Series B set. The dimensions of all ASTM blocks are given in ASTM E-127, which also presents the recommended steps for fabricating and checking aluminum alloy standard reference blocks. The recommended steps for fabricating and control of steel standard reference blocks are found in ASTM E-428. Figure 17 provides an example of the construction of ASTM calibration blocks.

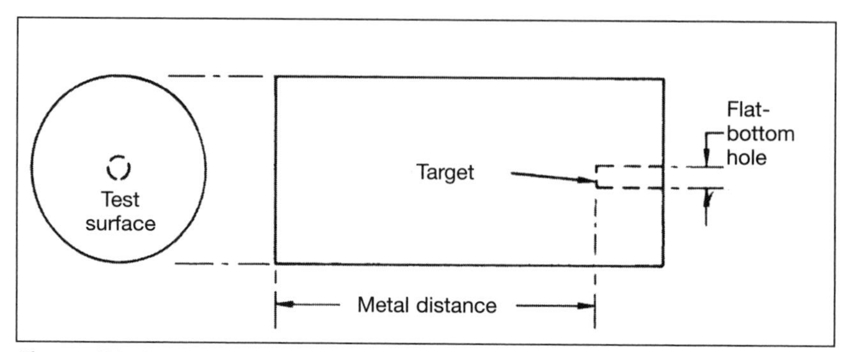

Figure 17: Construction of ASTM calibration blocks.

Special Blocks

The International Institute of Welding (IIW) reference block and the miniature angle beam field calibration block, both shown in Figure 18, are examples of other reference standards in common use.

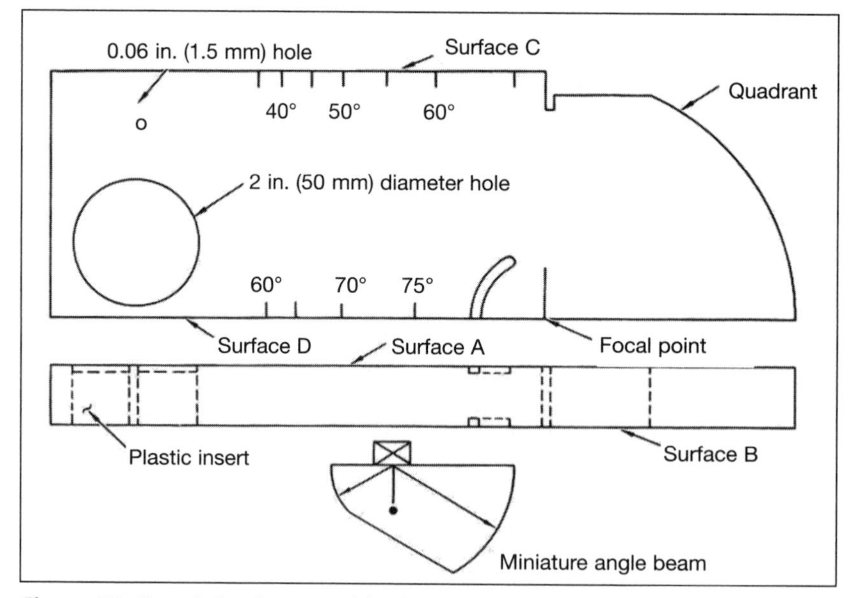

Figure 18: Special reference blocks.

These standards are adequate for many test situations, provided the acoustic properties are matched or nearly matched between the test object and the test block. In most cases, responses from discontinuities in the test object are likely to differ from the indications received from the test block hole. For this reason, a sample test object is sectioned, subjected to metallurgical analysis and studied to determine the nature of the material and its probable discontinuities.

In some cases, artificial discontinuities in the form of holes or notches are introduced into the sample to serve as a basis for comparison with discontinuities found in other test objects. From these studies, an acceptance level is determined that establishes the number and magnitude of discontinuities allowed in the test object. In all cases, the true nature of the test material is determined by careful study of the sample test object.

For irregularly shaped test objects, it is often necessary to make one of the test objects into a reference standard by adding artificial discontinuities in the form of flat-bottom holes, saw cuts, notches, and so on. In some cases, these artificial discontinuities can be placed so that they will be removed by subsequent machining of the test object. In other cases, a special standardizing technique is developed by carefully studying a test object ultrasonically and then verifying the detection of discontinuities in the test object by destructive investigation. Subsequently, the results of the study become the basis for the testing standard.

Calibration of Semiautomatic and Automatic Systems

When ultrasonic data is recorded using mechanical positioning, the accuracy of the position as it relates to the recorded data can be a critical factor when evaluating data. This becomes evident when measuring the distance to a discontinuity on a B-scan or attempting to accurately size discontinuities using a C-scan.

Semiautomatic systems are mechanically guided or mounted ultrasonic systems that are moved manually. The data is acquired by use of an encoder that records the position as the system moves along the scan plane. Typically, a scan is made in one direction and only one encoder is used. Calibration of the mechanical position is performed by moving the probe position over a known distance and comparing the accuracy of the system readout distance to the known distance. Accuracy can be a required percent of the known distance or a specified value.

Automatic systems are mechanically guided or mounted ultrasonic systems that are motor driven. When a single encoded axis is used, the requirements are similar to those for semiautomatic scanning. When multiple axes are used to scan and index, such as with an immersion system, there may be requirements in addition to positioning, such as the perpendicularity or parallelism between axes.

Digital Thickness Instrumentation

Modern ultrasonic thickness gages may be used to measure wall thickness of metals, glass, ceramics, and rigid plastics. They use the pulse-echo principle of ultrasonic application, where short pulses of energy are transmitted from a high-frequency transducer into the test object. The emitted pulses travel through the material to its inside surface and reflect back to the transducer. The elapsed travel time for a round trip is measured and converted to an accurate digital thickness measurement.

Today's digital thickness meters are small, lightweight, and capable of producing very accurate results. Most provide data logging capacity that allows for easy information gathering and transfer to computer-based data analysis programs.

Figure 19 shows a technician using a transducer to resolve and accurately display wall thickness readings of a heavy-wall pressure vessel. Smaller units display the thickness value only — not an A-scan.

Figure 19: Ultrasonic thickness measurement of a heavy-wall pressure vessel.

In the mid-1980s, several manufacturers developed a new generation of digital meters that use liquid crystal displays (LCDs) to provide waveform information on A-scan displays, in addition to the digital readout of the thickness value. The A-scan displays enable the technician to view the waveform and decide whether the digital thickness value presented results from an internal reflector or the actual inside wall of the test object.

Sound Velocity Measurements

Most applications of NDT rely on accurate measurements of the sound velocity in different materials. The basic principle of sound velocity determination is to measure the time between transmitted and received ultrasound signals. During the testing procedure, the measurement of the transducer displacement is more convenient and accurate than the measurement of the transducer/reflector distance. Such a technique allows the technician to eliminate additional artifacts caused by the time delay from the transducer and associated electronics. A good example of this technique is the use of step calibration blocks (see Figure 20).

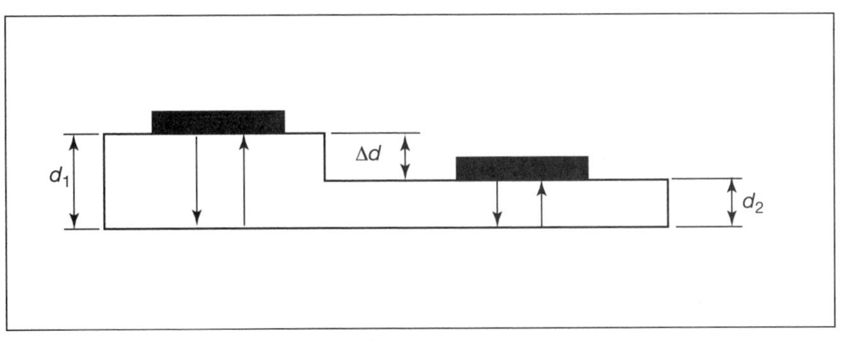

Figure 20: Step calibration block.

The latest microprocessor-based automatic discontinuity (flaw) detectors can evaluate sound velocity and the probe delay very accurately. When information about two reference levels (thicknesses of two steps, d_1 and d_2) is encountered, the device calculates Δd and indicates the time of the reflected signals from the bottom of both steps, namely t_1 and t_2. Then, the device automatically calculates:

(Eq. 1) $$\Delta t = t_1 - t_2$$

Now, sound velocity is calculated according to the formula:

(Eq. 2) $$v = \frac{2\Delta d}{\Delta t}$$

How does the discontinuity (flaw) detector calculate the probe delay? The piezoelectric crystal does not touch the calibration block due to the protective layer of the transducer. Based on the thickness of one of the steps of the calibration block and calculated sound velocity, the discontinuity (flaw) detector evaluates the anticipated time of the reflected signal from the bottom of the same step of the calibration block, t_3. The time difference between the recorded time of the received signal, t_1, and the anticipated time, t_3, is actually the *time delay*:

(Eq. 3) $$\Delta t_{\text{delay}} = t_1 - t_3$$

This time delay is indicated on the monitor of the discontinuity (flaw) detector as a *probe delay*. It is worth mentioning that the sound velocity in this procedure is evaluated for a longitudinal wave. A similar technique is used for evaluation of sound velocity and the probe delay using an angle-beam calibration procedure. In this case, the sound velocity is evaluated for shear (or transverse) waves.

Transducer Operation and Theory

Introduction

In ultrasonic testing, the essential sensor of the system is the transducer. As shown in Figure 1, the transducer is a combination of several elements. It performs many functions, all centering around the piezoelectric element and the work it performs.

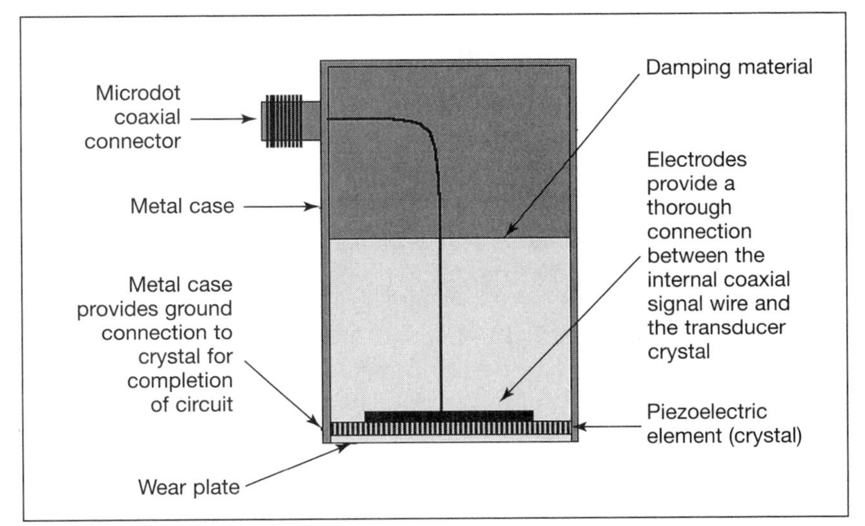

Figure 1: Transducer components.

Piezoelectric Effect

Piezoelectricity is a property of certain crystalline materials including natural crystals of quartz, rochelle salt, and tourmaline, plus manufactured ceramics such as barium titanate and lead zirconate titanates.

The prefix *piezo* is derived from a Greek word meaning "to press." When mechanical pressure is applied to one of these materials, the crystalline structure produces a voltage proportional to the pressure. Conversely, when an electric field is applied, the structure changes shape, producing dimensional changes in the material. Thus, the *piezoelectric effect* refers to a reversible phenomenon whereby a crystal, when vibrated, produces an electric current or, conversely, when an electric current is applied to the crystal, the crystal vibrates.

To produce an ultrasonic beam in a test object, a component of an ultrasonic instrument called a *pulser* applies high-frequency electrical pulses through a coaxial cable to a piezoelectric crystal contained inside of the transducer.

Transducer Materials

Early developers of ultrasonic transducers found that naturally occurring quartz crystal, when sliced into a very thin wafer and shaped into a coin-like disk, worked well for transmitting sound into and receiving sound from test materials. The most common piezoelectric materials used in ultrasonic transducers from the 1930s through the early 1980s were quartz, polarized ceramic, barium titanate, and lithium sulfate. Barium titanate was regarded as the best material to use as a transmitting crystal, while lithium sulfate was widely thought to be the best material for receiving ultrasonic vibrations. Today, the most common crystalline components of the ceramic transducer elements are barium titanate, lead metaniobate, and lead zirconate titanate.

Since the early 1980s, ultrasonic crystal elements have changed in an important way. The ability to manufacture crystals has improved on the single-dimensional crystals found in nature. Now, barium titanate, lead zirconate, lead titanate, and many others are available in precision-molded ceramic wafers that demonstrate improved performance compared to natural crystals.

The composition, shape, and dimensions of a piezoelectric ceramic element can be tailored to meet the requirements of a specific application. Ceramics manufactured from formulations of lead zirconate and lead titanate (known as *PZT materials*) exhibit greater sensitivity and higher operating temperatures, relative to ceramics of other compositions, and are the most widely used piezoelectric elements. These newer ultrasonic elements are commonly described as *polarized ceramics*.

Frequency

The frequency of a transducer is a determining factor in its use. For example, a technician making thickness determinations on thin-wall 0.06 in. (1.5 mm) tubing would choose a 10 MHz transducer to resolve signals returning from very short distances. A technician performing shear wave inspection may prefer to use a 2.25 MHz transducer, which provides a combination of good sensitivity and good penetrating ability because of its longer wavelength.

A technician may choose a transducer of a given frequency based on the sensitivity that a project specification requires. (Sensitivity is related to wavelength: the higher the frequency, the shorter the wavelength, which produces better sensitivity.) A higher frequency is required if the technician wishes to obtain higher levels of sensitivity.

Most ultrasonic testing is performed using frequencies between 0.2 and 25 MHz, with contact testing generally limited to 10 MHz and below because crystals ground for use above 10 MHz are too thin and fragile to be practical.

Transducer frequency and crystal thickness are integrally related:

- The thinner the crystal, the higher the frequency.
- The thicker the crystal, the lower the frequency.

Other considerations for selecting a transducer for a specific assignment include the following:

1. The higher the frequency of a transducer, the narrower the beam spread of the sound wave and the greater the sensitivity and resolution. The attenuation is also greater, but the penetration is poor.
2. The lower the frequency of a transducer, the deeper the penetration and the less the attenuation. However, with the greater beam spread, the sensitivity is less and the resolution is poorer.
3. At any given frequency, the larger the transducer, the narrower the sound beam but the less the sensitivity.
4. When testing cast metallic materials that have coarse grain structures, lower frequencies of no more than 1 to 2.25 MHz are required in order to penetrate to the opposite surface. Even lower frequencies (down to 200 kHz) are required for ultrasonic tests of wood and concrete.

Near Field and Far Field

In ultrasonic testing, the sonic beam is generally regarded as a straight-sided projection of the face of the transducer. In reality, the beam is neither straight-sided nor energy-consistent along the beam centerline. If sound-beam intensity is measured at various distances from the transducer, two distinct zones are always found within the sonic beam, as illustrated in Figure 2. These zones are known as the *near field*, or *fresnel zone*, and the *far field*, or *fraunhofer zone*.

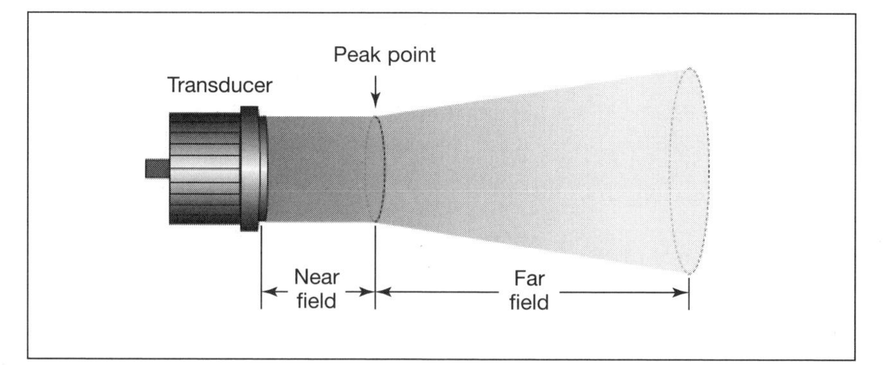

Figure 2: Zones within the ultrasonic beam.

Near Field

In the zone closest to the transducer, measurements reveal an irregular pattern of localized high and low intensities. This irregular pattern results from the interference between sound waves that are emitted from the face of the transducer. The transducer may be considered a mosaic of crystals, each vibrating at the same frequency but slightly out of phase with each other. Near the face of the crystal, the composite sound beam propagates chiefly as a plane front wave. However, the spherical front

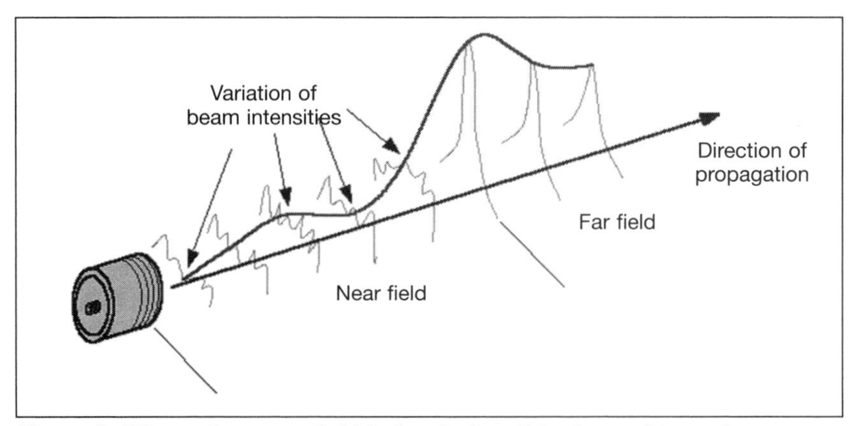

Figure 3: Ultrasonic wave field in front of a disk-shaped transducer.

waves, which emanate from the periphery of the crystal face, produce side-lobe waves that interfere with the plane front waves. This causes patterns of acoustical maximums and minimums where they cross, as shown in Figure 3.

The effect of these acoustical patterns in the near-field zone varies during an ultrasonic test. However, if the technician has proper knowledge of the near field, the correct reference block can be scanned and correlated with the indications from the test.

The length of the near field is dependent on the diameter of the transducer and the wavelength of the ultrasonic beam, and may be computed as:

(Eq. 1) $$L = \frac{D^2}{4\lambda}$$

where
- L = the length of the near field
- D = the diameter of the transducer
- λ = the wavelength of the ultrasonic energy

With reference to Equation 2 (Chapter 1), λ can be replaced with V/f, so this formula can be rewritten as:

(Eq. 2) $$L = \frac{D^2 f}{4V}$$

where
- V = the sound velocity of the material
- f = the frequency of the transducer

Since the wavelength of ultrasonic energy in a particular material is inversely proportional to the frequency, the length of the near field in a particular material can be shortened by lowering the frequency.

Far Field

In the zone farthest from the transducer, the only effect of consequence is the spreading of the ultrasonic beam and the natural attenuation effect of the material. The highest sound intensity occurs at the end of the near field/beginning of the far field. From that point on, the beam intensity is reduced by the attenuation characteristics of the material in which it is traveling and by beam spread.

Beam Spread

Fraunhofer diffraction causes the beam to spread starting at the end of the near field. At this distance, the beam originates at the center of the radiating face of the transducer and spreads outward, as shown in Figure 4.

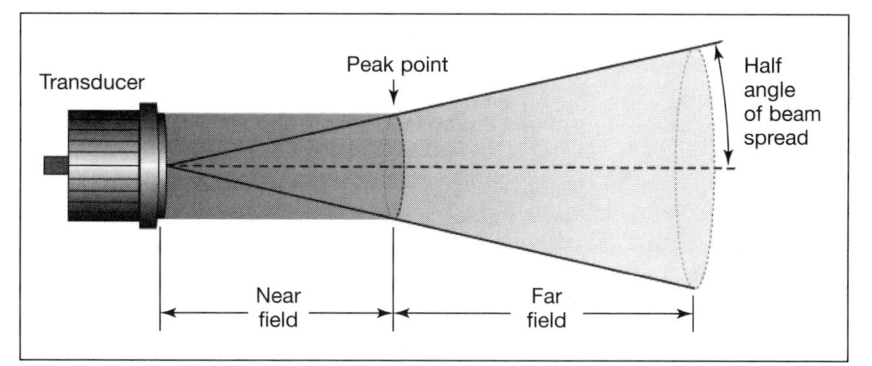

Figure 4: Beam spread computation.

The degree of spread may be computed as:

(Eq. 3) $$\sin\theta = 1.22\frac{\lambda}{D}$$

where

θ = the half angle of spread
λ = the wavelength of the ultrasonic energy
D = the diameter of the transducer

Again, by substituting V/f for λ, the equation becomes:

(Eq. 4) $$\sin\theta = 1.22\frac{V}{Df}$$

where

f = the frequency of the transducer
V = the sound velocity in the material

Calculations of the near field and far field are illustrated in Figure 5.

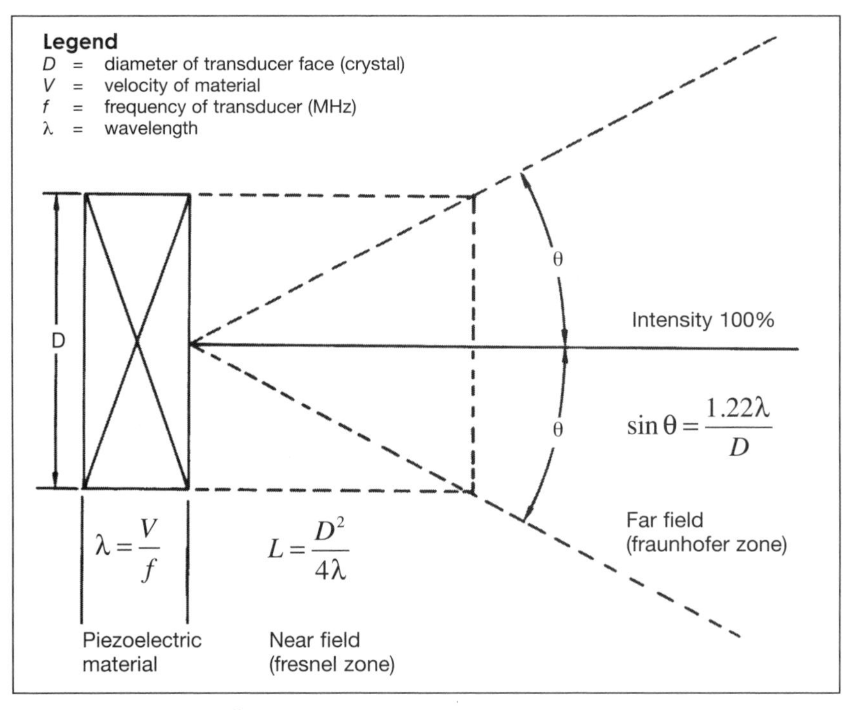

Figure 5: Beam profile.

At any frequency, the larger the crystal, the narrower the beam; the smaller the crystal, the greater the beam spread. Also, there is less beam spread for the same diameter of crystal at higher frequencies than at lower frequencies. The diameter of the transducer is often limited by the size of the available contact surface. Transducers as small as 0.125 in. (3.2 mm) diameter have been used. For shallow depth testing, 0.4 in. (10 mm) and 0.5 in. (13 mm) diameter transducers are used at higher frequencies of 5 to 25 MHz. A large-diameter transducer is usually selected for testing through greater depths of material.

Table 1 shows that as frequency is increased and as transducer diameter is increased, beam spread is decreased. Conversely, as frequency is decreased and as transducer diameter is decreased, beam spread increases. The ultrasonic technician must carefully choose a transducer to fit the job at hand. The proper combination of frequency and diameter has a strong influence on the success of the test.

Table 1: Beam spread in steel.

Frequency (MHz)	λ – in. (mm)	Transducer diameter – in. (mm)			
		0.375 (9.5)	0.5 (12.7)	0.75 (19.05)	1.0 (25.4)
1	0.2287 (5.8)	48° 10'	34°	21° 52'	16° 13'
2.25	0.102 (2.6)	19° 23'	14° 25'	9° 33'	7° 9'
5	0.0457 (1.16)	8° 34'	6° 25'	4° 16'	3° 12'

Side-Lobe Radiation

In addition to the main sound beam, *side-lobe beams* of ultrasonic energy are generated by the piezoelectric element or crystal. Side-lobe beams are produced as a function of transducer diameter and frequency. These waves may travel nearly parallel to the test surface, a phenomenon illustrated in Figure 6. If possible, the technician selects transducers that minimize side lobes so that the primary beam is the only one of consequence. Side-lobe beams must be considered when the geometry of the test object is such that they are reflected back to the transducer, causing nonrelevant reflections from the nearby top corner edges of a test object.

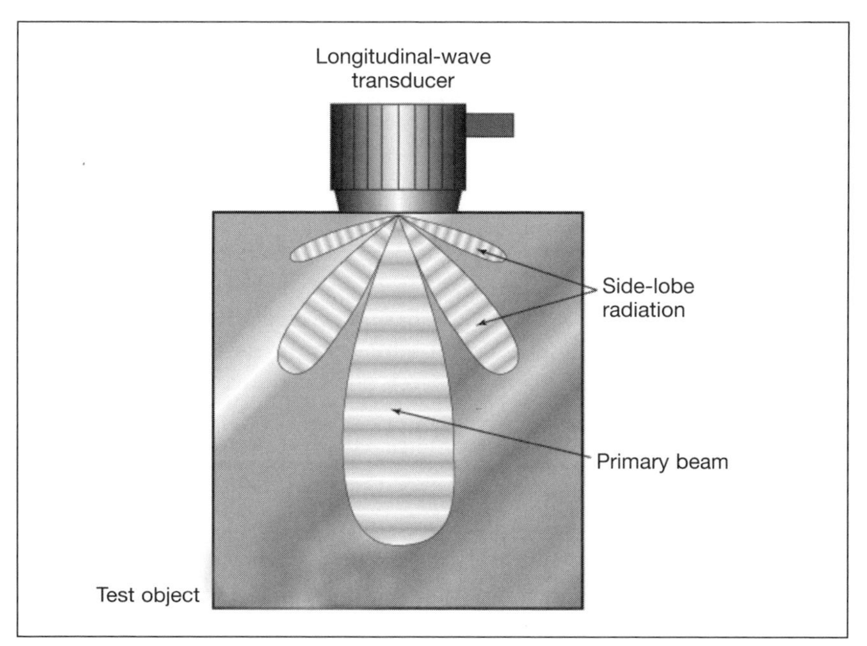

Figure 6: Side-lobe radiation.

Types of Transducers

Transducers are made in a limitless number of sizes and shapes, from diameters as extremely small as 0.008 in. (0.2 mm) to paintbrush transducers as wide as 6 in. (150 mm). The size of a transducer is a contributing factor to its performance. For instance, the larger the transducer, the narrower the sound beam (less beam spread) for a given frequency. The narrower beams of small, high-frequency transducers have greater ability for detecting very small discontinuities. Larger transducers transmit more sound energy into the test object, so they are used to gain deep penetration. Large, single-crystal transducers are generally limited to lower frequencies because very thin, high-frequency transducers are susceptible to breaking and chipping.

Paintbrush Transducers

Wide *paintbrush transducers* are made up of a mosaic pattern of smaller crystals carefully matched so that the intensity of the beam pattern varies very little over the entire length of the transducer. This is necessary to maintain uniform sensitivity. Paintbrush transducers provide a long, narrow, rectangular beam (in cross section) for scanning large surfaces. Their purpose is to quickly discover discontinuities in the test object. Smaller, more sensitive transducers are then used to define the size, shape, orientation, and exact location of the discontinuities. A typical paintbrush transducer is shown in Figure 7.

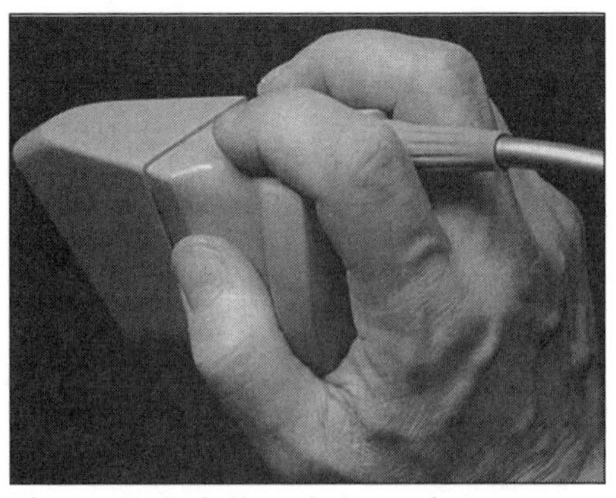

Figure 7: Paintbrush transducer.

Dual Transducers

Dual transducers differ from single transducers in that two piezoelectric elements are used. Whereas the single transducer may be a transmitter only, a receiver only, or both transmitter and receiver, the dual transducer is essentially two single transducers mounted in the same holder for *pitch-catch testing*. In the dual transducer, one transducer is the transmitter and the other, the receiver. They may be mounted side by side for longitudinal-wave testing or either stacked or paired side by side for shear-wave testing. In all cases, the crystals are separated by a sound barrier to block cross-talk interference. Figure 8 shows both types of dual transducers.

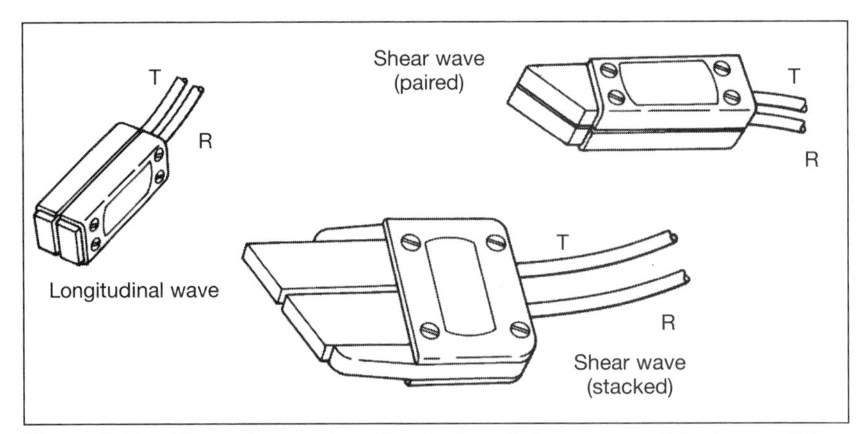

Figure 8: Dual transducers: longitudinal and shear wave (T = transmitting; R = receiving).

Longitudinal- and Shear-Wave Transducers

Transducers are also classified as either longitudinal-wave or shear-wave transducers. When the sound energy from the transducer is transmitted into the test object in a direction perpendicular to the test surface, an often-substituted name for a longitudinal-wave transducer is *straight-beam transducer* or *probe*.

Shear-wave transducers direct the sound beam into the test surface at an angle that is not perpendicular. An alternative term for a shear-wave transducer is *angle-beam transducer*. Shear-wave transducers are used to locate discontinuities oriented at angles to the surface and to determine the size of discontinuities oriented at angles between 90° and 180° to the surface.

Angled plastic (usually acrylic polymer) *shoes* are mechanically attached to longitudinal-wave transducers to propagate shear, surface, or plate waves into the test object by mode conversion. In contact testing, angle-beam transducers use a *wedge*, usually made of plastic, between the transducer face and the surface of the test object to direct the sound energy into the test surface at the desired angle. In immersion testing, control of the sound beam into the test object is achieved by means of an adjustable-angle transducer holder. Both straight- and angle-beam transducers are shown in Figure 9.

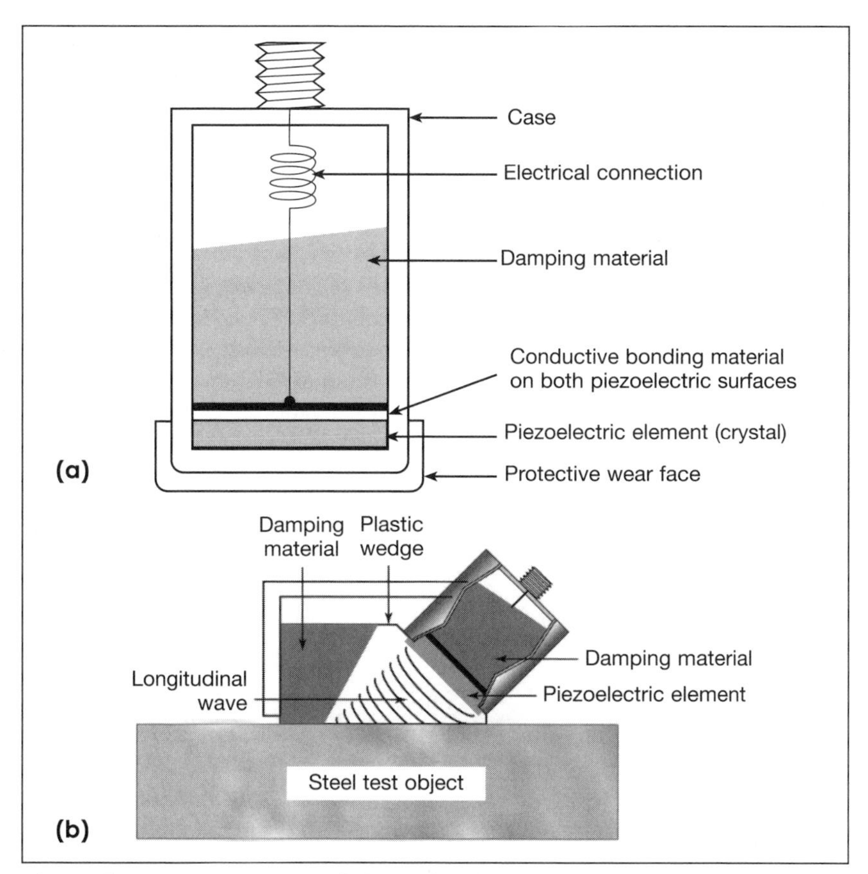

Figure 9: Transducer types: (a) longitudinal- and (b) shear-wave transducers.

Faced-Unit or Contour-Focused Transducers

In addition to wedges, other frontal members are added to the transducer for various reasons. On contact transducers, *wear plates* are often added to protect the front electrode and to protect the fragile crystal from wear, breakage, or the harmful effects of foreign substances or liquids. (Notice the protective wear face of the longitudinal transducer in Figure 9.)

Frontal units shaped to direct the sound energy perpendicular to the surface at all points on curved surfaces are known as *contour correction lenses.* These cylindrical lenses sharpen the front surface indication by evening out the sound travel distance between the transducer and the test surface. A comparison of flat and contoured transducers is shown in Figure 10.

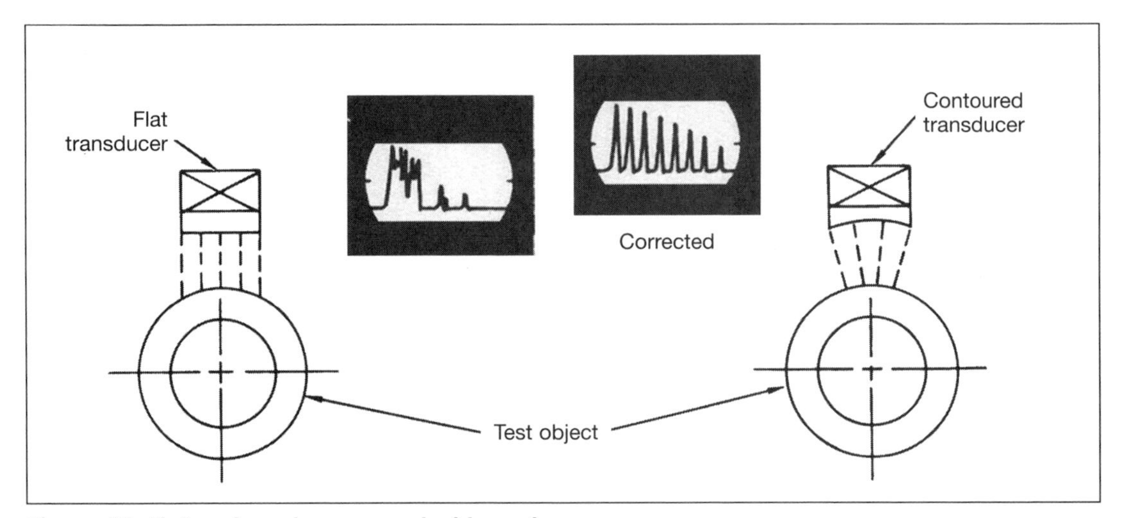

Figure 10: Flat and contour-corrected transducers.

Other acoustic lenses focus the sound beam from the transducer. Focused transducers concentrate the sound energy into a narrow, sharp, pointed beam of increased intensity capable of detecting very small discontinuities in a relatively small area. Focusing the sound beam moves its point of maximum intensity toward the transducer but shortens its usable range. The test object has the effect of a second lens because the beam is refracted, as shown in Figure 11, when the beam enters the test surface.

The increased intensity results in increased sensitivity. Moving the point of maximum intensity closer to the transducer, which is also closer to the test surface, improves the near-surface resolution. Disturbing effects of a rough surface and metal noise are also reduced by concentrating the sound energy into a smaller beam covering a smaller area. In a smaller area, true discontinuity indications are relatively large compared to the combined noise of other, nonrelevant indications. The useful thickness range of focused transducers is about 0.01 to 2 in. (0.25 to 51 mm).

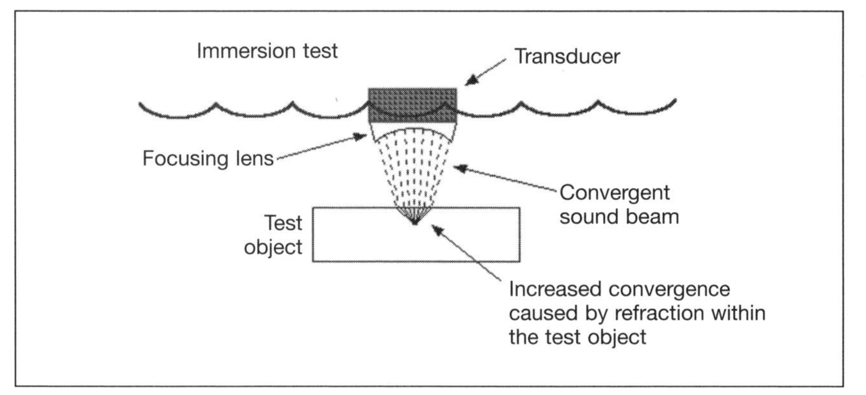

Figure 11: Focused beam shortening in metal.

Phased Arrays

Special transducers known as *linear arrays* or *phased arrays* can be focused using electronic phase control. A typical linear array is shown in Figure 12. The linear array is a collection of very small transducers, with each transducer able to act as a transmitter or receiver. Transducer width may be as small as 0.02 in. (0.5 mm) and an array may consist of several hundred small transducers. By selectively pulsing each transducer or group of transducers in a given order, the ultrasonic beam may be focused in depth or be made to sweep across the test object without moving the array. (More detailed information about phased array testing is provided in Chapter 10.)

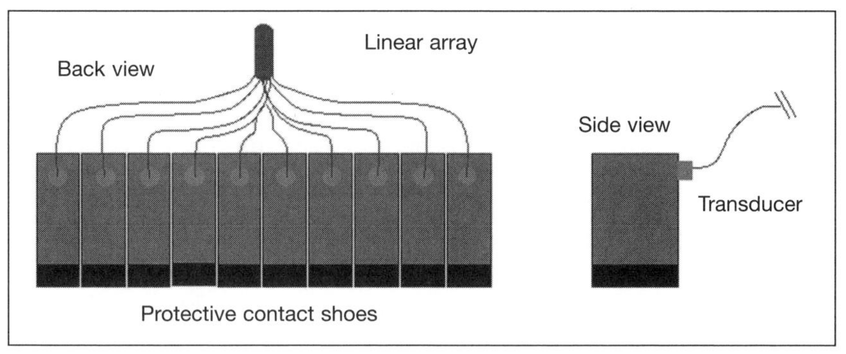

Figure 12: Linear array may be built to contain almost any number of transducers, and may be built to any shape required to perform a specific test.

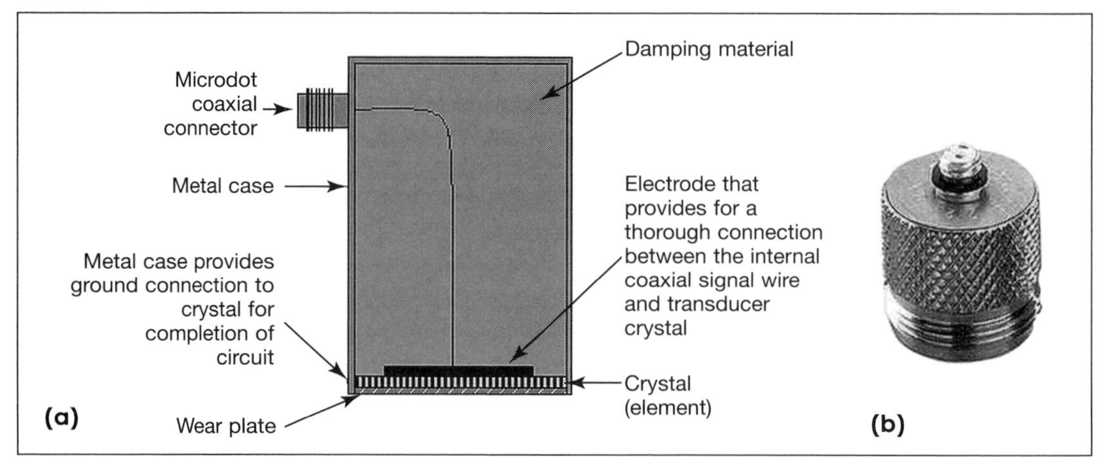

Figure 13: Longitudinal-wave transducers: (a) contact transducer construction; (b) transducer with threaded end for attaching a wedge or delay line.

Contact and Angle-Beam Transducers

As mentioned, transducers are made for both straight-beam and angle-beam testing. Figure 13(a) illustrates the construction of a longitudinal-wave contact transducer. Pictured in Figure 13(b) is a longitudinal-wave transducer designed to screw into a plastic wedge to be used for angle-beam testing. *Note:* This type of transducer may also be attached to a delay line to improve the resolution of near-surface discontinuities.

Beam Intensity Characteristics

The strongest intensity of the sound beam is along its central axis, with a gradual reduction in amplitude away from the axis. In the near field, the measurement of the sonic intensities reveals an irregular pattern of localized high and low intensities. This irregular pattern results from the interference between sound waves that are emitted from the face of the transducer. The effect that the presence of these acoustical patterns in the near field produces on ultrasonic tests varies, but if the technician has accurate knowledge of the length of the near field, the proper test block can be scanned and correlated to those indications that originate from within the test object.

In the zone furthest from the transducer (the far field or fraunhofer zone), the only effect of consequence is the spreading of the ultrasonic beam and the natural attenuation effect of the material.

Sensitivity, Resolution, and Damping

The capabilities of a transducer and testing system are for the most part governed by two factors: sensitivity and resolution.

Sensitivity

The *sensitivity* of a transducer is its ability to detect echoes from small discontinuities. Transducer sensitivity is measured by the amplitude of its response from an artificial discontinuity in a standard reference block. Precise transducer sensitivity is unique to a specific transducer.

Even transducers of the same size, frequency, and material by the same manufacturer do not always produce identical indications on a given display screen. A transducer's sensitivity is rated by its ability to detect a given size flat-bottom hole at a specific depth in a standard reference block.

Resolution

The *resolution* or *resolving power* of a transducer refers to its ability to separate the echoes from two reflectors close together in time; for example, the front-surface echo and an echo from a small discontinuity just beneath the surface. The time required for the transducer to stop *ringing* or vibrating after having been supplied with a long voltage pulse is a measure of its near-surface resolving power. Long tails or wave trains of sound energy from a ringing transducer cause a wide, high amplitude echo from all reflectors in the sound path, including the entry surface.

As illustrated in Figure 14(a), a small discontinuity just beneath the surface is easily masked by the ringing signal of the initial pulse. Figure 14, in general, shows that even reflectors at a greater distance are not displayed distinctly due to the same issue of too long a pulse length applied to the transducer. Figure 15 displays additional examples of poor versus good resolution in the far field.

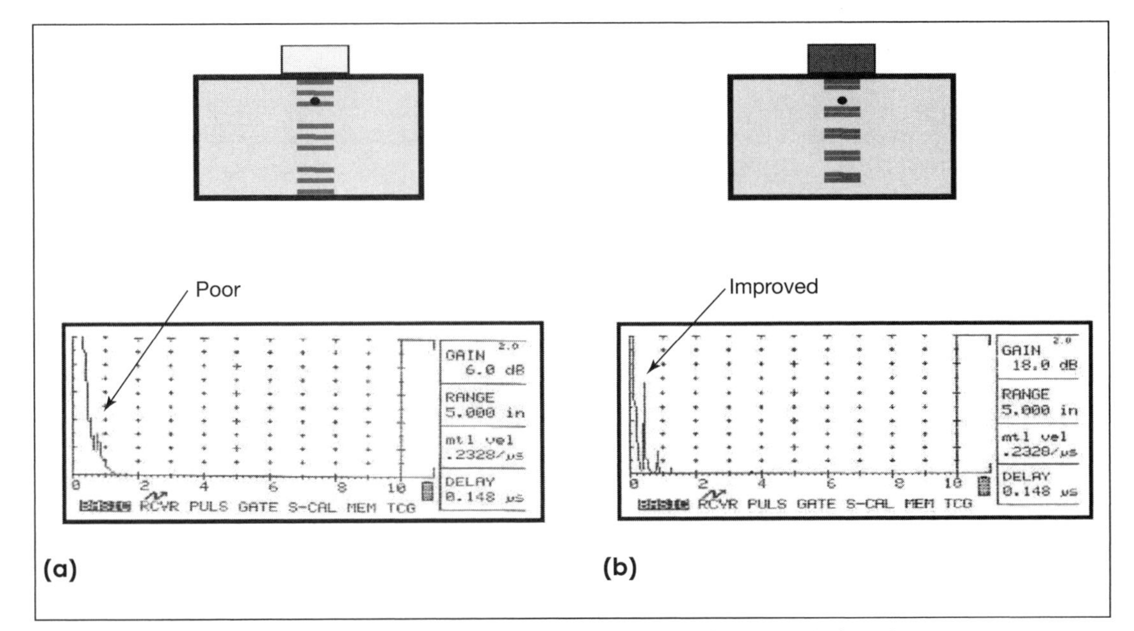

Figure 14: Near surface resolution: (a) poor resolution; (b) improved signal.

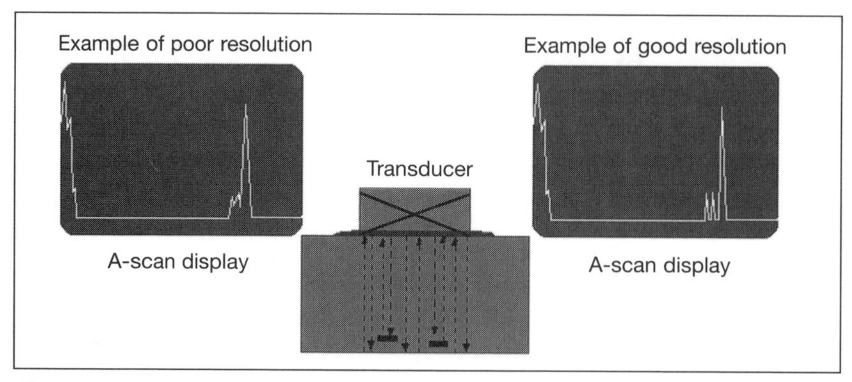

Figure 15: Resolution ability of the transducer.

Spatial Resolution

Spatial resolution relates to the ability of a transducer to differentiate between two or more reflectors that are closely spaced in a lateral plane perpendicular to the axis of sound-beam propagation, as shown in Figure 16. Spatial resolution is a function of the transducer's characteristic near field and beam spread.

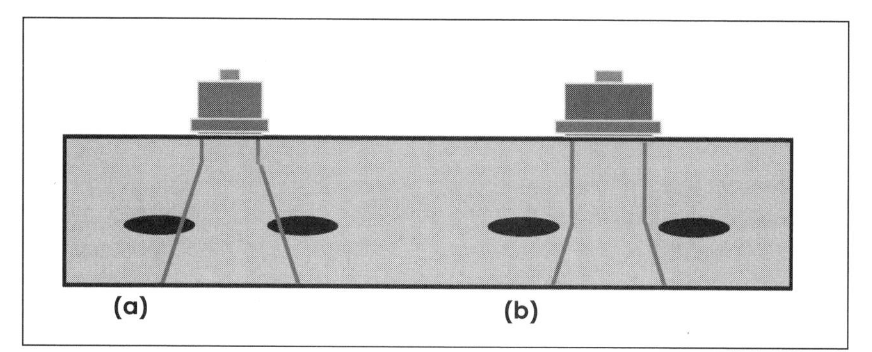

Figure 16: Spatial resolution: (a) good; (b) poor.

Damping

Damping refers to the time required for the crystal to quit vibrating after excitation. The resolution of the transducer is directly related to the *damping time.* The shorter the damping time, the better the ability of the transducer to resolve two signals arriving close together at a given time or to resolve signals from near the contact test surface. Figure 17 illustrates a *dead zone* that takes up 1/10 of the total screen range. Transducer damping and instrument setting are factors shown here.

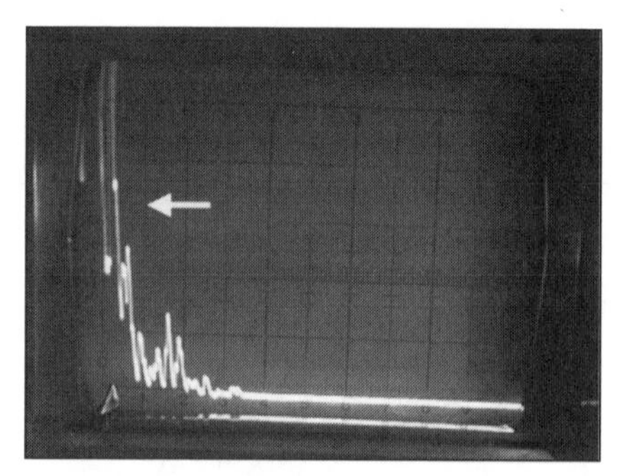

Figure 17: Transducer damping and dead zone.

Couplants

Purpose and Principles

As noted in previous chapters, one of the practical problems in ultrasonic testing is the transmission of the ultrasonic energy from the source into the test object. If a transducer is placed in contact with the surface of a dry test object, very little energy is transmitted through the interface into the material because of the presence of air between the transducer and the test material. The air causes a great difference in acoustic impedance at the interface. This is called an *impedance mismatch*.

Typically, a couplant is used between the transducer face and the test surface to ensure efficient sound transmission from transducer to test surface. The couplant, as the name implies, couples the transducer ultrasonically to the surface of the test object by filling in the gaps between the irregularities of the test surface and the transducer face, thus excluding all air from between the transducer and the test surface.

Materials

The couplant can be any of a vast variety of liquids, semiliquids, pastes, and even some solids that satisfy the following requirements:

1. Wets (fully contacts) both the surface of the test object and the face of the transducer and excludes all air from between them.
2. Is easy to apply.
3. Is homogeneous and free of air bubbles or solid particles in the case of a nonsolid.
4. Is harmless to the test object and transducer.
5. Is easy to remove when the test is complete despite a tendency to stay on the test surface.

Contact Couplant Selection

In contact testing, the choice of couplant depends primarily on the test conditions, such as the roughness or smoothness, temperature, and the position of the test surface (horizontal, slanted, or vertical).

One part glycerin with two parts water and a wetting agent is often used on relatively smooth, horizontal surfaces. For slightly rough surfaces, light oils with an added wetting agent are used. Rough surfaces, hot surfaces, and vertical surfaces require a heavier oil or grease as a couplant. Specialty couplants of varied viscocities for rough-surface and high-temperature applications may be necessary. In all cases, the couplant selected should meet the five criteria listed above.

Immersion Couplant Selection

Clean tap water is most commonly used as an immersion couplant. Several processes and additives are often applied to tap water to improve its performance or reduce its effect on the test material.

Deaeration is important to remove dissolved gases, which can come out of solution and deposit bubbles on the transducer or the test material, interfering with testing. Deaeration can be performed by holding the water at an elevated temperature for a few hours, by spraying through a nozzle, or by exposing it to a partial vacuum. Commercial systems exist for all three processes.

In addition to deaeration, wetting agents are occasionally used to reduce the surface tension of the water. This can improve coupling and help to prevent and remove air bubbles. However, some customers put restrictions on the use of such additives.

For test systems that do not replenish water frequently, algaecides are occasionally added to reduce the growth of algae. Generally, algae does not affect testing but is unsightly and unpleasant. As with wetting agents, some customers also restrict the use of algaecides.

In some circumstances, distilled or deionized water is used to reduce the amount of dissolved substances in the water, with subsequent deaeration. In general, dissolved substances do not affect testing, but certain substances, such as halogens and sulfur compounds, can be harmful to the test material.

In certain circumstances, glycerin is used instead of water, mainly for test material that can be damaged by water or where a slightly higher-performing couplant is needed. However, glycerin requires special processes for proper removal and is not commonly used.

Some test systems maintain the couplant bath at a constant temperature, typically around 70 °F (21 °C) for operator comfort and to eliminate temperature-related variability from the test.

Noncontacting Transducers

Historically, ultrasonic transducers have required a direct link to the test object. The transducer had to be in intimate contact with the test object and coupled by a liquid. In the case of direct contact techniques involving the scanning of large, very rough, or high-temperature surfaces, coupling results in transducers being damaged by mechanical wear or by temperatures above 212 °F (100 °C). In response, several types of *noncontacting transducers* have been developed. However, the noncontacting feature comes with certain constraints. For example, there is a drastic decrease in signal strength and signal-to-noise ratio compared to typical piezoelectric transducers.

Electromagnetic Acoustic Transducers

The development of noncontacting electromagnetic acoustic transducers (EMATs) has provided new and important opportunities for ultrasonic testing. EMATs can generate longitudinal, shear, plate, and surface waves in metallic test objects.

Practical electromagnetic probes consist of a coil wound into a geometrical shape to create a specific mechanical disturbance pattern. The probe also contains a magnet to aid the consistent vertical orientation to the test surface. Since many coil and magnet configurations are possible, many variations of wave patterns have been generated. Figure 18 shows one configuration that generates a 0° shear wave useful for thickness gaging.

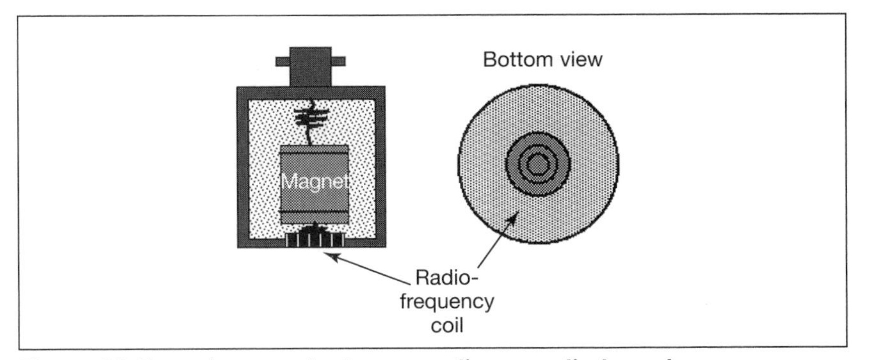

Figure 18: Zero-degree electromagnetic acoustic transducer.

Operating frequencies can be as high as 20 MHz, limiting thickness testing applications to material having wall thickness greater than about 0.04 in. (1.0 mm). The coil diameter, wire size, and magnet size depend on the application and the current available for driving the transducer. This type of transducer is used for thickness gaging in high-speed automatic testing stations.

Electromagnetic acoustic transducers are useful at elevated temperatures for testing metals in the early stages of forming, even while the material is red hot. Although it usually requires the addition of cooling systems for the transducer assembly (coil and magnet), EMAT technology is proving successful as a standard testing application for improving the quality of finished mill products.

Electromagnetic acoustic transducers are also effective when high-speed testing is needed, as in the case of pipelines and railroad wheels. Remote tests of pipelines have been performed from the inside using EMATs and remotely controlled robots called *pigs*. An EMAT's ability to generate lamb or plate waves results in indications of corrosion where the thickness of the pipe has been modified, as it often is near circumferential welds.

Being electrically controlled, EMATs can be combined with phased array technology when modifications of the interrogating ultrasonic beams are needed to improve testing. Where test objects must remain in a vacuum, as in electron beam welding, electromagnetic acoustic transducers also perform well.

The principal disadvantage of EMATs is that relatively low amounts of ultrasonic energy can be transmitted into the material due to air interference. This relative inefficiency often yields lower signal-to-noise ratios than can be achieved with conventional probes. Even though there are still problems with EMATs, scientists are working toward improving several issues that will broaden the applicability of this ultrasonic testing application.

Air-Coupled Transducers

An emerging technology for a broader application of ultrasonic testing is one that uses air (no liquid) as the coupling medium. All the restrictions that relate to the transmission of ultrasound through a low-density material, such as air, have been managed to a degree that the technology can be applied as another ultrasonic testing technique. Relatively low-frequency (under 200 kHz) transducers designed to acoustically match the impedance value of air are key elements to this approach. The transducers are designed to yield relatively large mechanical displacements in air.

Due to the low acoustic velocity of air, relatively small wavelengths can be achieved, although they are quickly attenuated when transmitted. Much of the science that has gone into the development of this technology has centered around improved pulser and receiver circuits within the instruments and transducers designed to transmit sound efficiently into air.

Thus far, most applications have focused on low-impedance materials, such as honeycomb composite structures, using the through-transmission mode. Figure 19 shows several low-frequency (400 KHz down to 50 KHz) transducers used in air coupling.

Figure 19: Low-frequency air-coupled transducers.

Laser-Induced Ultrasound

Another approach for introducing ultrasound into a test object without physical contact takes advantage of the energy stored in a short-duration pulse from a high-energy laser. A mechanical wave is generated by thermal expansion that takes place at the surface contacted by a laser beam. The expansion is oriented normal (perpendicular) to the surface and therefore creates a longitudinal wave within the material. (See Figure 20.)

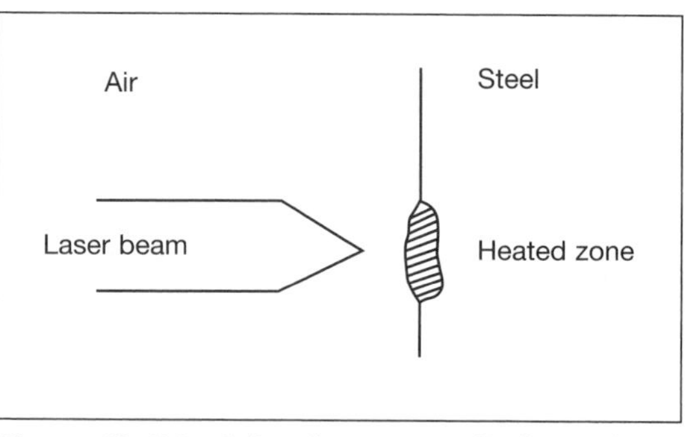

Figure 20: Principle of wave excitation using lasers on a thermal elastic or free surface.

Shorter pulses yield short-duration mechanical disturbances and higher-frequency ultrasonic waves. Regardless of the angle that the laser beam impinges on the test object, the resulting sound beam travels within the test object in a direction that is normal (perpendicular) to that surface. This makes it possible for laser-induced ultrasound to be effective at finding laminar discontinuities, even in curved test objects. Noncontacting and remote systems have been successfully developed using optical interferometers as the receiving sensor. As with electromagnetic acoustic and air-coupled transducers, the acoustic energy is very small and these systems tend to exhibit poor signal-to-noise ratios.

Summary

Table 2 summarizes the material characteristics found using laser ultrasonics, electromagnetic acoustic transducers, and air-coupled transducers to introduce ultrasound into test objects. Unless otherwise specified, the discussions and general examples used throughout the remainder of this book relate to requirements for through-coupling by use of denser materials, such as liquids.

Table 2: Comparison of noncontact ultrasonic generation and detection techniques.

	Laser ultrasonics	Electromagnetic acoustic transducer	Air-coupled transducer
Distance of operation	Large; several meters possible	Millimeters for bulk waves, less for surface, plate or angle beams; performance decreases rapidly with distance	Performance decreases rapidly with distance at 1 MHz and higher; at low frequencies (<50 kHz) many meters of separation is possible
Frequency range	Very large at generation; depends on optical receiver at detection	0.5 to 10 MHz typical	<1 MHz typical; performance decreases rapidly as frequency is increased
Type of waves	Longitudinal, shear vertical, surface, plate	Longitudinal, shear vertical and shear horizontal (both normal to surface and at oblique angles), surface, plate	Longitudinal, (shear vertical, surface, plate by mode conversion)
Orientation	No requirement; sensitivity may decrease at reception away from normal	Should follow the surface	Like conventional transducers
Material	Any, but high laser intensity may damage some materials more than others	Conductive (metals)	Works best with low impedance materials (soft, porous)
Degree of maturity	In development; not yet in industry use	Mature	Mature at low frequences; in development for frequencies >1 MHz
Cost	High (for lasers)	Moderate	Moderate
Safety	May require enclosure or limited access area	No limitation	No limitation
Other features	Operates in vacuum (in space), useful research tool	Operates in vacuum; can control angle of obliquely propagating beams by changing frequency	0.1 to 0.01 atmospheric pressure possible

Basic Ultrasonic Testing Techniques

Introduction

The type of test required for a particular component is usually given in a specification or test procedure that tells the technician the type of discontinuities to look for, the type of test required to locate the discontinuities, and the limits of acceptability. The specification typically provides other basic facts pertinent to the test. It is up to the technician to follow the specification. The sections that follow are intended to familiarize the technician with the basic steps required to conduct satisfactory ultrasonic tests.

Once test instrument controls are adjusted before testing, they are left unchanged because readjustments would negate the standardization and require restandardization of the test system.

Contact Testing

Ultrasonic testing uses one of two basic techniques: *contact testing* or *immersion testing*. In immersion testing, the transducer is separated from the surface of the test material by a significant distance. In contact testing, the transducer is placed in direct contact with the test object with a thin liquid film used as a couplant. On some contact units, plastic wedges, wear plates, or flexible membranes are mounted over the face of the crystal. Transducer units are considered to be "in contact" whenever the transducer or an accessory attached to it is physically touching the test material. The display from a contact unit usually shows the initial pulse and the front-surface reflection as superimposed or very close together.

Contact testing is divided into four techniques that are determined by the sound beam wave mode:

1. Transmitting longitudinal waves in the test object.
2. Generating shear waves.
3. Producing rayleigh (or surface) waves.
4. Producing lamb (or plate) waves.

The couplant is high enough in viscosity to remain on the test surface during the test. (Refer to Chapter 4 for more information on contact transducers and couplants.)

Longitudinal-Wave Technique

The longitudinal-wave technique is accomplished by projecting a sound beam perpendicular to the surface of the test object to obtain reflections from the back surface or from discontinuities between the two surfaces. This technique is also used in through-transmission applications using two transducers where the internal discontinuities interrupt the sound beam, causing a reduction in the received signal.

Pulse-Echo Techniques

Pulse-echo techniques may use either single- or dual-element transducers. Figure 1 shows the single-element longitudinal-wave transducer. The single-element transducer acts as both transmitter and receiver, projecting a pulsed beam of longitudinal waves into the test object and receiving echoes reflected from the back surface and from any discontinuity lying in the beam path.

The dual-element transducer is useful when the test material thickness is relatively thin, typically less than 0.5 in. (13 mm), when the test surface is rough, or when the test object shape is irregular and the back surface is not parallel with the front surface. One transducer transmits and the other receives in a *pitch-catch mode*, as shown in Figure 2. In this case, the receiver unit is receiving back-surface and discontinuity echoes.

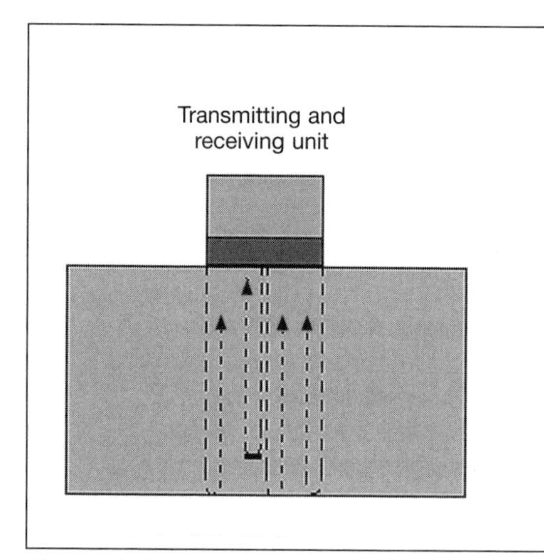

Figure 1: Longitudinal-wave single-element transducer.

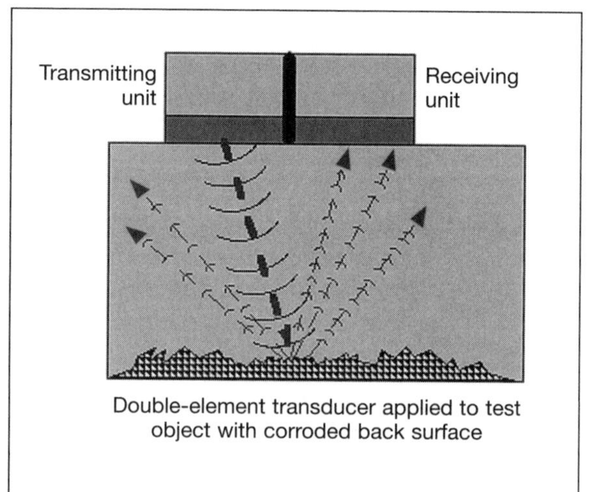

Figure 2: Dual-element longitudinal transducer.

Through-Transmission Technique

With the through-transmission technique, two transducers are used, one on each side of the test object, as shown in Figure 3. One unit acts as a transmitter, and the other as a receiver. The transmitter unit projects a sound beam into the material, the beam travels through the material to the opposite surface, and the sound is picked up at the opposite surface by the receiving unit. Any discontinuities in the path of the sound beam

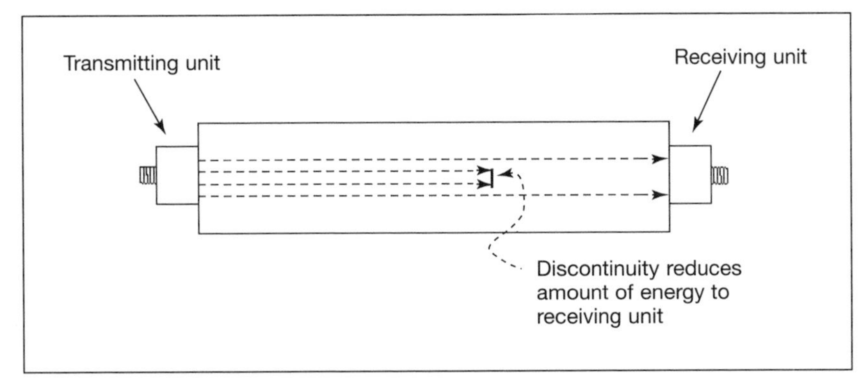

Figure 3: Through-transmission technique.

cause a reduction in the amount of sound energy reaching the receiving unit. For best results, the transmitter unit selected is the best available generator of acoustic energy and the receiver unit is the best available receiver of acoustic energy. Transducer alignment is critical for meaningful test results. Additionally, the front and back surfaces of the test objects must be parallel. Any misalignment or nonparallelism reduces the received signal and can falsely indicate a discontinuity.

Angle-Beam Technique

The angle-beam technique is used to transmit sound waves into the test object at a predetermined angle to the test surface. Depending on the angle selected, the wave modes produced in the test object may be refracted longitudinal and shear waves, shear waves only, or surface (rayleigh) waves. Of these options, the shear-wave mode is most common, particularly as it applies to weld inspection. Figure 4 illustrates shear-wave applications scanning plate and pipe material.

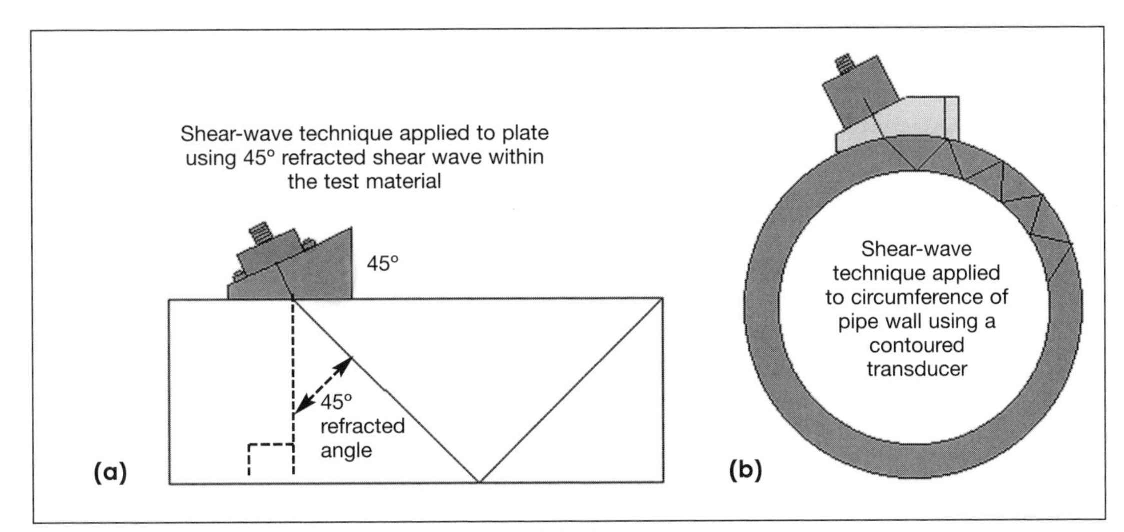

Figure 4: Shear-wave technique: (a) plate; (b) pipe.

Angle-beam techniques are used for testing welds, pipe or tubing, sheet and plate material, and for test objects of irregular shape where straight-beam units are unable to contact all of the surface. Angle-beam transducers are identified by case markings that show sound-beam direction by an arrow and that indicate the angle of refraction in steel for shear waves.

Surface-Wave Technique

Angles of incidence may cause the refracted wave within the test material to become a surface (or rayleigh) wave. This wave mode travels only at or near (within three wavelengths of) the surface of a solid material and exhibits a completely different wave motion than that of longitudinal or shear waves. The creation of a surface wave using a plastic transducer wedge requires that the incident angle in the wedge is greater than the second critical angle. In the case of test objects prone to near-surface discontinuities, especially where the test surface is fairly smooth, surface-wave techniques offer excellent testing results. Figure 5 illustrates this technique. Note the particle motion that the wave causes within the test material compared to that of the longitudinal or shear waves.

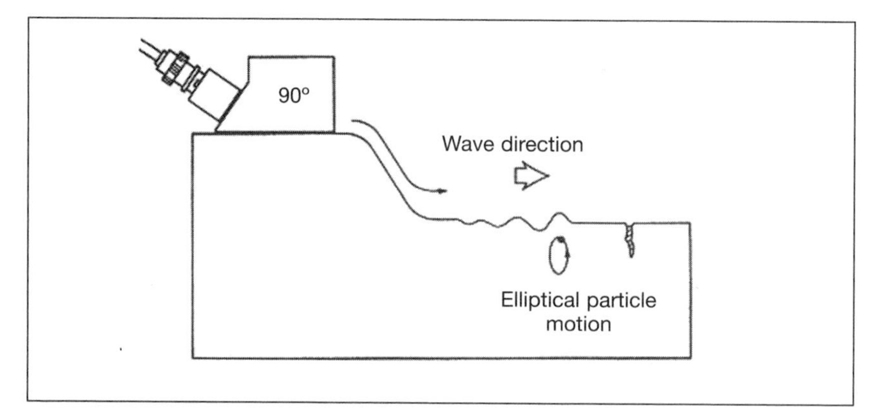

Figure 5: Surface-wave technique.

Immersion Testing

In immersion testing, a liquid-tight transducer is used at some distance from the test object, and the ultrasonic beam is transmitted into the material through a liquid path or column. The water distance appears on the display as a fairly wide space between the initial pulse and the front-surface reflection because of the reduced velocity of sound in the liquid couplant. The test requirements are given in the applicable specification.

The liquid couplant is almost always water, except for some wheel transducers (discussed below) and some exotic applications. For simplicity, the terms *water* and *water path* are often used regardless of the actual couplant composition.

Variations of Immersion Testing

Any one of three techniques may be used in the immersion testing method:

1. The immersion technique, where both the transducer and the test object are immersed in water.
2. The bubbler or squirter technique, where the sound beam is transmitted through a column of flowing water, as shown in Figure 6(a).
3. The wheel-transducer technique, where the transducer is mounted in the axle of a liquid-filled tire that rolls on the test surface, as shown in Figure 6(b).

In all three of these techniques, a *focused transducer* that concentrates the sound beam (much in the way that light beams are concentrated when passed through a magnifying glass) may be used to enhance the test.

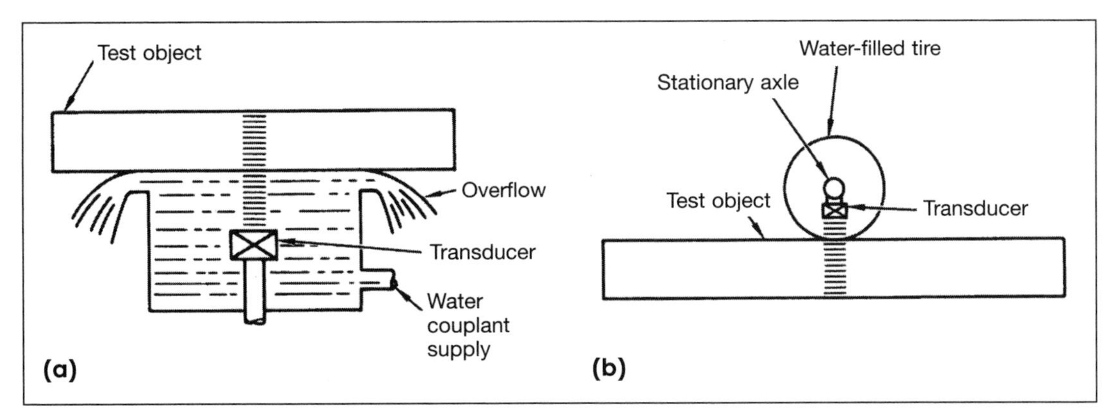

Figure 6: Two variations of immersion testing: (a) bubbler technique; (b) wheel-transducer technique.

Standard Immersion Technique

In immersion testing, both the transducer and the test object are immersed in liquid, typically water. The sound beam is directed through the liquid into the material, generating either longitudinal waves or shear waves in the material. In many automatic scanning operations, focused beams are used to detect discontinuities that are either very small or very close to the near surface.

In immersion testing, both longitudinal- and shear-wave testing of the submerged test object are possible. The entry angle of the ultrasonic wave is adjusted manually or by computer setting to produce the precise angle of wave travel (refraction) through the material that will result in a thorough test for anticipated discontinuity orientations.

Figure 7 shows a typical immersion setup, along with a representation of the display that may be expected in a longitudinal-wave examination.

Figure 8 shows a typical shear-wave immersion setup. Note that the signal from the front surface of the material is very faint, but a very strong signal is obtained from the crack on the far surface.

The correct water path is particularly important when the test area shown on the A-scan display is gated for automatic signaling and recording operations. The water path is carefully set to clear the test area of unwanted signals, in particular the second reflection from the front surface, which could cause misinterpretation.

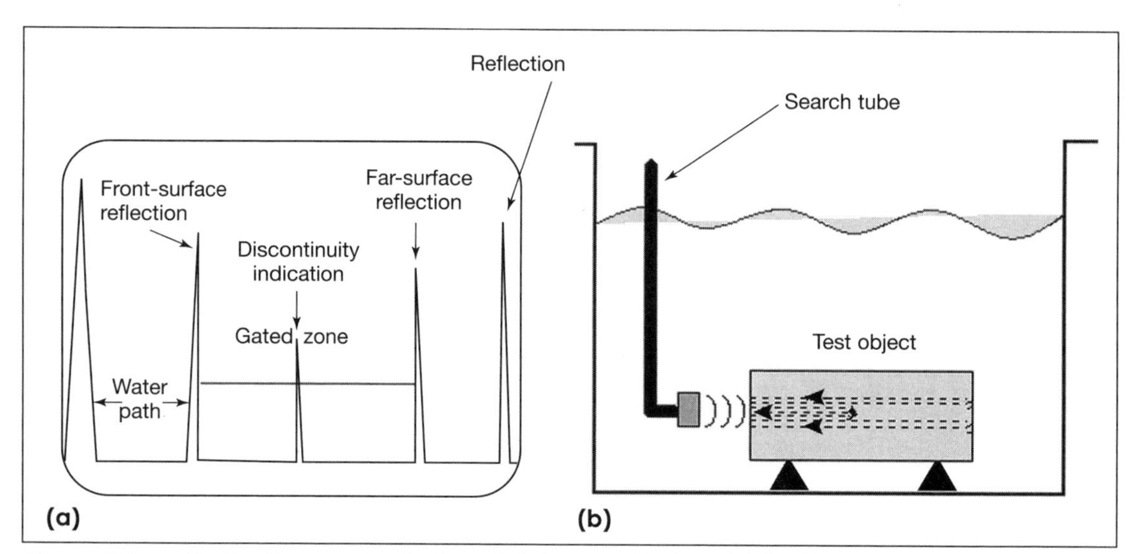

Figure 7: Longitudinal immersion testing: (a) A-scan display; (b) tank.

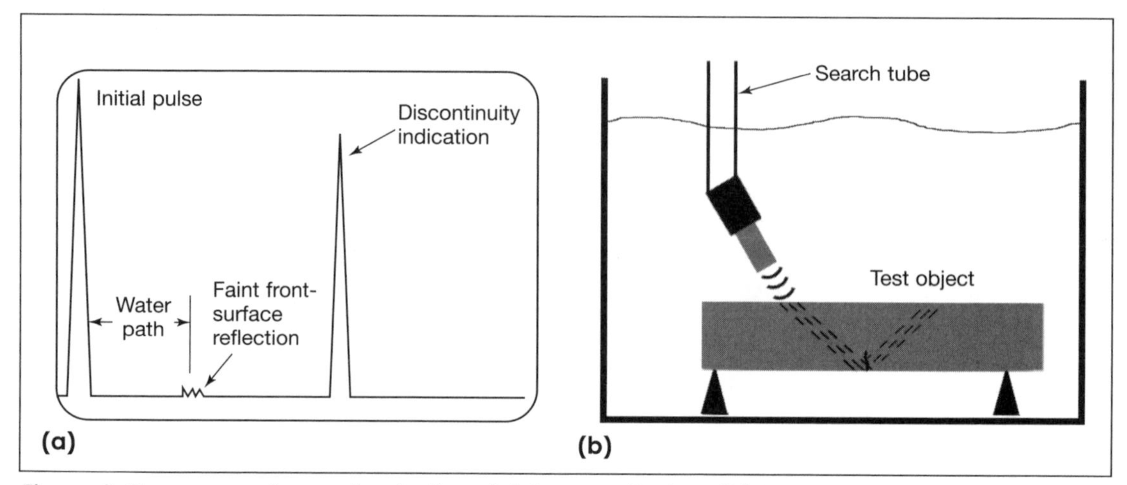

Figure 8: Shear-wave immersion testing: (a) A-scan display; (b) tank.

Bubbler Technique

The bubbler technique is a variation of immersion testing. The bubbler is typically used with an automated system for high-speed scanning of plate, sheet, strip, rail, tubing, and other regularly shaped forms. The sound beam is projected into the material through a column of flowing water and is directed perpendicular to the test surface to produce longitudinal waves. It can also be adjusted at an angle to the surface to produce shear waves.

Figure 9 illustrates a bubbler system that is used to test sheet metal moving over a fixed transducer station at high speeds. The same system is also adaptable for use in high-speed scanners that can be attached to large immovable objects, such as bridge girders or pressure vessels.

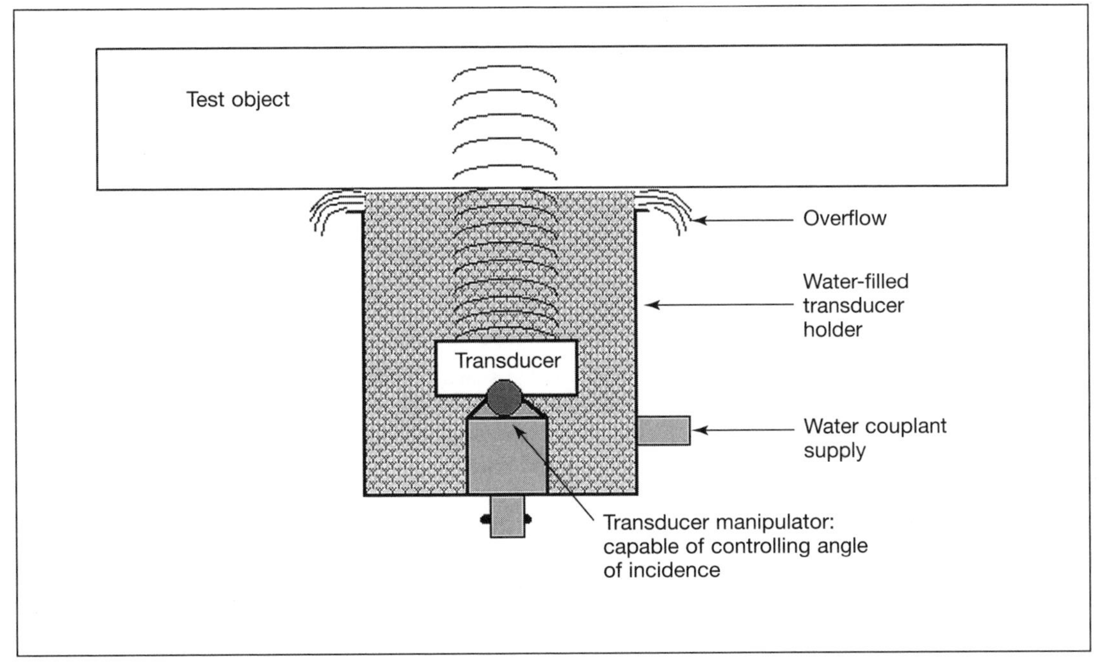

Figure 9: Bubbler technique.

Wheel-Transducer Technique

The wheel-transducer technique is a variant of immersion testing in that the sound beam is projected through a liquid-filled tire into the test object. The transducer, mounted in the wheel axle, is held in a fixed position while the wheel and tire rotate freely. The wheel may be mounted on a mobile apparatus that runs across the material, or it may be mounted on a stationary fixture where the material is moved past it.

It is common practice within the railroad industry to use this ultrasonic testing technique. Wheel transducers are fixed to carriages that are mounted to rail vehicles. Each of the wheels may contain several transducers, which may be positioned to perform longitudinal and shear tests to detect internal discontinuities within the rails.

Figure 10 illustrates the stationary transducer/moving wheel technique. The position and angle of the transducer mounting on the wheel axle may be adjusted to project the desired angle into the test object.

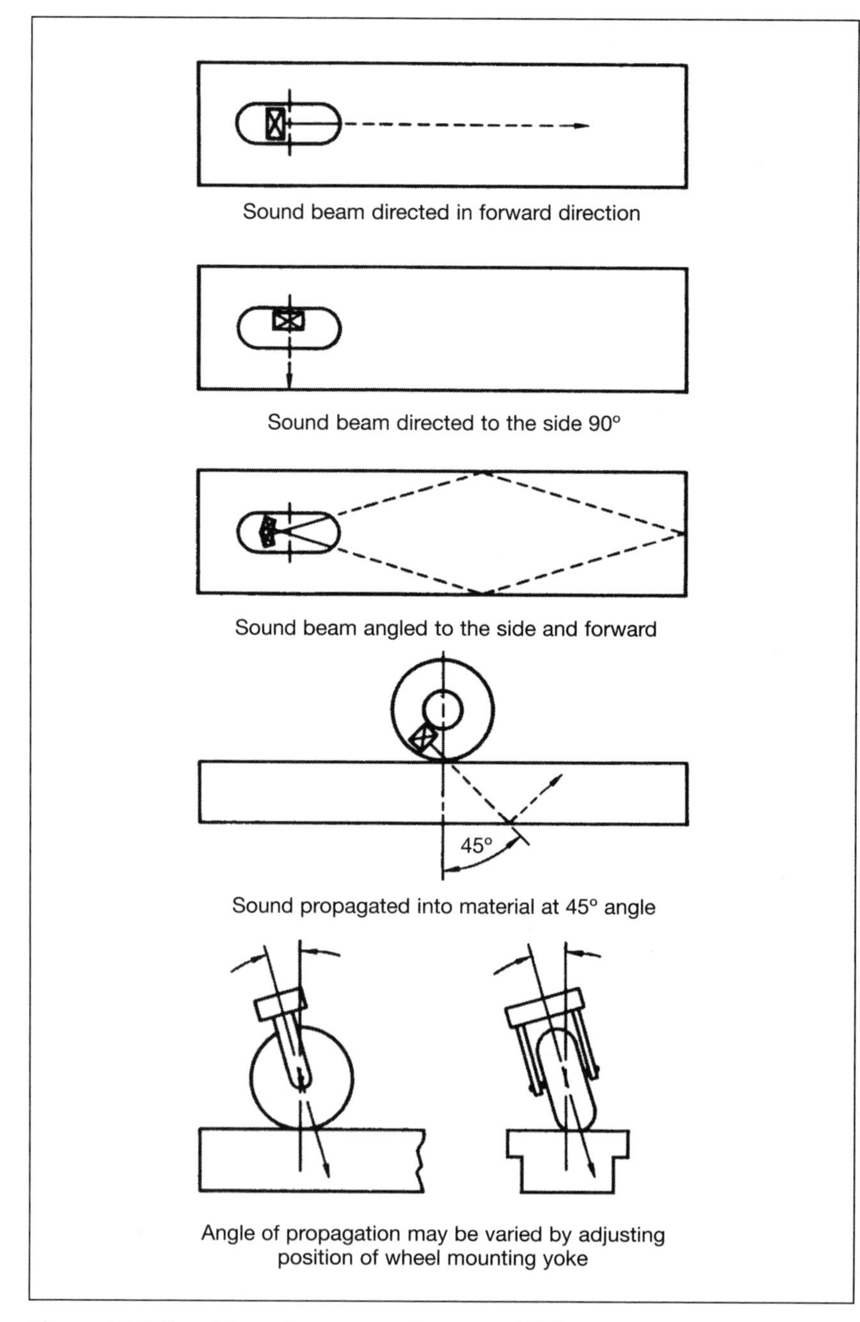

Figure 10: Wheel transducer angular capabilities.

LEVEL
II

Principles of Ultrasonics

Importance of Ultrasonic Testing

Materials used in the manufacturing of industrial products can sometimes have characteristics that adversely affect the product's intended performance. For example, a small crack in the steel used to build a bridge can grow to a size that reduces the steel's strength to a fraction of what the structure needs for safe operation. As seen in the previous Level I studies, ultrasonic testing is one of the nondestructive testing methods used to detect cracks and other service-threatening conditions that can lead to premature failure of critical structures and systems. This chapter reviews the fundamental concepts and various display presentations that allow the ultrasonic technician to investigate and understand the test material, as well as the ultrasonic testing techniques commonly applied in current industrial settings.

Overview of Ultrasonic Testing

Ultrasonic testing is a versatile nondestructive testing method used to detect service-threatening conditions in both raw materials and finished products. The test is based on a high-frequency mechanical vibration (sound wave) that is made to pass through a test object. To ensure reliable results, the sound wave must be introduced in a consistent and predictable manner. Since high-frequency sound waves travel similar to the beam of light from a flashlight, the sound beam can be aimed throughout a test object. Ultrasound is reflected by the boundary between dissimilar materials. For example, sound reflects from a water-solid interface as well as from a boundary between a solid and a gas. Voids or cracks in a material also form reflective interfaces.

Unlike light waves, sound waves cannot be seen. The mechanical vibrations used for nondestructive testing are sound waves at a relatively high frequency or pitch. Vibrations with frequencies above the human range of hearing are called *ultrasonic*. For most people, this occurs at frequencies of 20 kHz or higher.

Five Basic Elements of Ultrasonic Testing

There are five basic elements common to most ultrasonic testing systems:

1. Source of energy.
2. Probing medium.
3. Modifier.
4. Sensitive detector.
5. Display.

Figure 1 illustrates an ultrasonic testing system using these five basic elements.

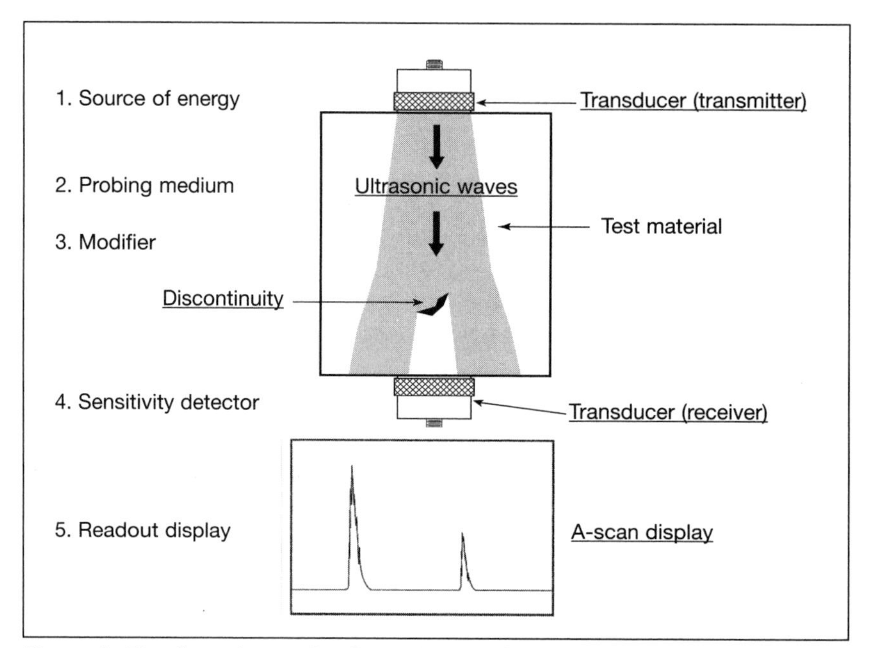

Figure 1: The five elements of nondestructive testing (numbered) used in an ultrasonic testing system (underlined).

Energy Source

The first element is the *source of energy* that creates the ultrasonic waves. Ultrasonic waves are usually created using transducers that convert electrical pulses into short bursts or pulses of mechanical vibration. Piezoelectricity is a unique material characteristic that converts electrical pulses into ultrasonic pulses and vice versa. Piezoelectric materials are important components of ultrasonic transducers.

Probing Medium

The ultrasonic wave, representing the second element of the test method, is referred to as the *probing medium*. It is used to penetrate test objects in search of discontinuities or other conditions.

Typical undesirable conditions include insufficient material thickness, the presence of cracks and voids, or poor bonding between layers of laminated structures. These conditions can exist in the raw materials from which an object is made or they may be introduced during a manufacturing process. Service-generated factors, such as corrosion, overloading, or cyclic stresses, can also degrade the usefulness of a critical test object or assembly.

Modifier

The third element of ultrasonic testing is some material feature that modifies ultrasonic waves as they pass through the test object. Since ultrasonic waves are mechanical, any change in the mechanical continuity of a test object alters the progress of probing sound waves. A wave can be reflected in a new direction, or, in the case of several small reflectors, it can be scattered into many different directions. For example, a crack in a steel bar represents a very large change in density at the surface of the crack. This is because the density of the air in the crack is much less than the density of the surrounding steel. An ultrasonic wave encountering a crack is reflected by the crack's surface.

Detector

The fourth element is a sensitive detector capable of registering changes experienced by the probing medium. Such changes can involve wave redirection or unexpected alterations to wave strength. In ultrasonic testing, a transducer is operated as a receiver of ultrasonic pulses and scanned over the external surface of test objects, identifying changes in sound-beam direction and pulse strength. Figure 2 shows a sound pulse emitted by the source (or sending) transducer. A receiving transducer detects the pulse when it is positioned face to face on the opposite side of

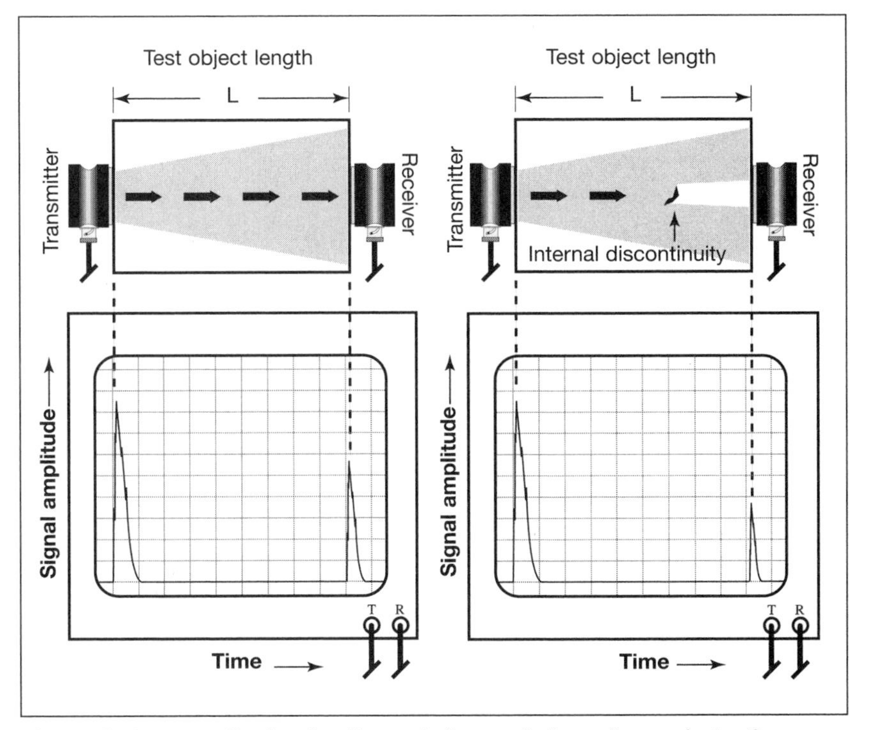

Figure 2: A-scan display for through-transmission ultrasonic testing.

the test object. This configuration, called *through transmission*, is often used to assess the uniformity of test objects throughout their thickness. It is particularly sensitive to the presence of voids, separations, and related irregularities found within test materials.

Display

The fifth element of ultrasonic testing is the readout display. Basic ultrasonic testing instruments display the pulses (amplitude and time of arrival) detected by the receiving transducer. More sophisticated systems gather this same information from many receiver sites and can present graphical displays showing how the acoustic characteristics of the test object vary throughout its cross section or its entire volume.

Ultrasonic Instrumentation

Many configurations now exist for ultrasonic testing instrumentation and system hardware. The increasing ability to interface computers with ultrasonic systems for interpretation, as well as the miniaturization of electronic components, has widened the scope of applications for the ultrasonic method.

The ultrasonic testing instrument has three basic functions.

1. To produce an electrical pulse that generates a stress wave in the transducer.
2. To amplify the weak echo signals received from within the test object.
3. To display the returned information in a meaningful way.

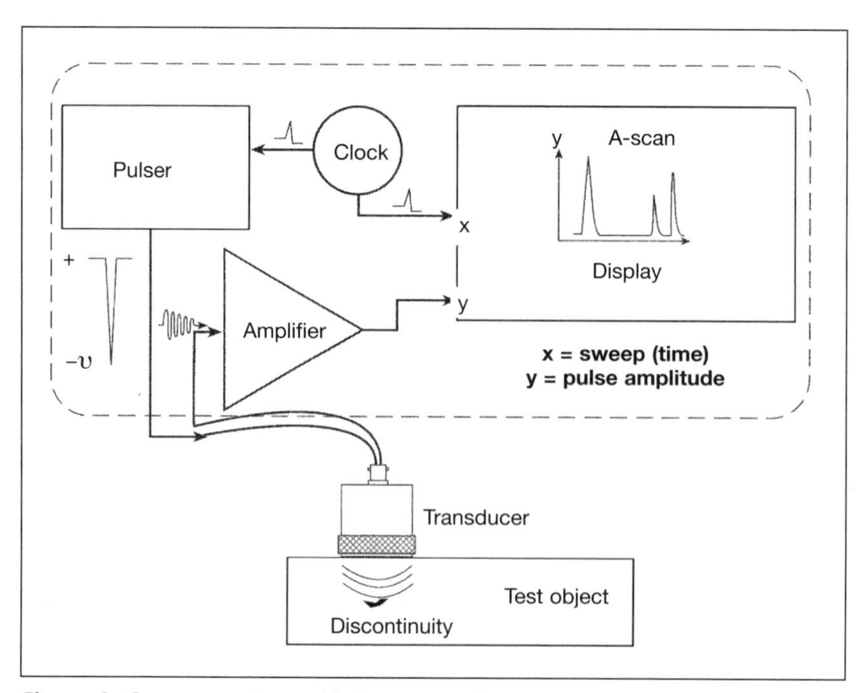

Figure 3: Components and interconnections of a basic discontinuity detector.

Each ultrasonic testing instrument has a pulser, an amplifier, and a display device. In order to refresh the information being displayed by the instrument, a system *timing circuit* is used to repeatedly pulse the transducer and to synchronize the display. Figure 3 shows the interconnection of these components along with the connection of a pulse-echo transducer (both transmitter and receiver).

Pulser

When triggered by the clock circuit, most pulsers emit a sharp, unidirectional, spiked pulse that is sent through the coaxial cable to the transducer. In older units, this voltage spike was as high as 1000 V. In newer, digitized instruments with highly efficient transducers and more powerful amplifiers, the excitation voltage may be only 200 to 300 V.

In some instruments, the pulser is adjustable to adapt the instrument to different testing conditions. Lower-voltage pulses tend to be shorter, yielding better resolution to signals from closely spaced reflectors. Higher voltages create stronger acoustic pulses that penetrate to greater depths in highly attenuative materials. To create an electrical match between the pulser circuit and the transducer, supplemental resistance can be used to attain better power transfer. Power transfer is best when the electrical impedance of the transducer matches the output impedance of the pulser circuit.

Pulse Characteristics

Certain pulse characteristics are controlled electronically by the ultrasonic testing instrument. Typically, pulse height (input energy) and duration are adjustable. Although the variability in an individual ultrasonic testing instrument might be limited, conventional units are available that generate pulses from 100 V to 1000 V.

The crisp, short-duration (single-cycle) pulse is used when high resolution of small reflectors is important. The longest pulse is used when penetration is particularly difficult in highly attenuative materials.

The pulse repetition rate (PRR) at which the pulser is excited is also variable. The PRR directly affects the speed at which materials can be tested, particularly in automatic systems. The degree of test coverage can be reduced if the transducer is scanned over a surface at a high speed while the PRR is relatively low.

The output pulse is converted to an elastic wave within the transducer and transmitted into the test object as a stress wave. Depending on reflector orientation and makeup, only part of the stress wave will return to the transducer. After the detected stress wave is reconverted into an electrical signal by the transducer, the magnitude of the pulse will be reduced from the electrical signal used to launch the stress wave.

Amplifier

The *amplifier* of an ultrasonic testing instrument boosts the signal strength of the received pulses to a level that can be readily displayed on the instrument's screen. It is the *adjustable gain* of the receiver's amplifier that is the key variable under the control of the technician.

The increase of incoming signal strength can be expressed as a simple linear relationship (relative increase expressed in percentages) or logarithmic relationship (in terms of decibels). Although relative signal strength is more intuitive (half as large, twice as large, ten times as large), decibel representations have become most common in ultrasonic testing. A signal level change of 2:1 is expressed as 6 dB. A 2:1 signal loss is –6 dB. A ratio of 100:1 is given as 40 dB, whereas a ratio of 10 000:1 represents an 80 dB gain.

Other Amplifier Functions

In addition to the relative signal strength, amplifiers can be adjusted to accept either a broad range of signal frequencies or a selected narrower range of frequencies. Amplifiers also filter echo signals in order to amplify the exact shape of the echo using the broadband setting or selectively key in on an individual frequency. When the natural resonance frequency of the transducer matches the narrow band frequency setting, a strong and relatively noise-free signal results.

Although the primary purpose of the amplifier is to increase received signal strength to meet the requirements of the sweep display unit, it is the technician who makes these modifications according to how the echoes appear on the screen. For example, excessively noisy signals can be filtered and clipped to clean up their appearance. Filtering is used to smooth the jagged appearance of signals, while the *reject control* eliminates lower-strength signals. The result is a clean baseline with clearly defined pulse shapes of consistent appearance.

Display Unit

Once the echo signals have been amplified, they are ready to be used in a display mode that gives information about the location and nature of echo surfaces within the test object. Three general formats — A-scan, B-scan, and C-scan — are commonly used, with several others incorporated in specific types of equipment.

A-Scan Display

The most common display is called an *A-scan*. In an A-scan display, the vertical axis represents signal strength. The horizontal axis represents time and displays pulse signal amplitude variations with increasing time from a specific reference point. The reference point at the left side of the display screen is usually the moment when the transducer is first excited with an electric pulse, sometimes called the *initial pulse* or *main bang*.

Figure 4 shows a typical A-scan. The vertical axis (from 0 to 100 units) reflects the strength or intensity of the mechanical wave activity at the transducer. The horizontal axis (from 0 to 10 units) reflects the sequence of wave activities as a function of elapsed time. The initial pulse is on the left side of the screen presentation. The left edge of the pulse corresponds to the instant the electrical pulse excites the transducer, while the remainder of the pulse is caused by the *ring-down* of the transducer.

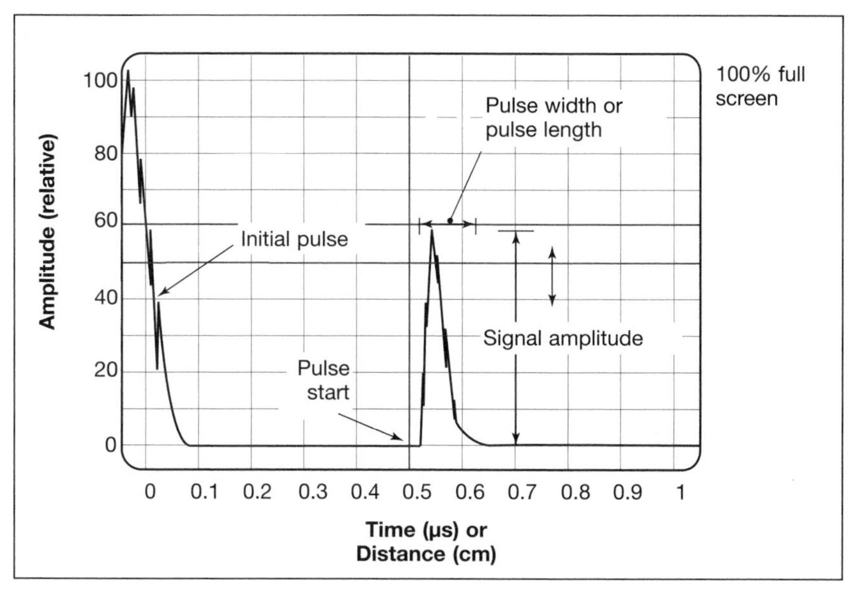

Figure 4: A-scan presentation.

After a little more than five units of time, an echo stress wave is detected by the transducer. The relative height of the received pulse is a measure of the echo stress-wave strength. The horizontal position of the pulse's left edge (labeled *pulse start* in Figure 4) is the time the echo pulse arrives at the transducer.

The bottom horizontal line is often referred to as the *horizontal baseline*. Signals from the material cause indications to rise upward from this baseline. In this mode, the entire display screen is available for estimating the relative signal's peak amplitude. *Note:* An alternative A-scan display, called the *radio-frequency* or *RF signal,* presents the signal with both positive and negative peaks.

B-Scan Display

The *B-scan* displays X-positional information in one direction and the time history of the horizontal scale of the A-scan in the other. The result represents a cross-sectional slice of the reflectors within the test object. Figure 5 shows the B-scan of a step wedge with internal discontinuities.

Ultrasound reflects the strongest signal when it encounters a reflector surface at a right angle to its direction of propagation. As a result, the B-scan only shows horizontal components of the step wedge and internal reflectors. Since internal reflectors reduce the strength of ultrasonic waves, a shadow of the internal reflector is often seen as a loss of signal in images of any subsequent reflecting surfaces. Thus, gaps appear in the continuity of the lines representing the wedge step surfaces.

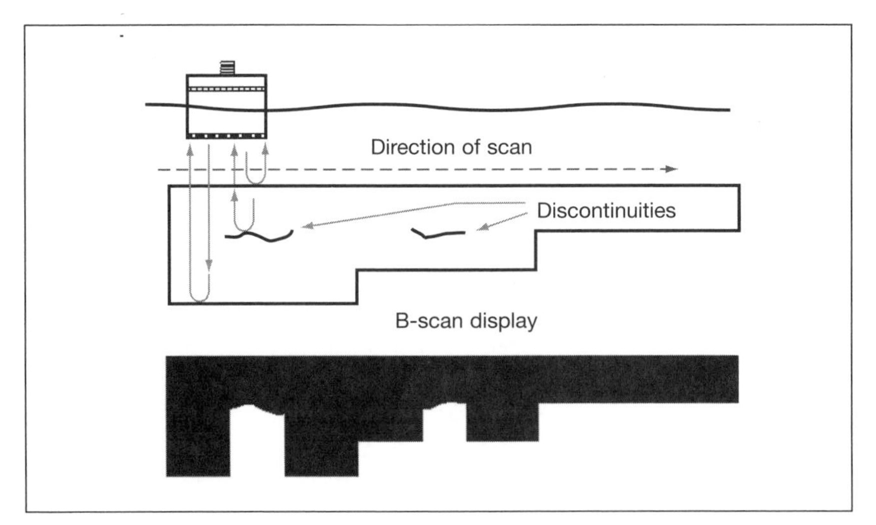

Figure 5: B-scan representation of a step wedge with internal discontinuities.

A series of B-scans taken with vertical orientations is used to build up a three-dimensional image. In practical applications, a particular region within a test object is usually of interest. Often, a single slice is sufficient to gather the information for determining a reflector's location, general size, and shape.

C-Scan Display

With a *C-scan*, the transducer is scanned in a regular pattern over an area of interest, often using an automatic mechanical positioning device. The received signals are converted to variations in color or grayscale density. From A-scan data, a *plan view* of the test object is generated using signal criteria based on pulse height and time of arrival to determine color or grayscale density at each X and Y location, similar to the floor plan of a house. Vertical and horizontal directions represent the directions in which the transducer is scanned.

The resulting patterns are directly correlated with the size and shape of reflecting surfaces within the test object. Similar to X-ray images, the patterns are intuitively easy to interpret.

Figure 6(a) shows the system layout for a C-scan of a plate, seeking to detect the portion of internal reflectors whose signal strength exceeds a predetermined threshold level.

For reflectors with sharply defined edges, a C-scan image is an accurate representation of the reflector size. A key measure of a C-scan is its ability to distinguish between closely spaced reflectors at the same depth. In this case, the lateral resolution of the system is important and is related to the diameter of the sound beam at the depth of interest and the scanning step size.

Figure 6(b) shows a C-scan of a test object, using the variations in received signal strength to vary the density of grayscale or color ranges. In this mode, the gradient or rate of signal change is directly

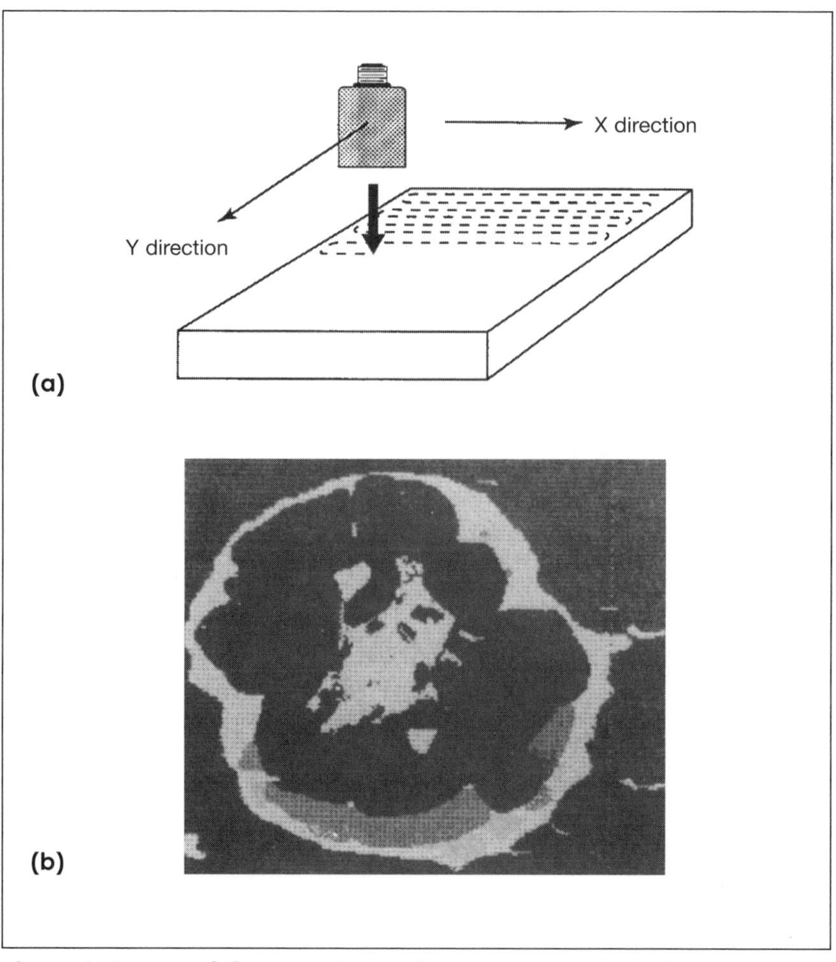

Figure 6: C-scan: (a) system layout for testing a plate for internal discontinuities; (b) computerized C-scan of impact damage in a graphite-to-epoxy laminate.

related to the rate at which the density or color changes. For a coarse increment between levels, the images can be made to look very similar to contour maps.

The major advantage of a C-scan representation is the intuitive information related to shape factors that are not readily seen when looking exclusively at an A-scan. When the images are created with narrow acceptance ranges and carefully correlated with depth information, the C-scan rendition becomes a slice of a three-dimensional rendering of the reflectors contained within the test object.

Computerized Systems

Devices used to display various scan modes can be based on analog or digital technologies. Older analog instruments are equipped with a cathode ray tube (CRT) to display A-scans. These systems are bulkier and heavier than their digital counterparts. However, they reproduce analog signals generated by ultrasonic transducers with very high fidelity and a virtually instantaneous response. They are relatively simple systems, designed to display time-varying signals. Their pulse repetition rates or *screen replenish rates* can be 1000× per second or more.

Digital devices transform analog signals into digital using a converter circuit. This process, plus the inherent delay in replenishing screen displays, results in a slower response time for digital systems. Typical computer screens are replenished at a rate of 60 frames per second. However, because of their small size, digital systems can be equipped with auxiliary features, such as automatic calibration, data storage, and external communication, which enhance their functionality well beyond that of analog systems. These features, plus smaller size and weight, facilitate better tests, especially in the application of manual ultrasonic tests.

Transducers

All parts of an ultrasonic test system — the instrument, the coupling agent, and even the relatively simple coaxial cable — are important in producing a comprehensive inspection of the test object. However, of all the significant advances produced by the scientists and manufacturers of ultrasonic equipment, none have been more important than the improvements made in the manufacture of *transducers*.

Transducers form the core of all nondestructive ultrasonic testing procedures. Whether an object can be tested or not depends on the appropriate acoustic properties of a transducer. The choice of the correct transducer is decisive for the quality and the reliability of test results.

A transducer is specified for a given test based on its ability to produce a beam of ultrasonic energy. This beam must be capable of penetrating the test object to a calibration standard (representative of the test material) to prescribed depths and producing reflections that are clearly discernable from fabricated reflectors of prescribed size. Whether the transducer meets the specification will depend on its frequency and its construction.

A transducer's frequency is determined by the thickness of the piezoelectric element (crystal). The thinner the crystal, the higher the frequency. Higher-frequency sound beams produce higher levels of sensitivity and resolution but less ability to penetrate test objects to greater depths.

Penetration versus Sensitivity and Resolution

Typically, a transducer is chosen to enhance the *sensitivity* and *resolution* of the system or to provide greater ability to penetrate coarse-grained materials or thick test objects. To gain good penetration, a transducer in the lower frequency range (less than 5 MHz) is used. Lower frequency ranges produce longer wavelengths that counter the natural attenuation of the test material. On the other hand, higher sensitivity to smaller reflectors and better resolution are achieved with higher frequencies (5 MHz and higher).

Transducer Damping

Damping improves the penetrating ability of a transducer as well as its sensitivity and resolution. In applications where good resolution is of primary importance, it is common to select a highly dampened transducer. A high degree of damping helps shorten interface ring-down or recovery time and allows the system to resolve closely positioned reflectors.

Performance characteristics of three transducer types are discussed below. The technician should remember that each application is unique and requires careful evaluation.

- **High-penetration/low-resolution transducers** – Low-resolution transducers are intended to provide excellent sensitivity where distance resolution is not of primary importance. Typically, these transducers have longer waveform duration and a relatively narrow bandwidth.
- **Medium-penetration/high-resolution transducers** – High-resolution transducers are manufactured to reduce the excitation pulse and interface echo recovery time while maintaining good sensitivity at the transducer center frequency.
- **Broadband transducers** – Broadband transducers are untuned transducers that provide heavily damped performance. They are the best choice in many applications where good axial or distance resolution is necessary. They also serve in tests that require an improved signal-to-noise ratio in coarse-grained, attenuating materials.

Testing and Documentation

Even transducers produced by the same manufacturer to be the same size, shape, and frequency can be highly individual. There is a need for carefully testing and documenting individual characteristics of ultrasonic transducers.

Manufacturers typically provide documentation of the transducer's actual radio-frequency waveform and frequency spectrum. Additionally, measurements of peak and center frequency, upper and lower (–6 dB) frequencies, bandwidth, and waveform duration are made according to the ASTM E-1065. This data is tabulated on a test form and included with the purchase of any transducer.

Piezoelectric Materials

The sound-beam characteristics of a transducer applied under normal testing conditions are generally derived from the diameter and the frequency of the piezoelectric element. While the technician knows the features of a given transducer, details regarding the physical and acoustic properties of the piezoelectric material used to manufacture the actual crystal may be unknown. However, this information is important. The material that the crystal is made from determines the efficiency of the overall piezoelectric process and has an important effect on the overall quality of the ultrasonic test.

Materials such as quartz, lithium sulfate, or barium titanate are almost never used today. Instead, new, powerful piezoelectric materials are available, but their basic acoustic and electrical characteristics are very different. Depending on the application, one material may be more advantageous because of physical or economic reasons or simply because of a less complicated manufacturing process.

Lead zirconate titanate is the most familiar piezoelectric material used to generate ultrasound. Additionally, lead titanate and lead metaniobate are two of the more frequently used ceramic piezoelectric materials. Another piezoelectric material used in transducers is polyvinylidene fluoride (PVDF). Manufacturers are also showing rapid progress in their ability to produce composite piezoelectric elements that produce improved signal-to-noise ratios.

Table 1 compares properties of piezoelectric materials. Relative energy conversion efficiency is compared to quartz. The *critical temperature* is the temperature at which the material loses its piezoelectricity, commonly referred to as the *curie temperature*.

Table 1: Selected piezoelectric material properties. (T = transmitting; R = receiving; T × R = total efficiency).

Material	Efficiency			Impedance (Mrayl)	Critical temperature °F (°C)	Density (g/cm³)
	T	R	T × R			
Quartz (x cut)	1	1	1	15.2	1069(576)	2.65
PZT5 (lead zirconate titanate)	70	0.21	14.6	33	379–689 (193–365)	7.5
BaTi (barium titanate)	8.4	–	–	31.2	239–302 (115–150)	5.4
PMN (lead metaniobate)	32	–	–	20.5	1022 (550)	6.2
LSH (lithium sulfate hydrate)	6.9	~2.0	–	11.2	167 (75)	2.06
LN (lithium niobate)	2.8	0.54	1.51	34	–	4.64
PVDF (polyvinylidene fluoride)	6.9	1.35	9.3	4.1	329–356 (165–180)	1.76

Testing Techniques

Ultrasonic Testing in Industrial Settings

Ultrasonic testing is used throughout the original manufacturing process and again as a tool for assessing the integrity of components during their useful lifetime. During new component or system manufacturing, ultrasonic testing is used to determine the integrity of basic materials and to monitor fabrication processes, including joining and forming of components. As is the case with most nondestructive testing methods, ultrasonic testing is best used in the early stages of manufacturing when test object geometry is simple.

During their useful lifetime, components and systems are monitored for progressive degradation caused by unexpected overloading, cyclic fatigue cracking, corrosion, or environmental conditions. The capacity to monitor the integrity of material from early in the manufacturing process to the very end of a structure's useful life is unique to the application of nondestructive testing in general and ultrasonic testing in particular. For that reason, ultrasonic testing applications are part of the maintenance programs of operating power stations, aircraft, petrochemical plants, and transportation facilities. Ultrasonic tests ensure that components and systems have been constructed in accordance with original design specifications and that they continue to meet inservice performance projections.

Acoustic Coupling

Unlike light, which can travel through a vacuum, ultrasonic waves require an intermediate medium to transfer the transducer's mechanical motion to the test object. The coupling of the transducer crystal's motion to the test object is best done if the two are rigidly attached to each other, but this is often not possible. If a gas, such as air, is trapped between the transducer and the test object, virtually all of the sound energy is reflected at the transducer-air boundary with very little reaching the test object. A liquid couplant is used as a transition medium between the two solid bodies to allow for ease of transducer movement and to displace any air between the transducer and the test object.

In contact testing, the transducer is in direct physical contact with the test object. Successful acoustic wave transfer is best performed when a thin layer of couplant is applied between the transducer and the test object, as shown in Figure 7. This couplant ensures effective acoustic energy transfer while lubricating the sliding surfaces between the transducer and the test object.

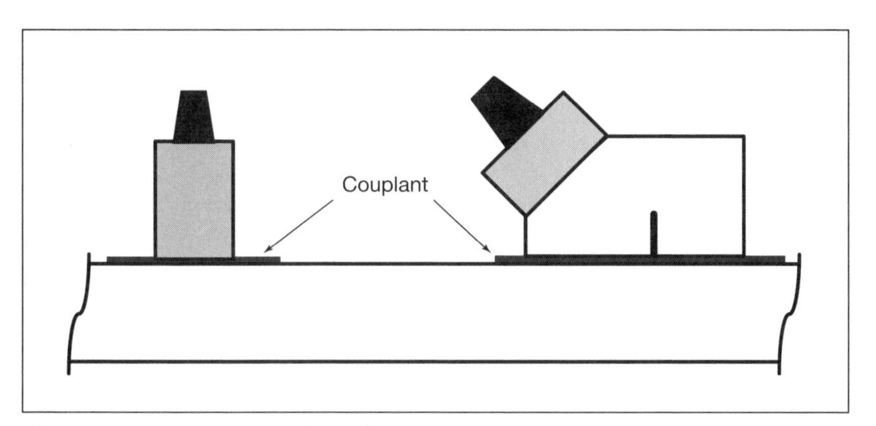

Figure 7: Acoustic coupling of transducer to test object.

Many angle-beam transducer-wedge combinations permit the transducer to be attached to the wedge by small screws or a spring-like snap ring. The wedge can be changed to allow the use of other wedge angles and permits combinations of various frequency transducers and angles at minimum cost. When this type of transducer-wedge combination is used, there is also a need to have couplant between the face of the transducer and the wedge, as shown in Figure 8. This couplant should be of high viscosity and of a type that does not rapidly evaporate or dry out. Loss of couplant at this point reduces the amount of sound transmitted into the test object. If the loss occurs after calibration, this results in lower amplitude signals than were used during calibration.

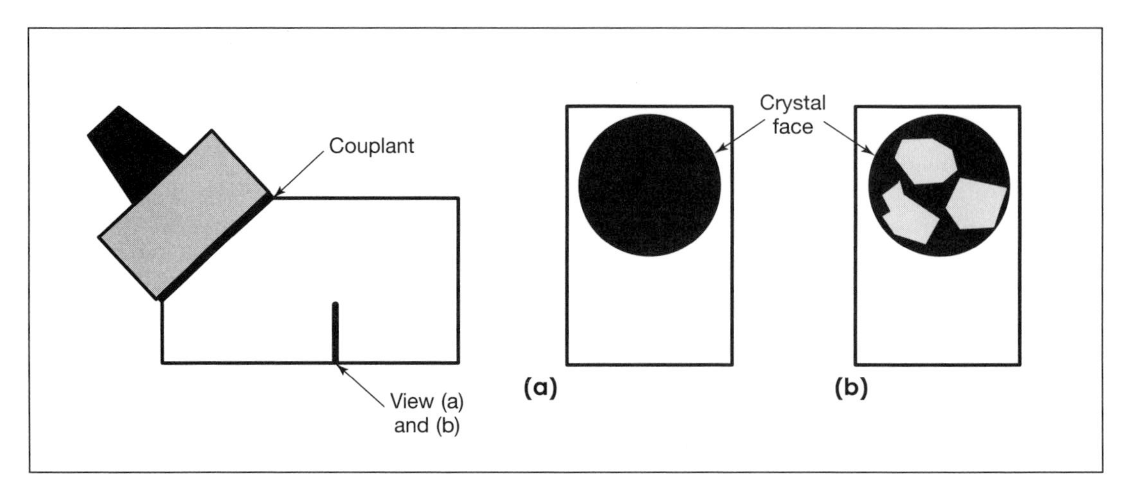

Figure 8: Acoustic coupling of transducer to wedge: (a) fully coupled transducer; (b) partially coupled transducer.

To determine if the transducer is fully coupled to the wedge, the technician should invert the probe, wet the scanning surface, and then look up the sound path toward the face of the transducer. If the crystal face is completely black, as shown in Figure 8(a), the transducer is properly coupled. If there are air gaps in the couplant, the crystal face will appear silver-colored or will have areas that are silver-colored, as shown in Figure 8(b). This indicates that there are air gaps in the couplant. If air gaps are present, the transducer must be recoupled to the wedge and the calibration checked.

Dry Coupling

Spurred by the need to perform some tests without the use of any liquid coming in contact with the test object, dry coupling has been achieved with special synthetic rubber cover materials placed between the transducer and the test object. This approach allows spot tests of objects that are subject to chemical contamination by any form of liquid.

Air Coupling

Air-coupled transducers can be configured to work in through-transmission mode, as with water-coupled transducers. However, a distinct feature of air-coupled transducers, usually in the 200 to 400 kHz

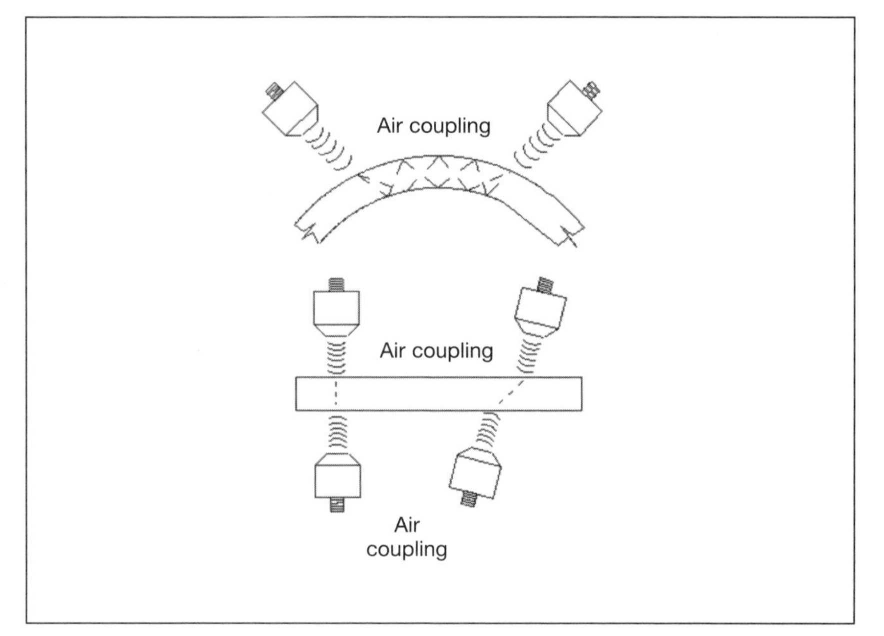

Figure 9: Configurations used to generate guided plate waves within test materials.

frequency range, is the ability to efficiently generate guided plate waves, which are otherwise rapidly dampened by the water couplant. Plate waves are used in the testing of many materials, honeycomb structures in particular. Figure 9 illustrates several configurations used to generate guided plate waves within test materials such as plate and tubing.

Typical objects tested with air-coupled transducers include:

1. Honeycombs.
2. Solar panels.
3. Foam sandwich panels.
4. Cork-coated honeycombs.
5. Aircraft brake disks.
6. Timber and wood products.

The combination of specially designed transducers with the proper driver/receiver instrumentation has made air-coupled ultrasonic testing a valuable tool for industrial ultrasonic testing. Air-coupled ultrasonic scanning is increasingly becoming the method of choice for those parts where water and other couplants are not practical.

Immersion Coupling

In immersion coupling, the transducer is positioned some distance away from the test surface. In most cases, the test object is submerged and the surrounding liquid acts as the coupling medium. In other cases, a discrete column of liquid is produced between the transducer and the test surface. Immersion coupling is most often used in automatic

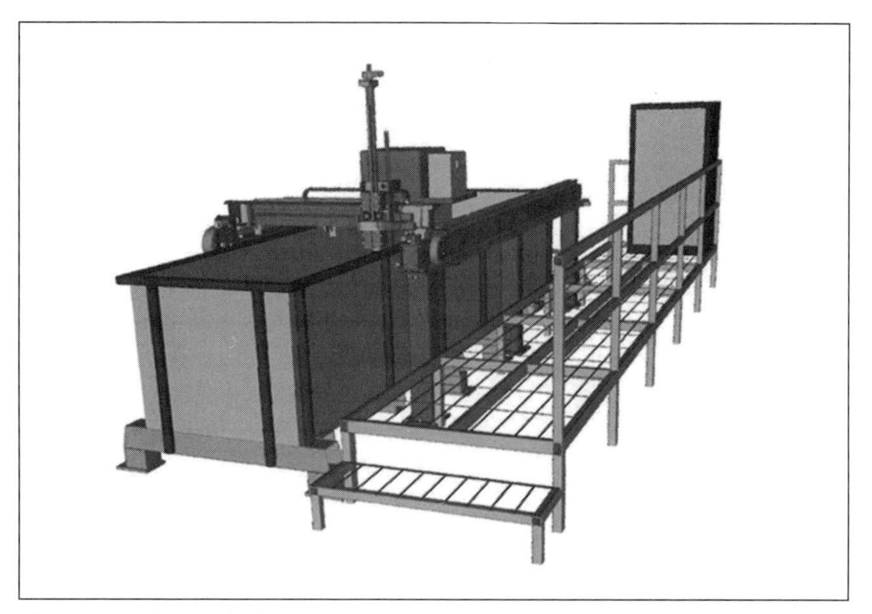

Figure 10: Ultrasonic immersion tank equipment configuration.

scanning applications because of its consistent coupling and the absence of transducer surface wear. Figure 10 illustrates a typical immersion setup.

Immersion systems are widely used in the metal manufacturing industries for offline tests of billets, bars, tubular products, and plates. They are also used for fabricated parts, such as jet engine turbine blades. System sizes range from small tabletop units for laboratory and research work up to large tanks suited for major assemblies.

Squirter Systems

Another form of immersion testing is known as the *squirter system.* As shown in Figure 11, the system is most often used with transducers aiming their pulsed or continuous wave beams through water columns that carry the beams to the surface of the test object. Squirter systems are used to test composite materials in aerospace manufacturing. These systems can be very large and complex. For example, systems greater than 40 ft (12 m) long are quite common, although much smaller systems are also manufactured.

Base Material Testing

Straight-Beam Testing

The straight-beam testing of base materials involves directing the sound beam through the test object perpendicular to the scanning surface. Since the sound beam travels through thickness, most test objects can be tested from one side. The transducer should be moved across the

Figure 11: Ultrasonic testing by use of water columns, known as the squirter system.

surface, as shown in Figure 12, so that each successive pass overlaps the previous scan. The amount of overlap is usually defined in the governing code or specification.

On large plate, it is common to perform straight-beam tests using a grid pattern of scanning. The grid is laid out in accordance with the governing code or specification and the transducer is moved along those grid lines. If a discontinuity is found, the test is concentrated in that area until the full area of the discontinuity has been outlined and marked on the surface of the test object.

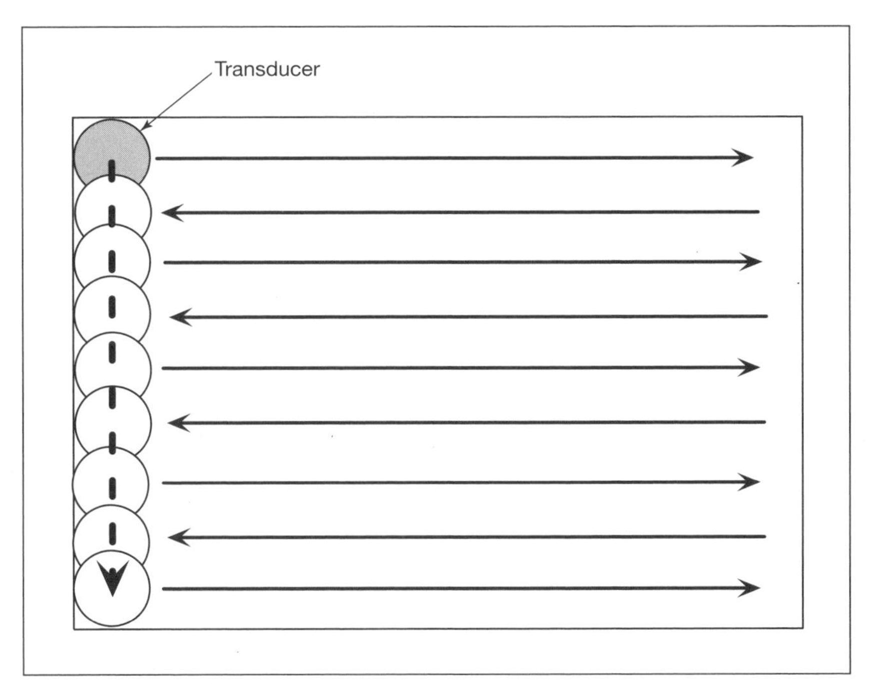

Figure 12: Straight-beam scan pattern on plate.

Angle-Beam Testing

When performing angle-beam tests on plate, a full test will require scans in four directions to detect discontinuities aligned both parallel and perpendicular to the rolling direction, as shown in Figure 13. Scanning in opposing directions in both the axial and transverse directions will detect skewed discontinuities that might not be oriented perpendicular to the sound beam in one direction.

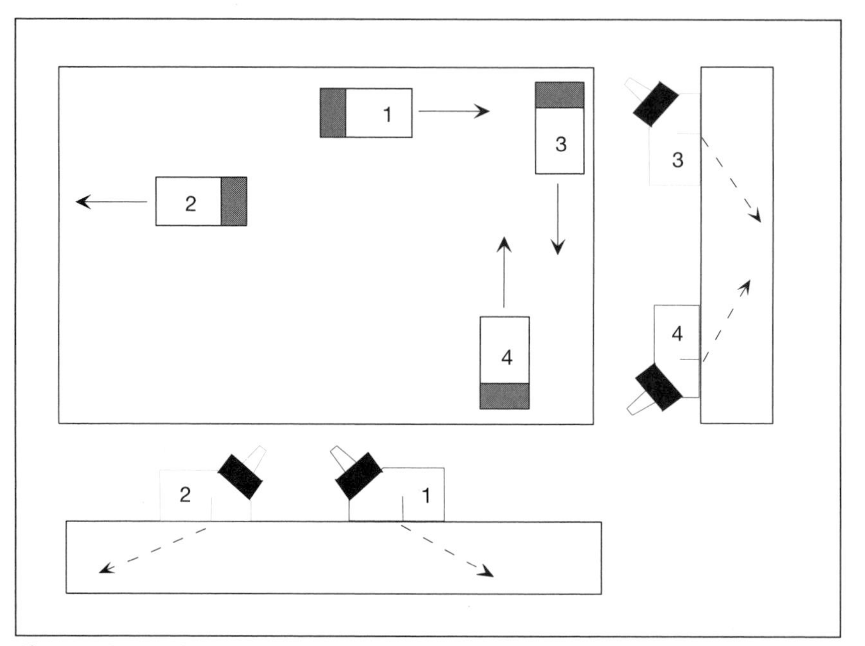

Figure 13: Angle-beam scan patterns for plate.

Angle-beam testing of pipe is performed in a similar manner, with two scans around the circumference in opposite directions and in two opposing directions parallel to the axis of the pipe. On circumferential scans, a wedge specifically contoured to match the pipe's outer diameter is usually required.

Weld Testing

Straight-beam testing of welds can only be performed on welds that have had the weld reinforcement ground flush or from the back side of tee or corner welds and then only if permitted by the governing code or specification.

Angle-beam testing can be performed on full-penetration plate welds, including butt, corner, and tee welds, and on pipe welds. The first step in the testing process is to determine the accessibility to the area of interest. Many codes and specifications require ultrasonic testing of the base material scanning surface beyond the toe of the weld, as described previously. The available distance back from the weld should be taken into consideration when selecting a wedge angle and determining the length of the scanning area.

Weld Configurations

Figure 14 shows three common weld configurations:

- Two variations of butt welds in a plate (a).
- A corner joint made by two plate ends set at 90° to each other (b).
- A tee joint between two plates as typically seen in a structural beam-column connection (c).

The surfaces adjacent to or, in the case of corner and tee welds, the face directly behind the weld are the surfaces from which the weld can be ultrasonically scanned. As shown in all four figures, these are commonly labeled Faces A, B, and C, where applicable.

The two weld diagrams in 14(a) show plates with two weld configurations: a single-vee butt weld at the top and a double-vee butt weld at the bottom. While the scanning surfaces for both are labeled the same, the location of the root of the weld is different and affects the location of certain types of discontinuities. Face A is on the plate side with the weld crown for a single-vee weld with Face B on the root side. In the case of a double-vee weld, Face A is usually the side of the weld that is most easily accessible.

Figure 14(b) shows a typical corner weld with the Face A scanning surface on the weld crown side of the beveled plate, Face B on the opposite side of the same plate, and Face C directly opposite of the beveled plate on the reverse side of the other plate. These face designations are the same for a typical tee weld, as shown in Figure 14(c). Scanning from Face C is done with a straight-beam transducer and is used primarily to detect laminar tears in the vertical member behind the weld or sidewall lack of fusion at the vertical face of the weld groove. In all tests, the face from which the weld is being tested should be recorded on the test report form.

Once the scanning face has been selected, it is necessary to determine how much of that surface will be required to perform a test that provides full coverage of the *area of interest*. This is determined by the material thickness and the choice of wedge angle if this is left to the technician and not specified by code. In order to attain full volumetric coverage, it is necessary to ensure that the weld area is scanned by both the first and second legs of the sound beam. If an additional portion of the base metal requires testing, that distance must be added to the scanning area.

Scanning Patterns

Figure 15 shows the minimum scanning distance required on each side of a plate butt weld to provide full coverage of the weld volume. At position A1, where the nose of the transducer hits the edge of the weld crown, the sound beam only covers a small portion of the bottom of the weld. At position B1, from the other side of the weld, only an additional small volume that was not covered by A1 is scanned. However, as the

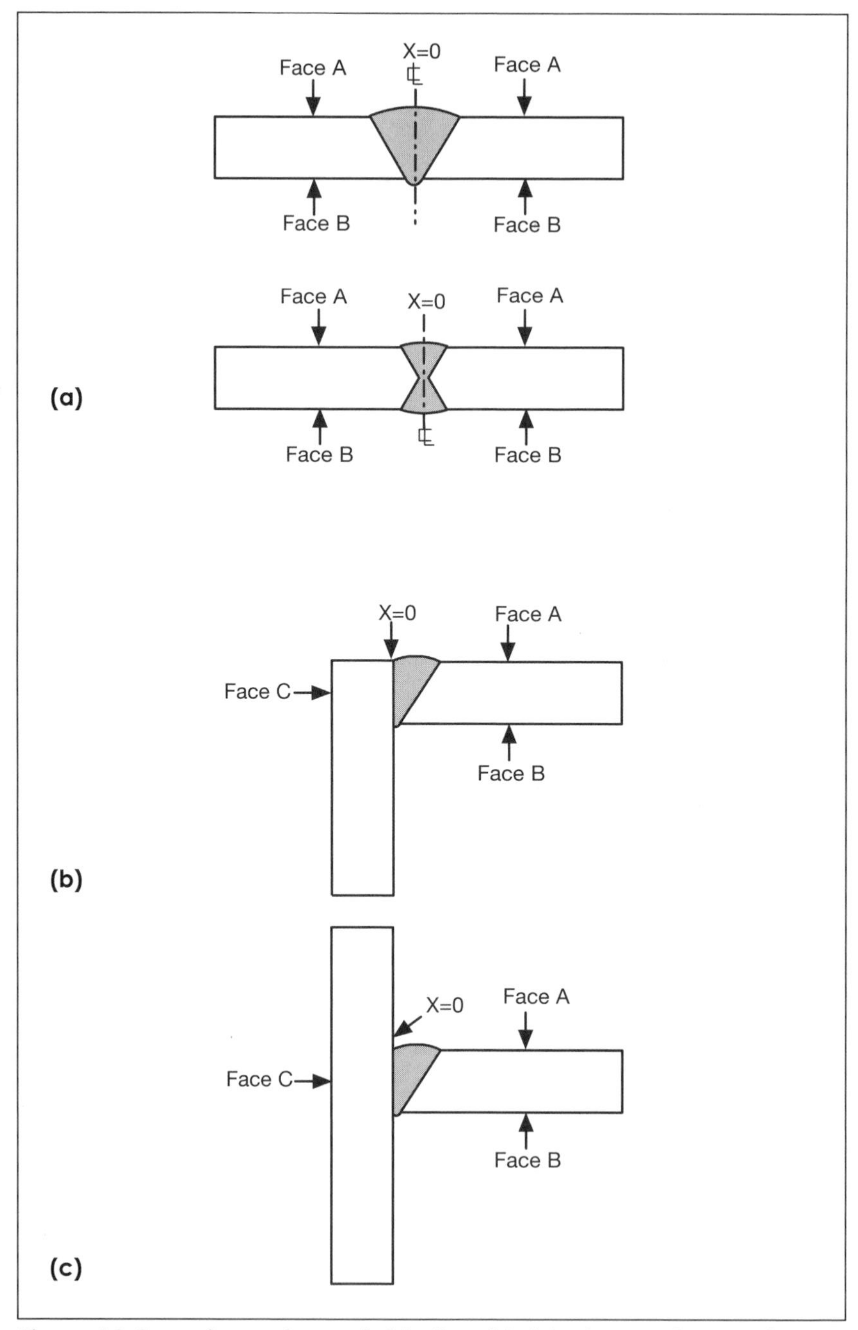

Figure 14: Scanning surfaces: (a) butt welds (single-vee, top, and double-vee, bottom); (b) corner joint; (c) tee joint.

transducer is moved back away from the weld, toward positions A2 and B2, respectively, the sound beam results in full coverage of the weld volume.

If the governing documents require that a portion of the base metal also be interrogated, then that distance must be included when the

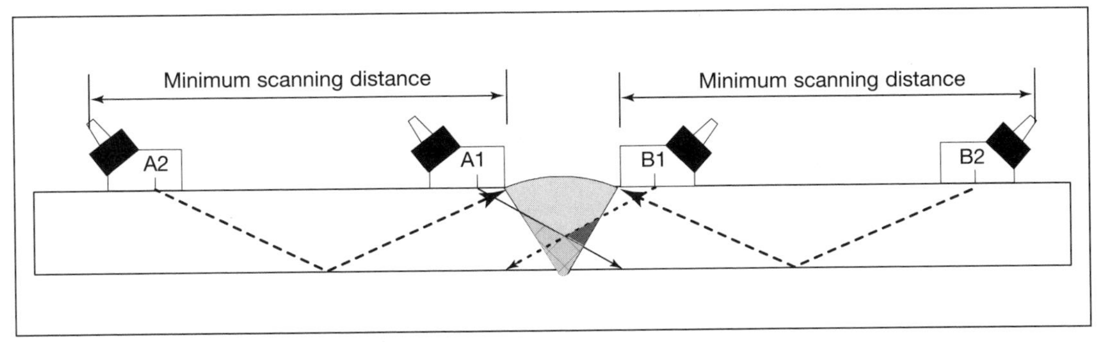

Figure 15: Minimum scanning distances.

scanning surface is prepared. Technicians should keep in mind that a 70° transducer will require a much longer scan path than a 45° probe, but a 45° sound beam may be too short to get the second leg clear through the weld cross section before the nose of the probe hits the edge of the weld crown.

To prepare the scanning surface, that portion of the plate must be free of any loose scale, rust or other foreign material that might cause a bad coupling that would prevent the sound from entering the test object. If weld spatter is present, it may be necessary to use a cold chisel to remove it. A 3 in. (76 mm) wide chisel is a good tool for this purpose, as it is wide enough to clean a large area quickly and, if used properly, will not gouge the plate surface. Once the scanning surfaces have been prepared, the couplant can be applied and the weld scanned.

In order to detect both transverse and axially oriented discontinuities, the weld has to be scanned in two directions from both sides of the weld. For axial discontinuities (those that run parallel to the weld length), the transducer is aimed at the weld and moved back and forth on side A of the plate surface, as shown in Figure 16. For

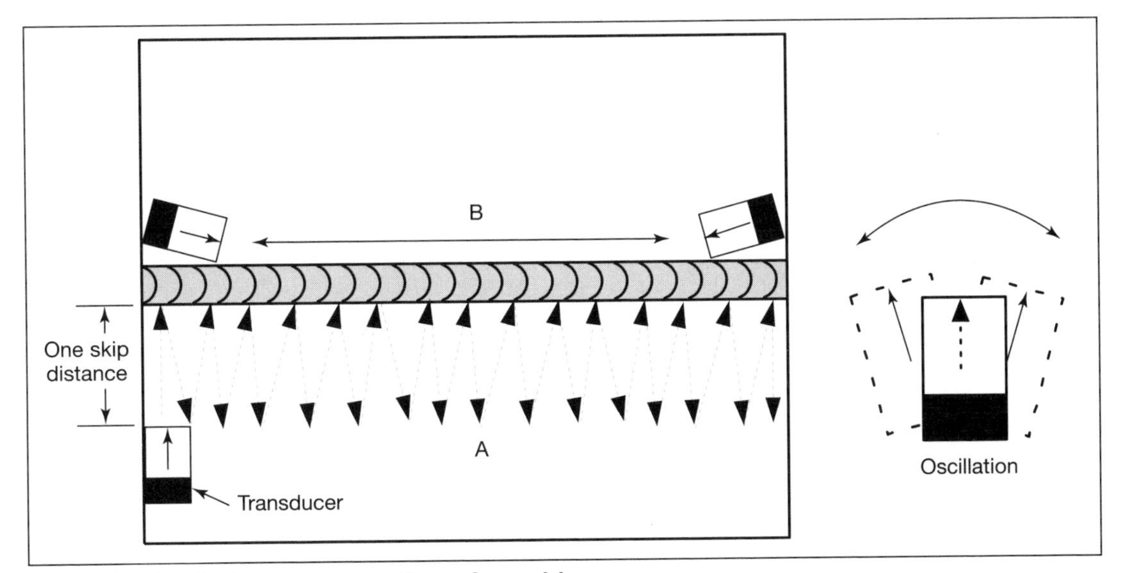

Figure 16: Angle-beam scan patterns for welds.

transversely oriented discontinuities (those that run across the weld width), the transducer is slid along the side of the weld in both directions, as shown on the B surface. Both types of scans are performed from both the A and B surfaces to ensure that all orientations of discontinuities are found.

As the probe is moved back and forth, the sound beam is required to overlap the previous scan by some percentage. The scan on the left side of Figure 17 shows a scan pattern using a 50% overlap. If the amount of overlap is not detailed in the governing documents, a 20% to 50% overlap is usually used. The easiest way to estimate the percentage of overlap is to look at the tracks the transducer makes in the couplant on the plate surface.

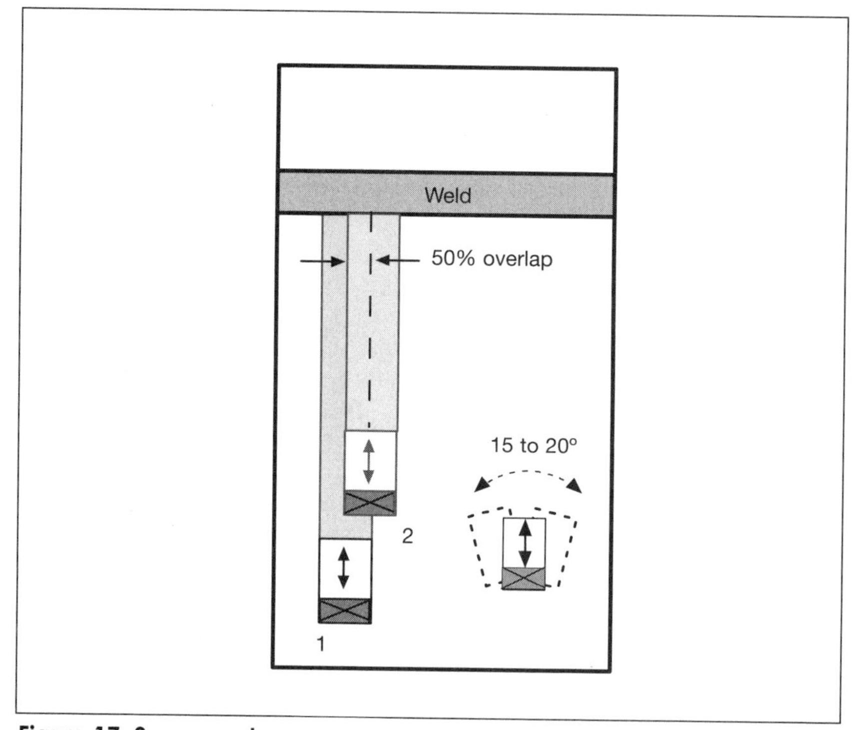

Figure 17: Scan overlap.

As the transducer is moved back and forth, it should also be oscillated from side to side in order to detect discontinuities that may not be perfectly oriented at 90° to the sound beam. If no oscillation requirement is specified in the governing code or specification, a range of approximately 15° to 20° can be used, as shown in Figure 17.

Although these manipulations seem relatively straightforward, all of this needs to be done while the technician is watching the display screen, not the probe. Many technicians routinely use probes varying from 0.25 to 1 in. (6.4 to 25.4 mm) in diameter (or greater), so the difficulty in maintaining a good scanning pattern with a consistent overlap becomes apparent. It is only with practice that this ability is developed.

To further complicate the process, most codes or standards require that the scanning rate not exceed a maximum travel speed. A common restriction is that the scan speed cannot exceed 6 in. (152 mm) per second, though the actual scan speed will be detailed in the governing specification or a referenced document. The purpose of this restriction is to ensure that any reflected sound has time to return to the transducer before it has moved on.

Selecting Reference Points

The final step before beginning the test is to select a set of reference points so that the locations of any discontinuities can be accurately located. To do this, the most common system is to use an X-Y coordinate system, where the X axis represents the distance across the weld and the Y axis represents the distance along the length of the weld. The typical locations for these points for the different weld types are shown in Figure 18.

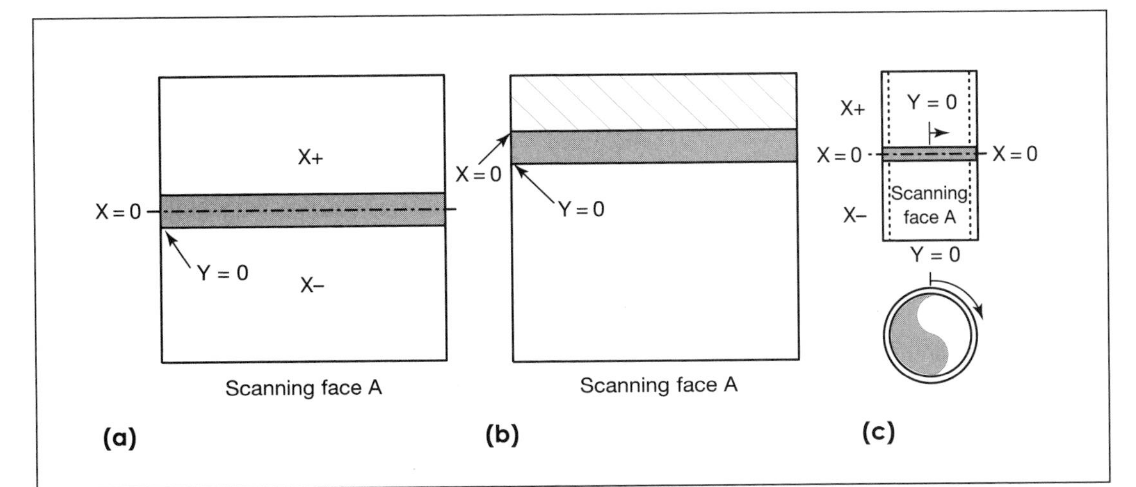

Figure 18: Reference locators: (a) centerline weld; (b) corner or tee weld; (c) pipe weld.

As can be seen in Figure 18(a), the zero point for X on a plate weld is the centerline of the weld (X=0) and the zero point for Y (Y=0) is the left end of the weld. For corner and tee welds, the X zero point is at the backside of the weld, as shown in Figure 18(b). For pipe welds, diagrammed in Figure 18(c), it is common to place the Y=0 reference point on top of the pipe for horizontal runs and in line with an elbow or fitting on vertical runs. The X=0 point is again the centerline of the weld. However, some codes and specifications have specific conventions for these locations, so they should be checked prior to the setting of locating marks. If no specific location instructions are given, the technician should select one set of conventions and record them on the report form. It is also smart to mark Y=0 on the weld so that if repairs are needed, the welder will know where to start measuring from.

The distance of a discontinuity from Y=0 is fairly obvious, as it is measured from the left end of the weld to the nearest end of a discontinuity. Therefore, a discontinuity that starts at 6 in. (152 mm) from the left end of the weld and ends 8 in. (203 mm) from the left end would be listed as a 2 in. (51 mm) indication at Y=6 in. (Y=152 mm).

To locate a discontinuity on the X axis requires a little more thought. Centerline indications are easy; they're at X=0, as shown by indication A on the shaded weld in Figure 19. Discontinuity B is 0.5 in. (13 mm) from the centerline away from the technician and would be recorded as being at X=+0.5 in. (X=+13 mm). Because indications C and D are both on the near side of X=0, they would be recorded as being at X=–0.5 in. (X=–13 mm) and X=–0.25 in. (X=–6.4 mm), respectively. When scanning the weld from the other side, the technician should make sure that the X+ and X– conventions are not accidentally reversed.

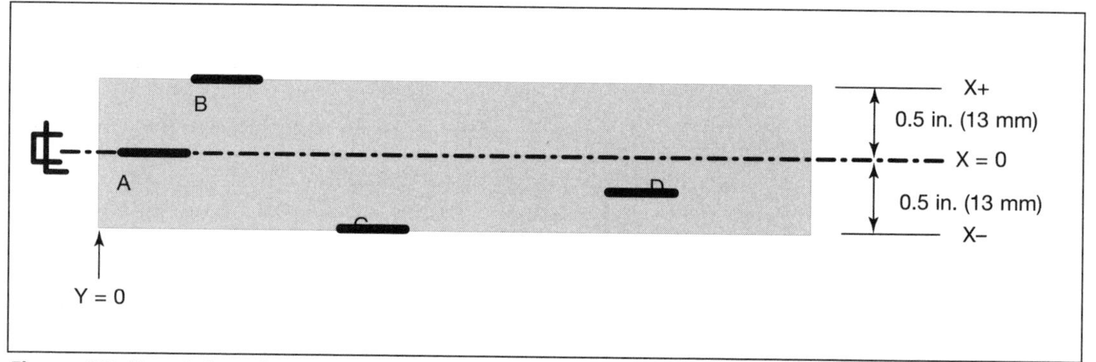

Figure 19: X-axis locations +/–.

Sizing Discontinuities

When sizing a discontinuity for length, the technician should refer to the governing documents for direction. However, if a specific method of determining the endpoint is not given, it is common practice to use the 6 dB drop method for making that determination. If used, that fact should be recorded. The *6 dB drop method* refers to a gain decrease of 6 dB resulting in a decrease in screen amplitude of 50%. To begin, the technician manipulates the transducer to maximize the signal from an indication.

Once that is done, the maximized signal is set to 80% full screen height (FSH), as shown in Figure 20(a). The transducer is then slowly moved to the left, parallel to the axis of the discontinuity, until the screen signal drops to 40% FSH or 50% of the maximized signal (a 6dB drop), as shown in Figure 20(b). A mark is then made on the plate surface at the centerline of the transducer to denote that end of the discontinuity. The transducer is then moved back toward the other end of the discontinuity until the signal peaks at 80% FSH and again drops to 40% at the other end of the indication, as shown in Figure 20(c). This end is marked using the centerline of the transducer as before, and the distance between the two marks is recorded as the length of the discontinuity.

Since many discontinuities are irregular in shape, the technician should continue the sizing scan past the point at which a 50% amplitude drop is first seen. It is entirely possible that a discontinuity will have a varying orientation that will drop off in amplitude at one point and then increase in amplitude farther away from the center of the discontinuity. If this condition occurs and the scan is stopped when the signal first drops to 50%, the recorded length will not reflect the actual discontinuity length. If the acceptance-rejection criterion being used is based on a combination of length and decibel rating, miscalculation of the length could have serious results.

The depth of a discontinuity can also be calculated using a trigonometric function based on the sound path or surface distance and the test angle. It can be read directly from a graphic ultrasonic testing calculator or, on newer machines, automatically calculated by pushing a button. Regardless of how the depth is calculated, the technician should bear in mind that the depth calculation is based on the nominal wedge

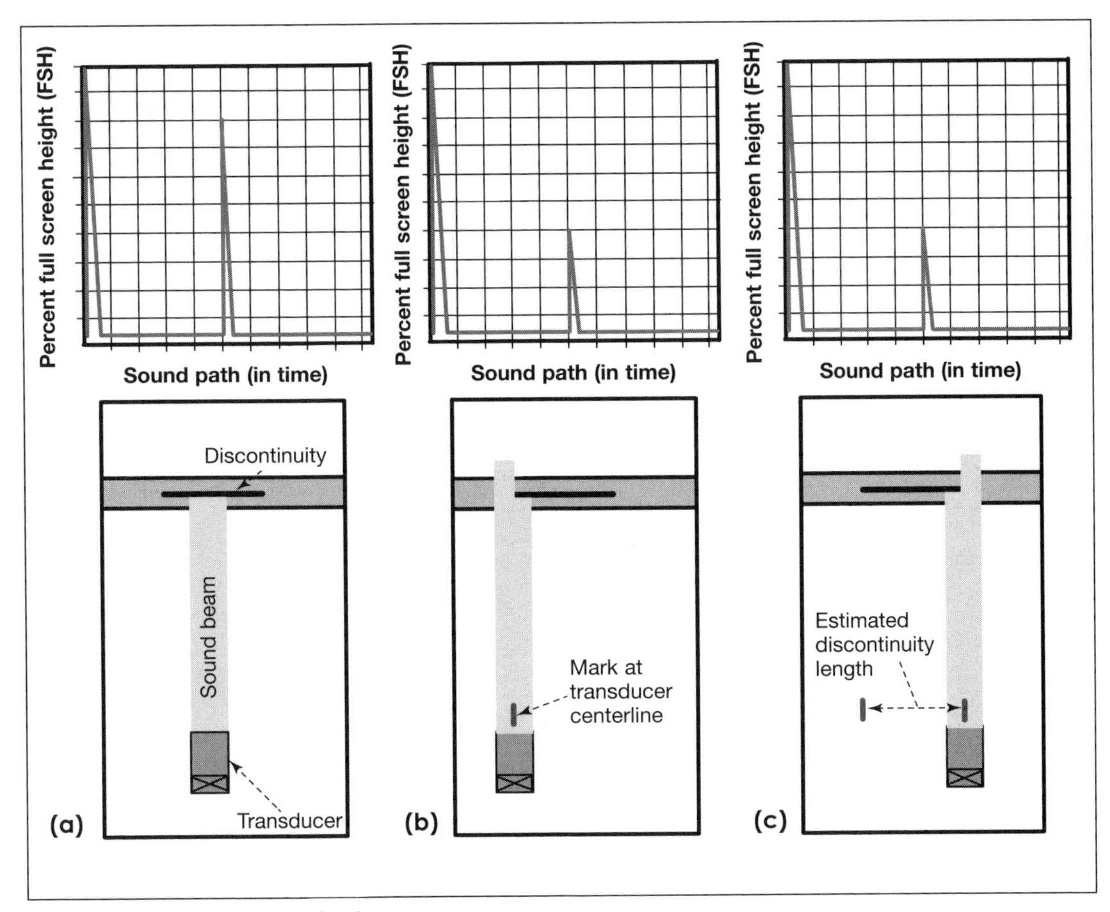

Figure 20: Sizing using 6 dB drop.

angle (45°, 60°, or 70°), and most codes and specifications allow the transducer to vary within a range of ±2°. As a result, a three decimal place depth of 0.001 in. (0.025 mm) may not be as accurate as the technician might think.

Directivity Pattern of Piezoelectric Transducers

The directivity pattern of piezoelectric transducers and the calculation of the beam spread are presented in Chapter 4. As described above, one of the practical ultrasonic testing procedures that use the knowledge of beam spread is the 6 dB drop technique. Specifically, this technique is used for evaluation of the size and shape of a discontinuity.

After calibrating the ultrasonic instrument with the calibration block made of the same material as a test object, the technician can perform evaluations of various discontinuities by observing the amplitude of the echo. The surface of the test object should be scanned and the position of the transducer on the test object at which the echo amplitude drops by half (6 dB) should be recorded. This indicates that the acoustic axis of the transducer is on the boundary of the discontinuity, as shown in Figure 21. Scanning the transducer on the surface of the test object, the technician can determine other boundary points and draw the contour of the discontinuity.

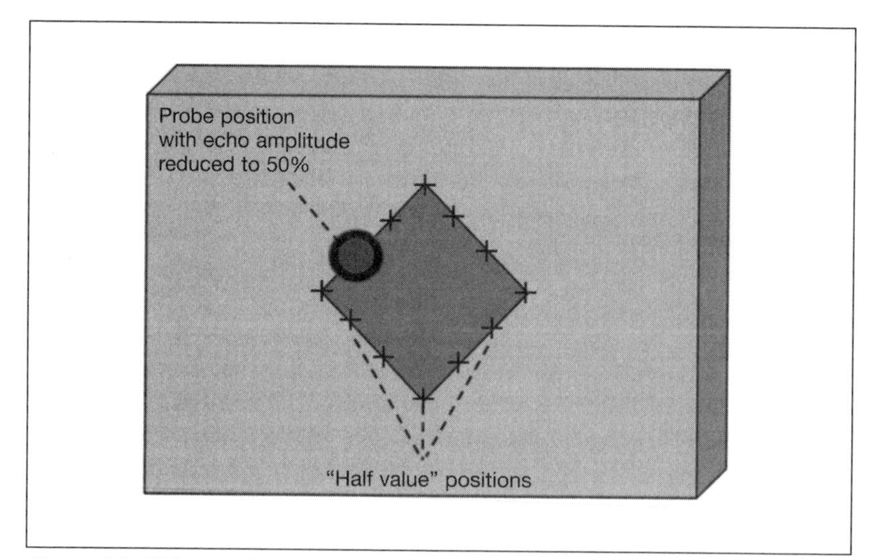

Figure 21: Sizing a discontinuity using the 6 dB drop technique.

An example of the scanned plate is shown in Figure 22.

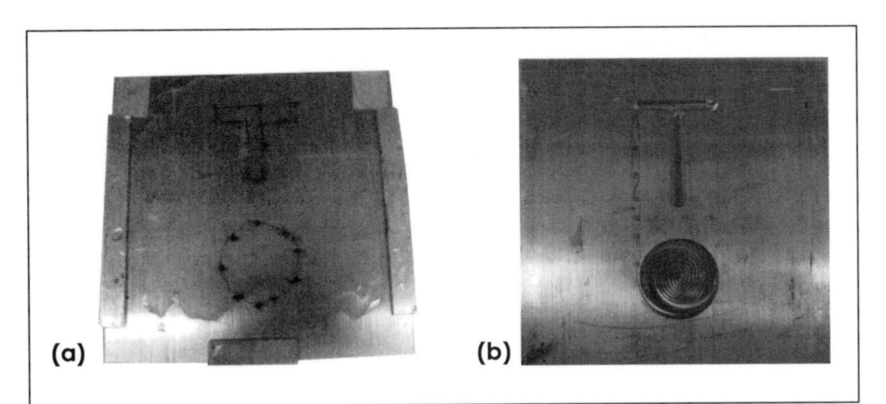

Figure 22: Scanned plate: (a) drawing; (b) actual discontinuities.

7

Equipment Calibration

Introduction

The equipment used in ultrasonic testing involves electronic and mechanical devices working together to accurately capture the way ultrasonic waves interact with various features of test materials. Ultrasonic interaction within a given material is analyzed by measuring the strength and the nature of returning waves. Location of reflectors is deduced by knowing the direction of the wave's propagation and the time elapsed in the wave's travel from the sending source to the receiving device. The speed of sound in the test object must be known for accurate distance estimations.

For simple test object geometries like plates, the ultrasonic testing instrument can be used to interpret features such as thickness and the presence of major discontinuities. As the geometric complexity of test objects increases, interpretation of detected ultrasonic wave signals becomes more difficult. To interpret results precisely, the fundamental characteristics of the ultrasonic testing system must be known.

Equipment calibration is the process of repeatedly verifying that the ultrasonic equipment is performing as intended. It is carried out at the:

- transducer level,
- instrument level, and
- integrated system level.

The frequency of calibration is based on practical field experience and is often mandated through consensus codes and standards.

Before tests, transducers are usually checked for their general condition and conformance to specified performance criteria, such as beam angle, depth resolution, and absence of excessive reverberation noise. The instrument's general condition is also checked. An ultrasonic test system's conformance to linearity performance limits is occasionally checked in a calibration laboratory; however, it is routinely adjusted to meet specific amplitude and distance calibration criteria before each field test. Finally, the transducer instrument positioning system is monitored for ongoing conformance to settings established at the beginning of each test.

The frequency of system checks is usually mandated by test procedure specification and is based on the risks of losing valid test data caused by the system falling out of calibration.

This chapter discusses how transducers, ultrasonic testing instruments, and overall testing systems are calibrated during normal test practices.

Transducer Performance Checks

In general, the performance characteristics of transducers can be measured as they relate to fundamental generation and reception of ultrasonic energy or as part of checking their practical behavior related to testing effectiveness. The former is typically done in a laboratory equipped with special testing and positioning apparatuses. The latter is done by the technician before, during, and after routine field tests.

Considered as standalone components, transducers are characterized by their electrical and acoustic responses. Typical features include electrical amplitude and frequency responses, such as relative pulse-echo sensitivity, center frequency, frequency bandwidth, time response, electrical impedance, and sound-field measurements. Typical approaches to transducer characterization can be found in documents such as ASTM E-1065, *Standard Guide for Evaluating Characteristics of Ultrasonic Search Units.*

Transducers designed to generate angled shear waves are checked for depth resolution, beam exit point location, and refraction angle within a specified material. A standard widely used for this purpose is the International Institute of Welding calibration block (the IIW block).

Instrument Calibration

Amplitude Linearity

In analog instruments, measurements of signal strength (pulse height) and transit time (related to the distance from the sending transducer) are taken directly from the display screen. It is important in these instruments that the visual A-scan axes be directly proportional to incoming signal strength (vertical axis) and expended time (horizontal axis).

Both axes must remain linear with respect to these two incoming signals throughout the operating range of the instrument. Since these variables are exclusively in the domain of the instrument's electronic circuitry, their calibration for linearity is often performed by laboratory technicians during routine maintenance.

Onsite checks of amplitude linearity (vertical axes) can be performed by observing how pairs of pulses, which differ in amplitude by some fixed amount, maintain their relative amplitude difference while the instrument's display of the two pulses will remain the same as the gain of the instrument is changed over its operational range. An example is shown in Figure 1. In Figure 1(a), two signals are set to 80% and 40% of full screen height (FSH). The gain setting is then decreased by 6 dB,

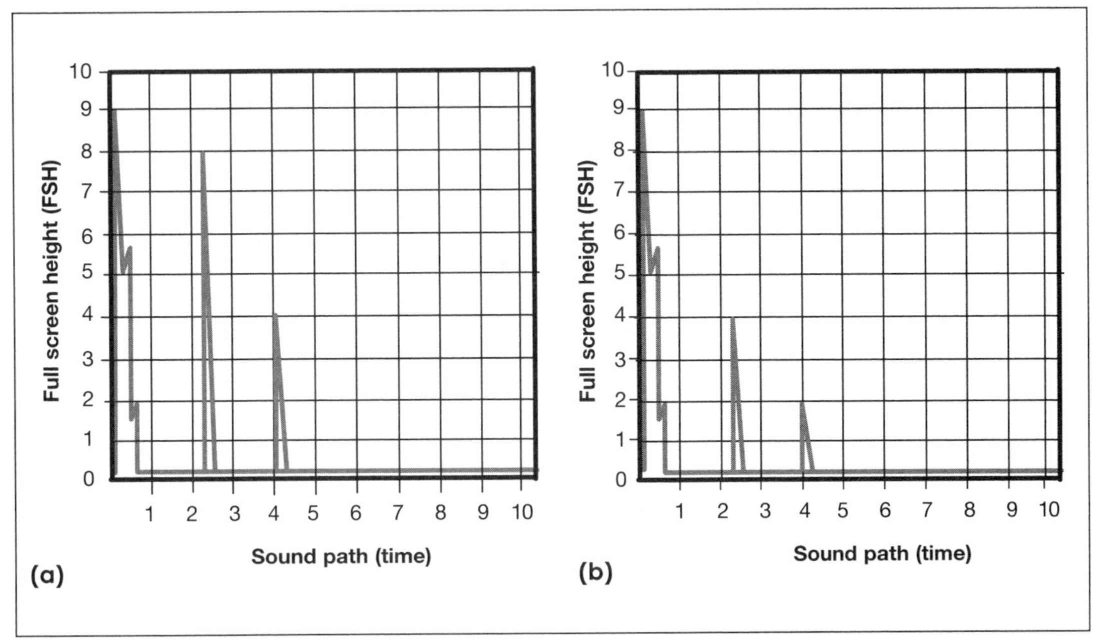

Figure 1: Vertical linearity check: (a) two signals at 80% and 40% full screen height; (b) same signals at –6 dB; 40% and 20% full screen height.

which should decrease the signal amplitudes by 50%, resulting in the signals dropping to 40% and 20% FSH respectively, as shown in Figure 1(b). If similar checks across the full vertical range (0% to 100% FSH) are within tolerance, the instrument is considered to be linear in the vertical direction. Tolerances can be found in ASTM E-317, Figure 3.

Calibration Steps

The basic calibration steps before a test include:

- establishing the horizontal axis scale to correspond to the physical region of interest within the test object, and
- setting a basic sensitivity level based on a standard reflector.

When tests are made over extensive sound travel paths, assessments of effective sound attenuation are also included in the calibration process. When test objects have contours and surface conditions different from those of the calibration block, these differences need to be assessed and compensated for when interpreting test results.

Straight-Beam Calibration

For a simple longitudinal-wave transducer (straight-beam test instrument), system level calibration typically uses a calibration block with a known thickness or depth to establish the range of thicknesses directly displayed on the screen. Using the multiple echoes as a relative gage, the screen width can be set to represent any distance significant to the test. Figure 2 shows a linear screen capable of displaying echoes at depths up to 5 in. (12.5 cm).

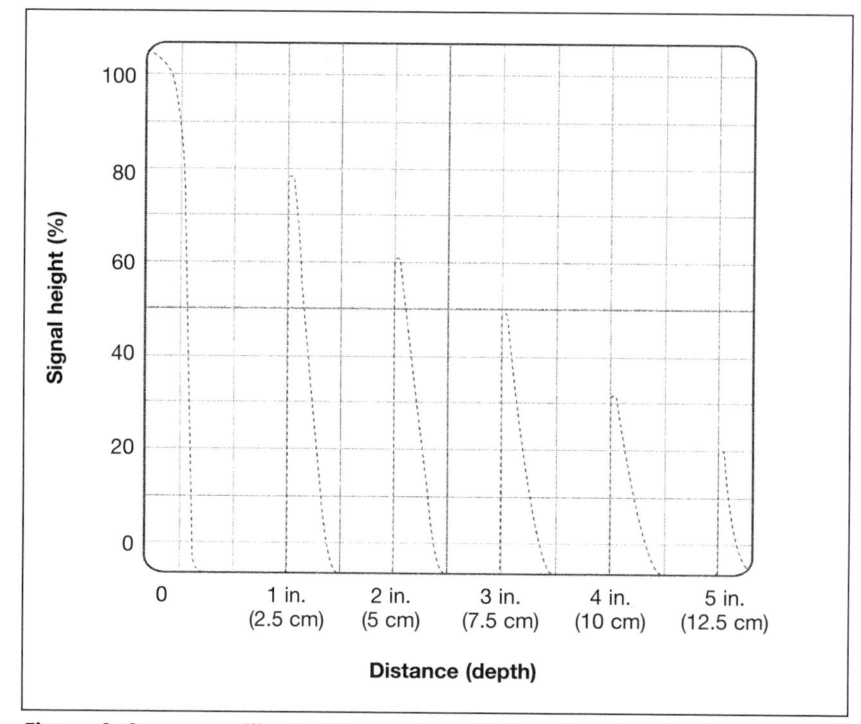

Figure 2: Screen calibrated for region of interest up to 5 in. (12.5 cm).

System Sensitivity

The sensitivity of the system is adjusted based on a standard reference reflector. Both side-drilled holes (SDHs) and flat-bottom holes (FBHs) are used for this purpose. In special cases, custom reflectors placed in test-object mockups are used to simulate the actual condition and testing environment of specific critical components.

Area-Amplitude Blocks

Flat-bottom holes have historically been used as the basis for calibrating straight-beam testing systems. Calibration blocks, called *area-amplitude blocks*, are available in sets with a range of hole sizes. This allows setting basic sensitivities for relatively large reflectors (low sensitivity) through very small reflectors (requiring a highly sensitive detection system). Typical area-amplitude blocks have FBH diameters that range from 1/64 in. to 8/64 in. (0.4 mm to 3.2 mm).

With area-amplitude blocks, the sound path remains constant and the hole diameter changes. As a result of the reduced FBH surface area interrogated by the sound beam, the amplitude decreases as the FBH diameter decreases (amplitudes A, B, and C in Figure 3, not to scale). However, the location of the screen signal does not change horizontally since the sound path remains constant.

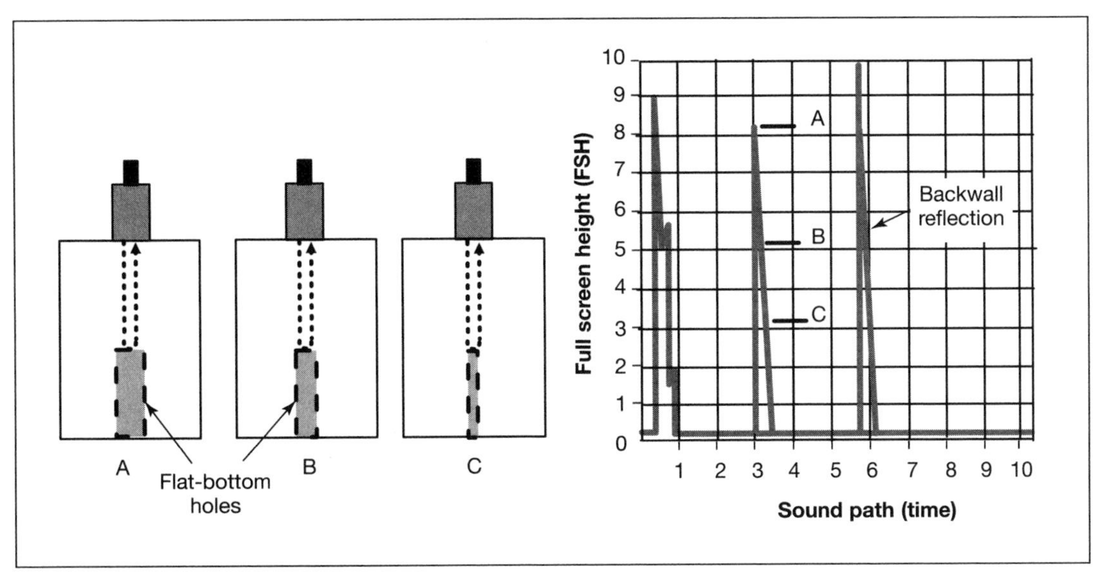

Figure 3: Area-amplitude blocks.

Distance-Amplitude Blocks

When the region to be tested involves relatively thick sections, the calibration process needs to determine the effective drop in sound energy with increasing distance. For straight-beam applications, this is often done using *distance-amplitude blocks*. These sets of blocks typically have FBHs of the same diameter, such as 3/64 in., 5/64 in., or 7/64 in. (1.2 mm, 2.0 mm, or 2.8 mm). Each set of blocks comes with sound-path distances ranging from 0.625 in. to 5.75 in. (16 mm to 146 mm). They are used sequentially to establish the pattern of changes in reflector echo signal strength with increasing distance from the transducer.

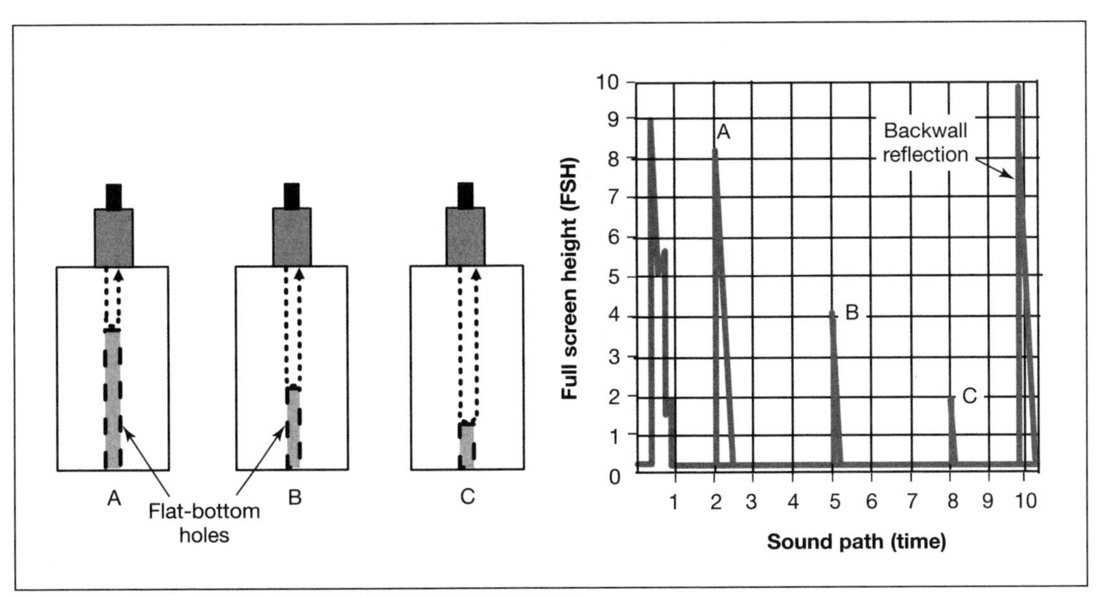

Figure 4: Distance-amplitude blocks.

Figure 4 shows a general representation of three distance-amplitude blocks and a typical screen presentation for each block.

Distance-Amplitude Correction Curve

The decrease in screen amplitude is due to the increasing length of the sound path, not a change in FBH diameter. Unlike area-amplitude blocks, the signal location moves horizontally to the right as the sound path increases. The loss in amplitude is due to beam spread and attenuation that result in less of the sound beam reflecting the FBH. If a curve were drawn from the peaks of each signal, that curve would be called a *distance-amplitude correction (DAC) curve.* Figure 5 shows a typical DAC curve for a 13-block set.

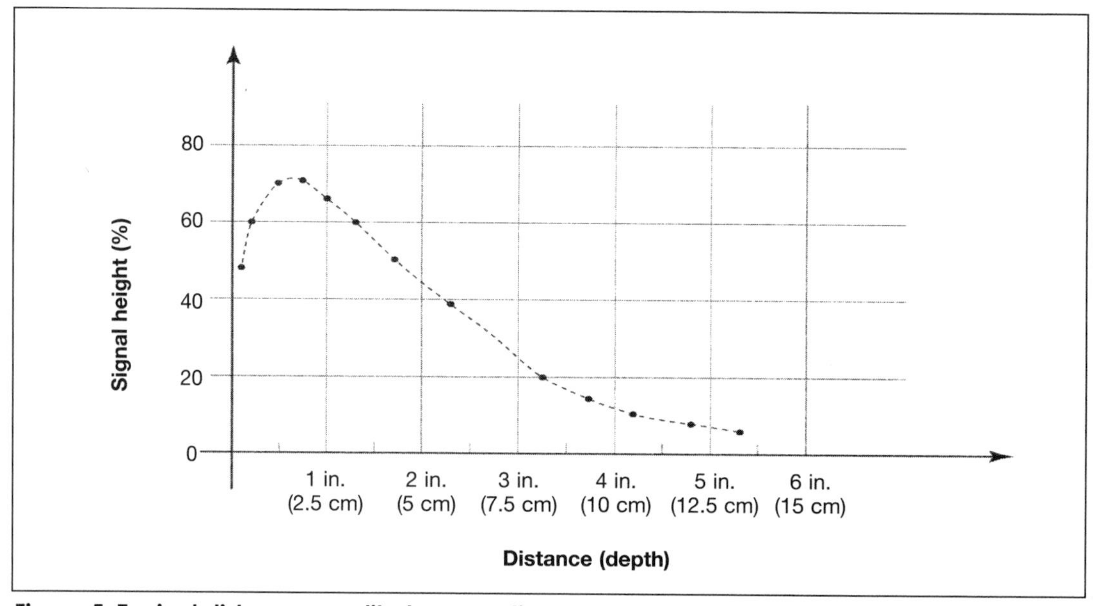

Figure 5: Typical distance-amplitude correction curve using a set of distance-amplitude blocks.

The response curve derived from the distance-amplitude holes is the basis for correcting readings taken during actual tests. For example, a discontinuity at a depth of 2 in. (50 mm), with the same effective reflecting area as another at a depth of 4 in. (100 mm), will appear on the screen to be four times bigger than the deeper reflector.

When using calibration blocks for ultrasonic testing, the required sensitivity is based on the size of the reference reflector, typically an FBH or SDH. For tests with longer sound paths, the attenuation of the sound is estimated by plotting of an appropriate DAC curve. Additional corrections used to compensate for surface curvature, roughness, or differences in the acoustic properties of the block and test object may also be required in special cases. Some of these cases are discussed in the context of certain standards covered in Chapter 13.

Angle-Beam Calibration

Side-drilled holes (SDHs) have traditionally been used as the basis for calibrating angle-beam test systems. Calibration blocks with SDHs have an added advantage: the amount of sound reflected from an SDH remains the same regardless of the transducer angle. Several of the more common blocks used for angle-beam calibration are the:

- Basic calibration block.
- International Institute of Welding (IIW) block.
- Distance sensitivity calibration (DSC) block.

Let's consider these one at a time.

Basic Calibration Block

The basic calibration block, shown in Figure 6, is rectangular and of varying size and thickness. Thickness selection is based on the thickness of the test object. The diameter of the SHDs varies based on the thickness, increasing in diameter as the block thickness increases. The holes are drilled and reamed to size so that the inner surface of the holes is as smooth as possible to provide a uniform reflector.

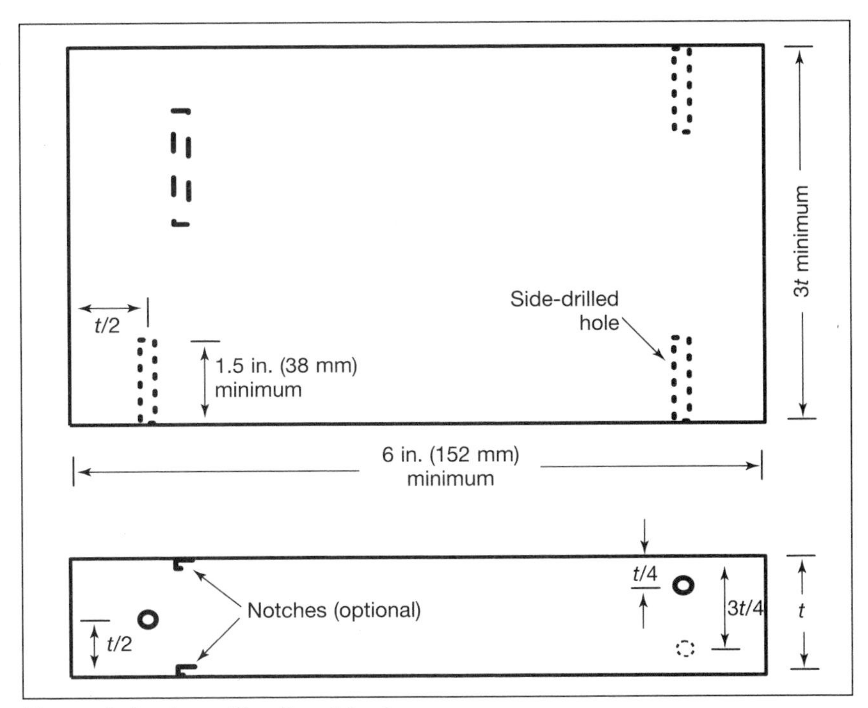

Figure 6: Basic calibration block.

The block must be long enough to allow a full skip distance for the transducer that is to be used but may not be less than 6 in. (152 mm). As the thickness increases, a longer block will need to be selected to accommodate the longer *skip distances. Note:* In angle-beam testing, the skip distance is the surface distance from the beam entry point to the point where the beam reaches the same surface after being reflected.

The most common way to calibrate with the basic calibration block is to use the depth of each hole from the scanning surface to set the screen width. Figure 7 shows the sound paths for the first legs for 1/4*t*, 2/4 (1/2)*t* and 3/4*t* hole locations and the corresponding screen locations for each signal. *Note:* Hole depths are designated in 1/4*t* increments.

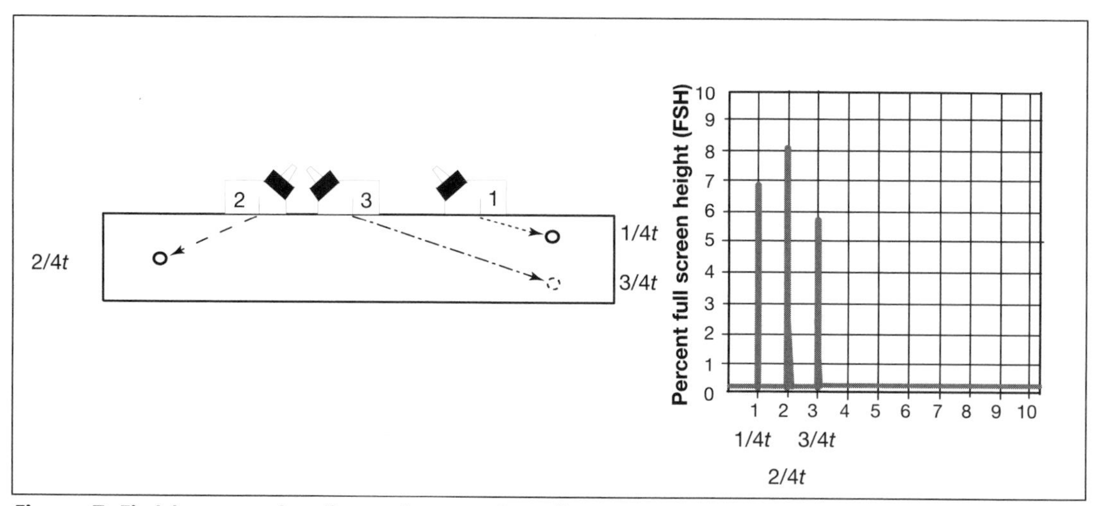

Figure 7: First-leg sound paths and screen locations.

Figure 8 shows the same holes being interrogated in the second leg of the sound beam. Because the backwall of the block would be 1*t*, or 4/4*t*, and the sound hits the backwall at an angle, there is no reflection at 4/4*t*. However, when the 3/4*t* hole appears in the second leg, the resulting sound path would be the same as if the hole was 1-1/4*t*, or 5/4*t*, below the scanning surface.

This can be seen graphically by imagining a mirror image of the block and the sound path continuing in a straight line, as shown by the shaded section in Figure 8. Similarly, when the 1/2*t* hole is seen in the second leg, the projected depth would be 6/4*t* and the 1/4*t* hole would show up at the 7/4*t* location. The 8/4*t* depth would be the scanning surface after a full skip distance. As with the 4/4*t* depth, no reflection is seen. Because the sound paths are longer than those of the first leg, less sound is reflected and the resulting screen amplitudes are correspondingly lower, as shown.

Now the use of the depth designation in one-quarter thickness increments becomes apparent. Each one of the depths can be depicted on the screen at the corresponding graticule marker. That is, the 1/4*t* signal can be set at the first major graticule, the 2/4*t* signal at the second and so on. By doing this, the screen, from zero to the eighth graticule, accurately represents twice the thickness of the calibration block being used.

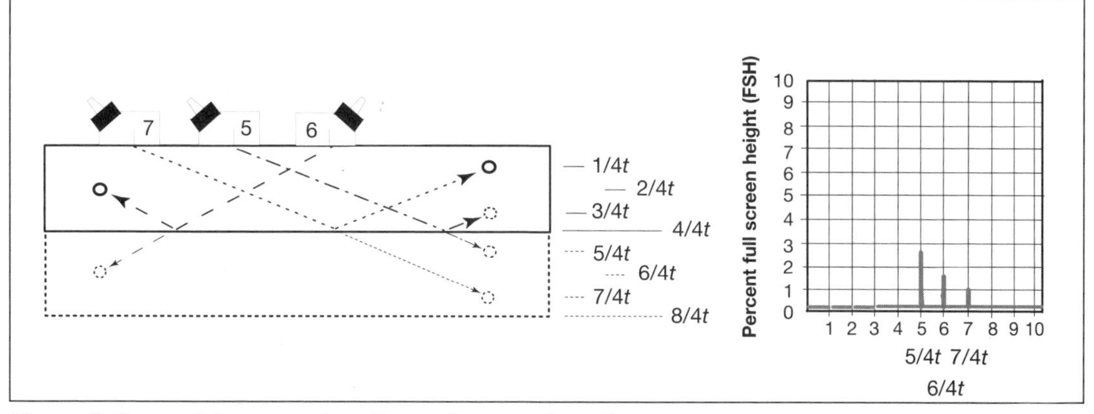

Figure 8: Second-leg sound paths and screen locations.

Calibration Procedure

To begin this type of calibration, the technician should maximize the return signal from the 1/4*t* hole, set the amplitude to 80% full screen height (FSH), and then place it over the first graticule. The transducer is then slid backward on the block until the 1/4*t* hole appears in the second leg (7/4*t* location). This signal is then placed over the seventh graticule. The transducer is then moved forward again to hit the 1/4*t* hole in the first leg. Using the range and delay controls and repeating this process, the technician adjusts the screen until the 1/4*t* and 7/4*t* holes line up over the first and seventh graticules, as shown in Figure 9.

At this point, the signals from the other four locations (2/4*t*, 3/4*t*, 5/4*t*, and 6/4*t*) should line up over the second, third, fifth, and sixth major graticules, respectively. If they do not, the range and delay controls should be adjusted until all signals line up where they belong. As noted previously, there will be no screen signals at the 4/4*t* and 8/4*t* locations.

In some instances, the signal amplitude from the 2/4*t* hole may be higher than the amplitude of the signal from the 1/4*t* hole. If this occurs,

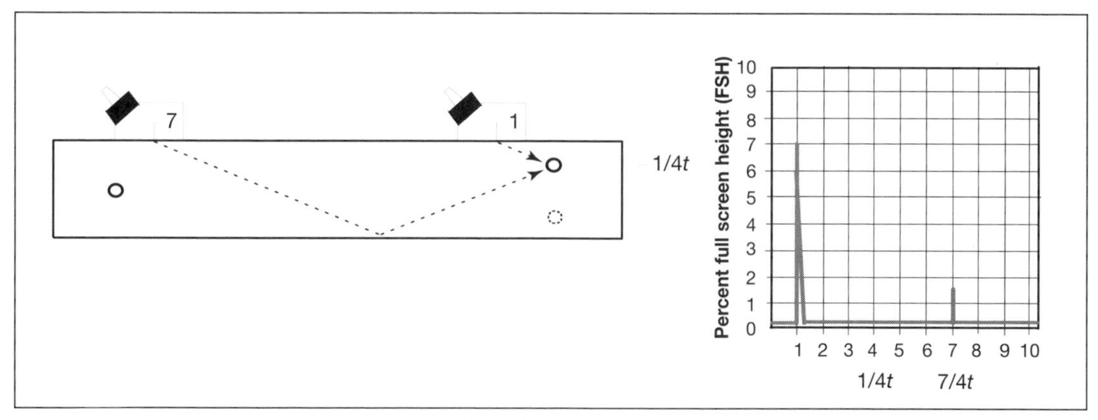

Figure 9: Initial calibration steps: basic block.

the gain (decibel level) should be set so that the signal from the 2/4*t* hole is set at 80% FSH (or whatever screen height is specified in the governing code or specification), and the signal locations from all six hole positions should be rechecked. This gain setting should be recorded, as it becomes the reference level for the inspection process.

Plotting a Distance-Amplitude Correction Curve

Without changing the reference level gain setting, the peak of each maximized signal can be marked on the screen and those points can be connected to create a distance-amplitude correction (DAC) curve. This curve, shown in Figure 10, then becomes the rejection level for signals found during the test. (*Note:* Some codes require that a line be marked at 50% DAC height, which is shown by the light dashed line in the figure.) Since there are no signals from the scanning surface at the zero (0) and 8/8*t* positions, the DAC curve should be extrapolated back to zero and out to the 8/8*t* screen position.

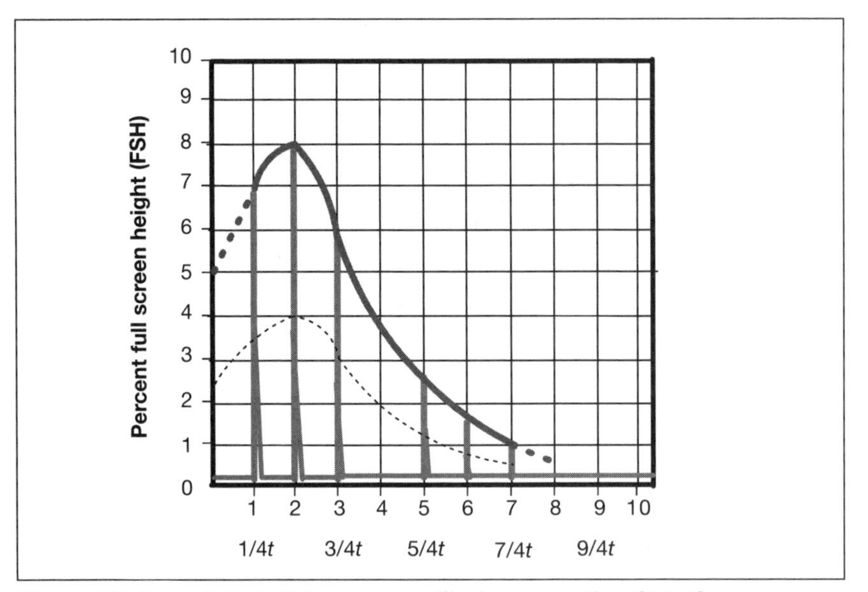

Figure 10: Completed distance-amplitude correction (DAC) curve.

When inspecting using a DAC curve, scanning is performed at a gain level above the reference level (as described in the governing code or specification), and if an indication is found, the gain is reset to the reference level. If the signal amplitude at reference exceeds the DAC, the indication is rejectable.

International Institute of Welding (IIW) Block

Another commonly used calibration block is the International Institute of Welding (IIW) block. This block comes in several different types and in multiple materials. For this discussion, the Type 1 IIW block, shown in Figure 11, will be used. *Note:* A metric block is available in addition to the U.S. customary block. The SI units that follow are the measurements of the equivalent metric block.

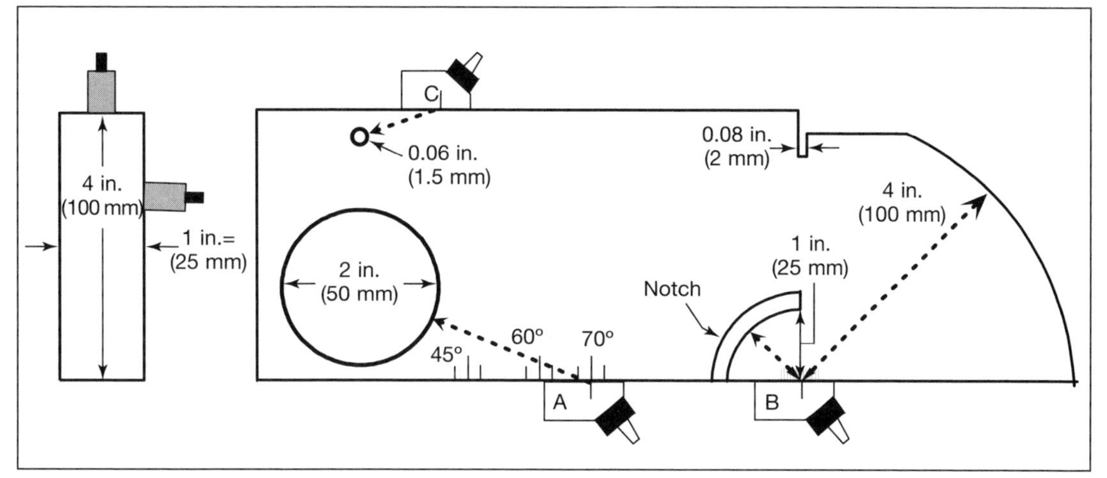

Figure 11: Type 1 IIW block.

This block provides the technician with many options. For straight-beam calibration, the block can be scanned from the side (1 in. [25 mm] thickness) to set up screen widths in 1 in. (25 mm) multiples or from the edge through the 4 in. (100 mm) width for wider screen widths. The 0.08 in. (2.0 mm) notch can be viewed from the opposite side of the block to check transducer resolution. Performance of a straight-beam inspection of the base material adjacent to a weld, looking for laminations or small laminar reflectors, is required by AWS code prior to shear-wave inspection.

Angle-Beam Inspection

For angle-beam work, the exit point of the wedge must first be determined by maximizing the signal from the 4 in. (100 mm) radius and noting the location of the focal point scribed on the side of the block. The angle of the transducer wedge can be placed in position A on the IIW block and the return signal from the 2 in. (50 mm) diameter hole maximized. With the signal maximized, the technician can see where the exit point of the wedge is located. In Figure 11, the transducer exit point is shown on the 70° line, so this transducer wedge angle is within acceptable tolerance.

Many codes and specifications require that the actual wedge angle be within ±2° of the nominal angle (45°, 60°, or 70°). If the actual wedge angle is outside of the specified range, the transducer may not be used for inspection work until it is brought back into the acceptable range.

Note: Most wedges can be corrected by sanding the scanning face on a flat surface. For wedges that have a low angle (<68°), the rear of the wedge should be sanded down. For wedges with high angles (>72°), the nose should be sanded down.

Setting the Screen Width

Prior to beginning a calibration using the IIW block, the technician must determine what screen width will be required to perform the test. Unlike

DAC curve calibrations on a basic block, when the IIW block is used, the screen width is not determined by the depth of reference holes. Screen width selection in an IIW calibration is based on the length of the full sound-path skip distance in the material to be tested, with the selected screen width sufficiently wide to allow a full skip distance to be completely seen on the screen. However, screen width should not be excessively wide, since that can cause signals to display too closely to each other on the screen, making it difficult for the technician to discriminate between individual signals.

Two of the most commonly used screen widths are 5 in. (12.5 cm) and 10 in. (25 cm). One advantage to using these screen widths is that for the 5 in. (12.5 cm) screen, each major graticule along the baseline will be equivalent to 0.5 in. (1.25 cm) of sound path and on a 10 in. (25 cm) screen, each major graticule will be equivalent to 1 in. (2.5 cm) of sound path.

To choose the appropriate screen width, the technician should determine which wedge angle is to be used (this may be dictated by the governing code or specification) and the thickness of the material to be tested. The technician then calculates one full skip distance for that material thickness. If the full skip distance is less than 5 in. (12.5 cm), a 5 in. (12.5 cm) screen width should be sufficient. If the full skip distance is greater than 5 in. (12.5 cm), then a wider screen width, such as 10 in. (25 cm), must be used. For example, on a 0.75 in. (19 mm) thick test object using a 70° wedge angle, a full skip distance will be approximately 4.125 in. (104.8 mm), so a 5 in. (12.5 cm) screen width can be used. However, on 1.25 in. (31.75 mm) thick material, the full skip distance for a 70° wedge will be approximately 6.875 in. (174.6 mm), so a 10 in. (25 cm) screen would be appropriate.

Cautionary note: If the screen width selected is less than a full skip distance, then the far end of the second leg of the sound beam will not show on the screen and the upper portion of the material or weld being tested will not be seen by the technician, invalidating the testing process.

Calibrating with the IIW Block

Once the screen width is selected, the transducer is placed at position B on the IIW block, as shown in Figure 11. The signal from the 1 in. (25 mm) radius notch is maximized and is set at the appropriate graticule on the screen display that represents 1 in. (25 mm) of sound path (signal A in Figure 12). The transducer is then aimed at the 4 in. (100 mm) radius at the end of the IIW block and that signal is set over the graticule representing 4 in. (100 mm) of sound path (signal B in Figure 12). By using the range and delay controls as described previously, the two signals are adjusted so that they both align at the proper locations on the screen. For a 5 in. (12.5 cm) screen, the signal from the notch is set at position A over the second major graticule and the signal from the end radius is set at position B over the eighth major graticule.

Once the screen width is selected and set, the transducer should be placed in position C, as shown in Figure 11, and the signal from the 0.06 in. (1.5 mm) side-drilled hole maximized. The amplitude of that signal should be set to 80% FSH (or as required by the governing code

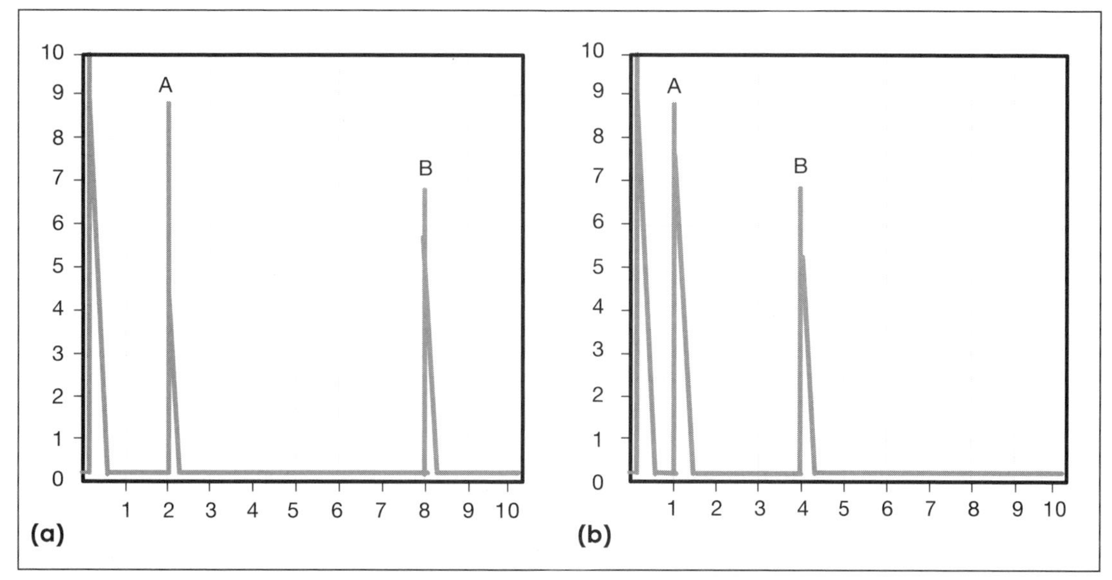

Figure 12: IIW block: (a) 5 in. (12.5 cm) screen; (b) 10 in. (25 cm) screen.

or specification) and that gain setting is recorded as the *reference level* for the tests performed using this calibration.

Defect Level and Defect Rating

With this type of calibration, as opposed to that with a DAC curve, the acceptance and rejection criteria are based on variations in signal amplitude related to sound path. Scanning is done at higher gain settings, as described in the governing code or specification. When an indication is seen, the signal is maximized and the amplitude is set to 80% FSH or the FSH percentage used for calibration. This gain setting is called the *defect level* (or *indication level).*

The sound path (SP) to the maximized indication is then read from the screen. With these three values, the *defect rating* (or *indication rating)* can be determined. The defect rating (D) is calculated as:

(Eq. 1) $$A - B - C = D$$

where

A = the defect level in decibels
B = the reference level in decibels
C = the attenuation factor

The attenuation factor (C), is twice the sound path to the indication minus 1 in. (25.4 mm) or:

$$C = (SP - 1) \times 2.$$

Here is an example of how this formula is used (in inches): Assume an indication was found at a sound path of 3 in. The reference level B

is 40 dB at 80% FSH and the indication amplitude, when set to 80% FSH, required a gain setting of 46 dB (defect level A).

Based on this data, A is 46, B is 40 and the attenuation factor $C = (3 - 1) \times 2 = 4$. Plugging these values into the $A - B - C = D$ formula, we get:

$$46 - 40 - 4 = 2$$

Therefore, the defect level for this indication is 2.

The defect rating by itself is just a number (without units). To determine whether or not the indication is rejectable, the governing code or specification has to give ranges of values for rejection. A typical set of ranges might be as follows:

If D (defect rating) is less than +5, the indication is rejectable regardless of length. If D is from +6 through +9, the indication might be rejectable if the length is greater than 0.75 in. (19 mm). If D is from +10 through +12, the indication might be rejectable if the length is greater than 2 in. (51 mm). If D is greater than +12, the indication might be acceptable regardless of length.

The above ranges are only examples of how a code or specification might define defect ratings. For actual values, the governing code or specification should be consulted.

Distance Sensitivity Calibration Block

A third commonly used calibration block is the distance sensitivity calibration (DSC) block. This block has two radii, 1 in. (25 mm) and 3 in. (75 mm), as shown in Figure 13. The focal point of each radius is at the point where the scribed line on the side of the block hits the scanning surface. To calibrate with this block, the appropriate screen width is selected and then the transducer is placed on the flat scanning surface. Several signals will be seen on the screen, from the

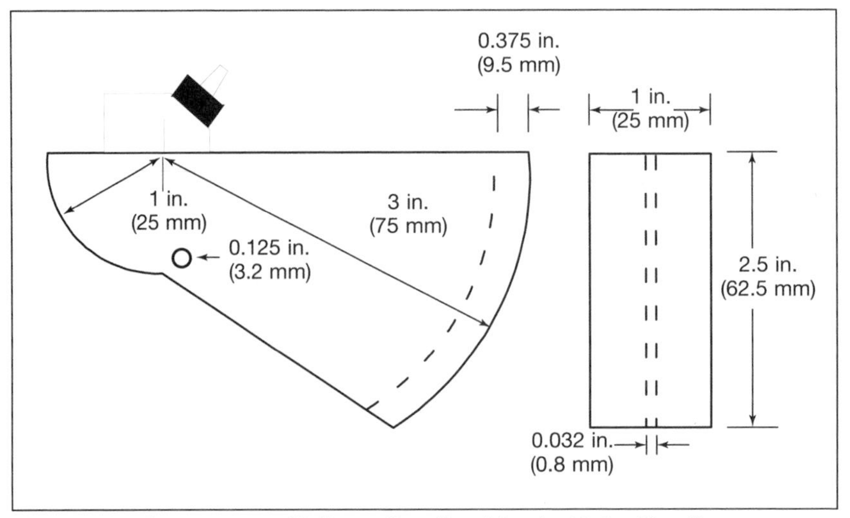

Figure 13: Distance sensitivity calibration block: *Note*: SI units are measurements of equivalent metric block.

1 in. (25 mm) radius, from the 3 in. (75 mm) radius, and from the notch in the 3 in. (75 mm) radius.

Screen Setup

For a 5 in. (12.5 cm) screen, the signal from the 1 in. (25 mm) radius (A in Figure 14) is maximized and set over the second major graticule or at a sound path of 1 in. (25 mm). The signal coming from the 3 in. (75 mm) radius (B) is then set over the tenth major graticule (5 in. [12.5 cm] sound path), and the range and delay controls are used to adjust the locations of these signals as described previously. (*Note:* The signal from the notch will appear just before [to the left of] the signal from the 3 in. [75 mm] radius. For now, that signal will be ignored.) The transducer is then aimed at the 3 in. (75 mm) radius and if the screen was properly set initially, that signal (B) will come up at the sixth major graticule, or at 3 in. (75 mm) of sound path. When this occurs, it verifies that the screen width has been accurately set.

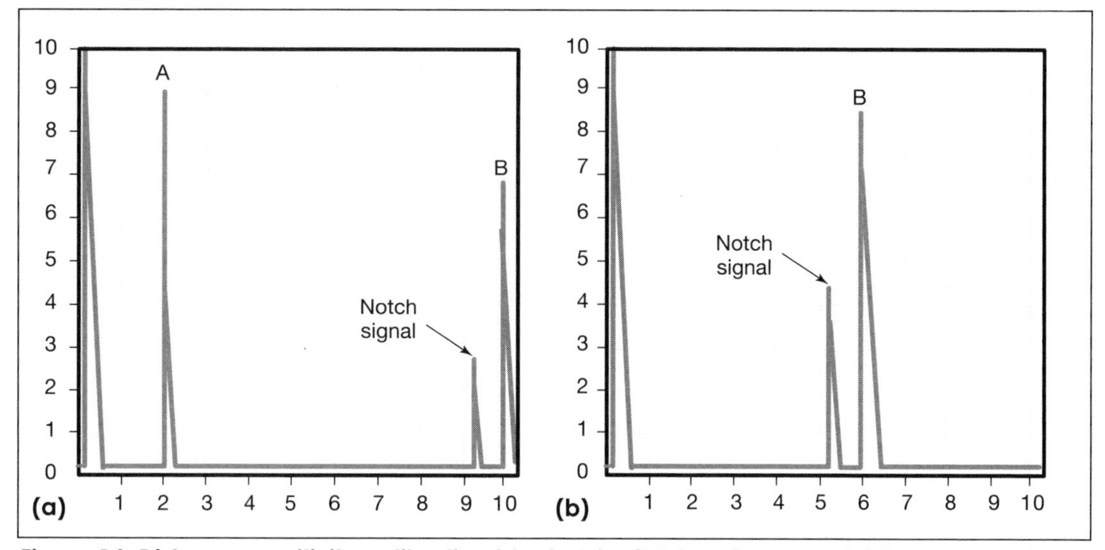

Figure 14: Distance sensitivity calibration block, 5 in. (12.5 cm) screen: (a) transducer aimed at the 1 in. (25 mm) radius; (b) transducer aimed at the 3 in. (75 mm) radius.

To set up a 10 in. (25 cm) screen, the same process is used, but with the transducer aimed at the 1 in. (25 mm) radius, that signal (A) is set over the first major graticule. The first return signal from the 3 in. (75 mm) radius (B) is set at the fifth major graticule and the second signal from the 3 in. (75 mm) radius (C) is set at the ninth major graticule. This is shown in Figure 15(a). The transducer is then aimed at the 3 in. (75 mm) radius and the first signal (B) is set over the third major graticule and the second signal (C) is set over the seventh major graticule, as shown in Figure 15(b). Signal A, from the 1 in. (25 mm) radius, does not show on this screen. When the display is adjusted so that these signals all show in the proper location, the 10 in. (25 cm) screen width is set. The notch signals will appear just to the left of the radius signals at the seventh and ninth graticules, as shown.

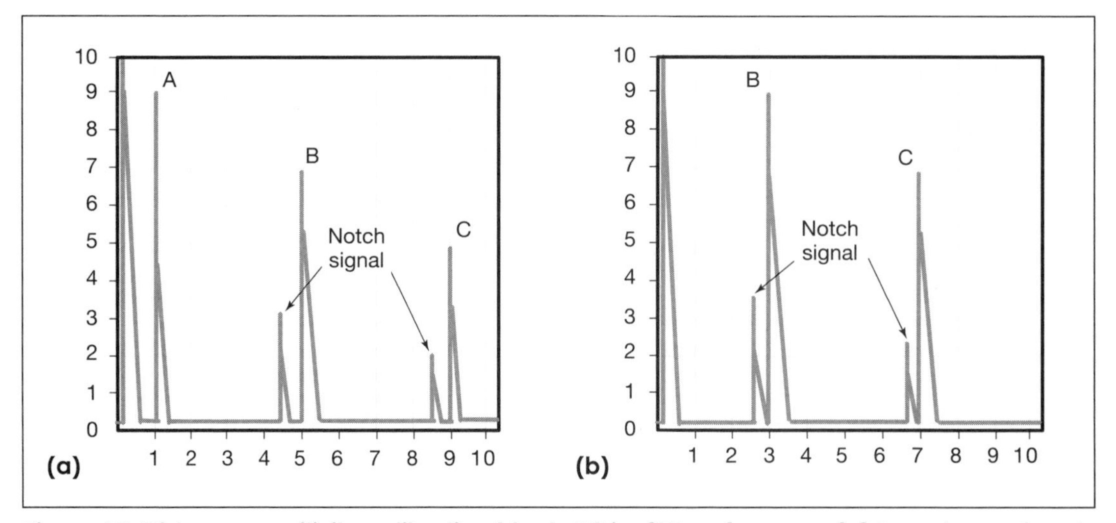

Figure 15: Distance sensitivity calibration block, 10 in. (25 cm) screen: (a) transducer aimed at the 1 in. (25 mm) radius; (b) transducer aimed at the 3 in. (75 mm) radius.

Reference Level

To set the reference level for either screen width, the transducer is aimed at the 3 in. (75 mm) radius and the gain control is used to set the signal amplitude from the 3/32 in. (2.4 mm) notch to 80% FSH (or as required by the governing code or specification). On the 10 in. (25 cm) screen, the first notch signal, just before the third major graticule, is used. As with the IIW block calibration, this calibration uses the $A - B - C = D$ formula, and the requirements described previously should be followed.

Sound Paths in the DSC Block

One question often asked about DSC block calibration is: Since the larger radius is 3 in. (75 mm), why do multiple signals show up at 4 in. (100 mm) intervals? This is due to the nature of reflection and refraction.

When the sound beam hits a material interface at an angle (such as between the wedge and the material being tested), the majority of the sound beam is reflected, with only a small percentage of the sound being sent (refracted) into the second material. The remaining sound reflects back from the interface and ricochets around until it attenuates to zero.

In the DSC block shown in Figure 16, the initial sound beam follows arrow A, striking the 1 in. (25 mm) radius and returning to the transducer. However, most of the returning sound is reflected along

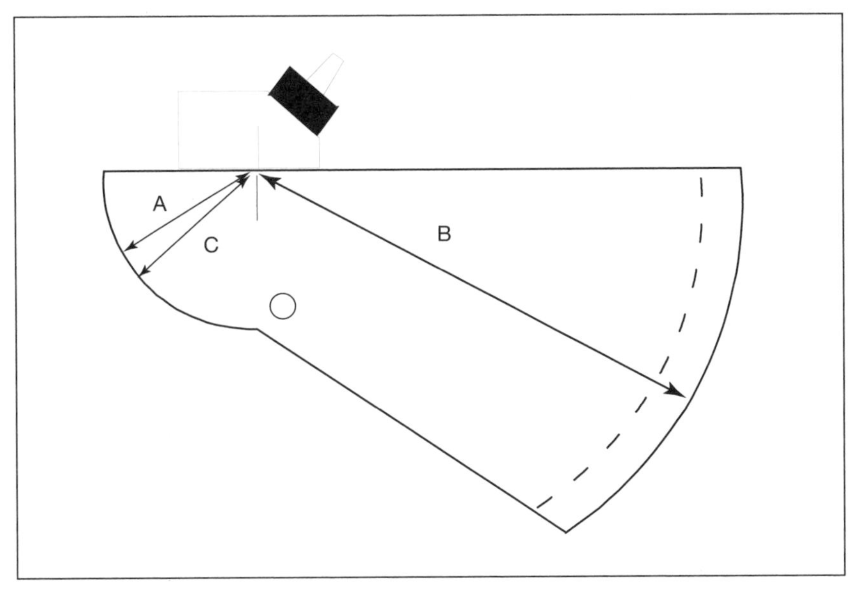

Figure 16: Distance sensitivity calibration block signal intervals.

arrow B, striking the 3 in. (75 mm) radius and returning back to the scanning surface. The sound beam that does not hit the scanning surface in the proper orientation to enter the transducer reflects from the scanning surface down to the 1 in. (25 mm) radius as shown by arrow C, then returns to the transducer. Because this second trip goes to both the 3 in. (75 mm) and 1 in. (25 mm) radii, the total distance traveled is 4 in. (100 mm), which is why the interval between signals is
4 in. (100 mm) on the screen display.

Miscellaneous Calibration Blocks

There are many other types of calibration blocks available, but most can be used in a similar manner as has been discussed here. Additional information on other calibration blocks can be found in Volume 03.03 of the *Annual Book of ASTM Standards* and in Section V of the *ASME Boiler & Pressure Vessel Code.*

Evaluation of Base Material Product Forms

Introduction

This chapter focuses on various types of materials processing, fabrication, and product technology and how they relate to ultrasonic testing. The discussion will focus on ingot pouring and continuous casting followed by subsequent processes for:

- rolling plate, sheet, bar, rod, pipe, and tubular products; and
- forgings, castings, composite structures, and weldments.

Emphasis will be on the discontinuities that are found in these types of materials and products.

Steelmaking Process

The traditional steelmaking process starts with iron ore being melted down in blast furnaces to produce molten iron. This iron, often along with scrap steel, is then heated in other furnaces along with lime and various fluxes to create *carbon steel.* There are alternate processes that do not use molten iron but start with scrap steel and/or other solid feedstock. The mix resulting from either process is called a *heat.*

In some cases, additional alloying elements such as silicon, nickel, chromium, and molybdenum are added to the heat to create specific *alloy steels.* When the heat is fully mixed and the impurities have been removed (via slag), the furnace is emptied into large fire-brick-lined ladles which can be used to fill (cast) ingot molds or are sent to a continuous-casting process referred to as *concast.*

Ingots

Ingot molds are large, rectangular, tapered forms placed on a nonflammable surface, as shown in Figure 1. After filling, the molten steel cools and solidifies into a granular solid. Once the steel has solidified, the molds are removed and the ingots are placed in soaking pits for heating, which equalizes the temperature throughout the ingot. After this process, the reheated ingots are sent to large primary rolling mills to be formed into *slabs* or *billets.*

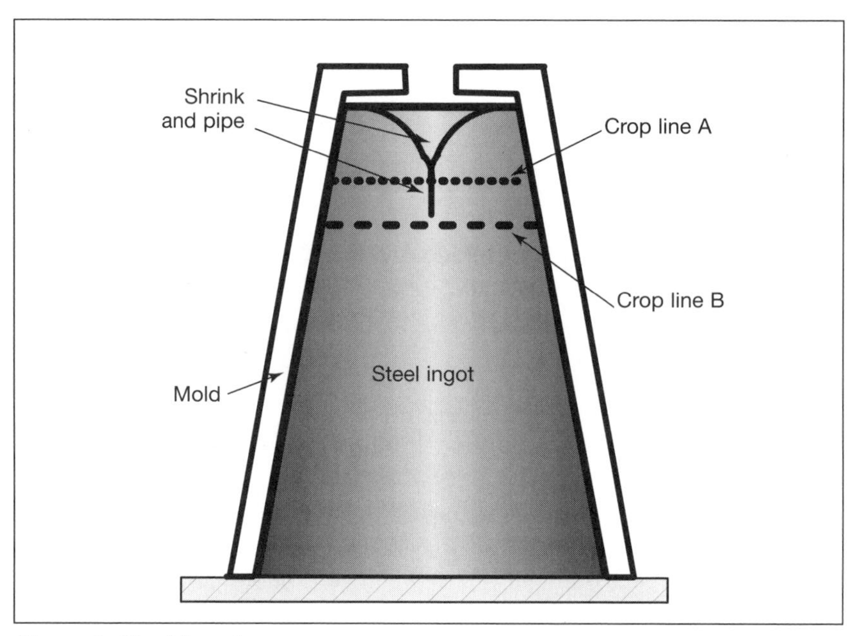

Figure 1: Steel ingot.

Because the ingots cool from the outside surface inward and the cooling steel contracts, the upper center portion of the ingot often shrinks inward and down into the ingot, causing shrinkage cracks, slag, and gases. When the gases are trapped in elongated stringers as they try to come to the surface of the ingot, this condition is called *pipe*, which can extend downward near the center of the ingot.

After cooling, the top section of the ingots are cut off, or *cropped*, in a process known as *hot topping*, to remove any shrinkage discontinuities that formed during the cooling process. If an ingot is properly cropped, as shown by crop line B in Figure 1, all or most of the defective area is removed. If the ingot is cropped too high (crop line A), the ingot may still retain some discontinuities, a condition that will affect subsequent forming processes.

Continuous Casting

Continuous casting is the process by which molten steel is poured into an insulated distribution tank called a *tundish*, which in turn feeds the steel into a water-cooled rectangular mold to form a 8 to 12 in. (203 to 305 mm) thick slab of steel of a width determined by the size of the casting machine. A side view of a typical continuous caster is shown in Figure 2. Many continuous casters use a turret system that permits ladles to continuously feed the tundish and the casting process can be maintained as long as molten steel is fed into the tundish, which is why the process is called *continuous casting*.

To initiate this process, a *dummy bar* is inserted into the base of the mold to act as a floor for the molten steel. As the mold is filled and the outer surfaces of the steel solidify, the dummy bar is slowly pulled down

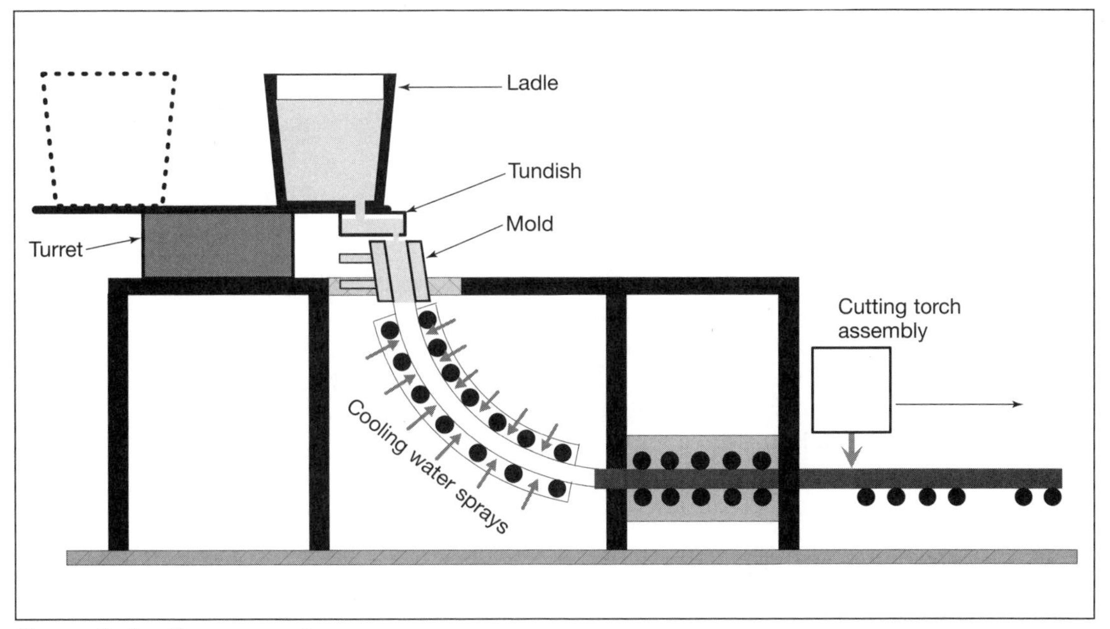

Figure 2: Continuous caster.

through the curved series of rollers, as shown. After the dummy bar passes through the final set of rollers, it is removed, leaving a continuous length of new steel extending from the mold to the cutting area beyond the last set of rollers.

During the entire casting process, the steel is sprayed with water to control the *solidification process*. As with ingots, the solidification process occurs from the outside inward, so the steel starting down the caster has a solid outer shell with a molten core. As the process continues, the steel solidifies completely and is rolled to the desired thickness as it passes through the final set of rollers. Once the steel exits the final rollers, a cutting torch system clamps to the new slab, cutting it to the desired length.

Discontinuities in Steel

Inherent discontinuities in the ingot-casting and continuous-casting processes are similar to those of other castings and include segregation, nonmetallic inclusions, shrinkage voids, cracks, and pipe.

Segregation occurs when individual elements either are not fully mixed in the heat or separate during the cooling process. Segregated elements do not have the same sound velocity as the parent metal, but unless the areas of segregation are relatively large, they cannot be easily detected ultrasonically. *Nonmetallic inclusions*, such as slag and other contaminants, are generally larger in size than segregations and can be more easily detected using ultrasonic testing.

Shrinkage voids and *cracks* are both good reflectors of sound and can be detected ultrasonically much more readily than segregation due to the sharp edges of the resulting voids and the large change in acoustic impedance between the void and the metal. Because the entrapped gas tends to form rounded tubes with smoother sides, *pipe* does not result in as sharp a reflector as *shrinkage* and *shrink cracks*. But because of the change in acoustic impedance between the gas and the metal, it too can be easily found ultrasonically.

Slabs and Billets

Because of their size, *slabs* and *billets* must be processed to reduce them to a manageable thickness. This is done in hot-rolling mills where the heated slab or billet is repeatedly passed through correspondingly tighter rollers. As the slab or billet is rolled, it increases in length, resulting in a longer, thinner shape. During this process, the metal grains in the steel are elongated in the direction of rolling, as are most discontinuities. Depending on the intended use of the steel, the product may be cut to length between rolling passes to make handling more manageable.

Plate and Sheet

The rolling process permits slabs and billets to be reduced in thickness into plates, and, if the process is continued, the plates can be rolled into *sheets*. Since the thinning process continually elongates the product form, rolling sheet steel results in a very long product. To reduce the physical size of the forming area and to make handling easier, the sheet is often formed into a coil. These coils can then be transported, stored for additional forming processes, or sent back through the same rollers set at closer tolerances to further reduce the thickness of the sheet. During the rolling operation, several types of process discontinuities can occur, as shown in Figure 3.

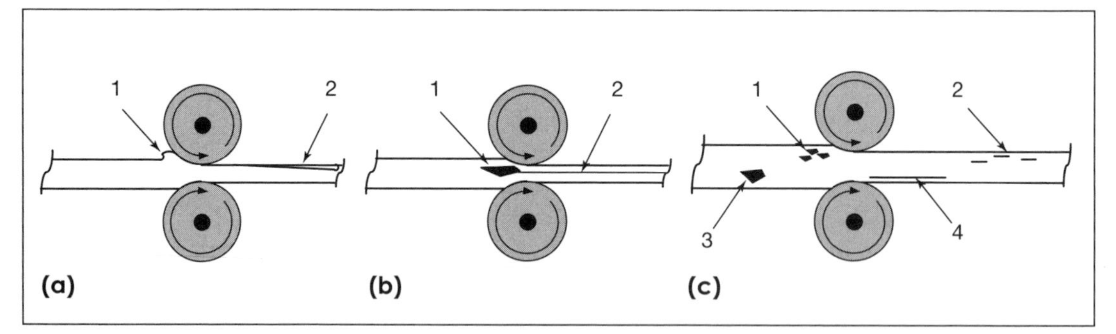

Figure 3: Rolling discontinuities: (a) rolling lap; (b) centerline delamination; (c) segregation and inclusion laminations.

Discontinuities in Plate and Sheet

One such discontinuity is a *rolling* or *surface lap*, shown in Figure 3(a). This occurs when some of the metal humps up in front of one of the rolls (1) and then is folded back over the unrolled sheet and pulled through the rollers. This results in an elongated sliver of steel that has been pressed back into the surface of the plate (2). The lap may be visible on close inspection but may also be smeared closed, making it invisible to the naked eye. During straight-beam ultrasonic testing, a lap on the scanning surface side may result in a loss of backwall signal when the transducer passes over it or in a very slight shift in the backwall signal if the lap is on the opposite side of the part from the transducer. If a lap is suspected, magnetic particle testing should also be performed to determine if a lap is present.

Laminations occur when any of the inherent discontinuities found in ingots, slabs, or billets make it into the rolling process. Because the rolling operation compresses the thickness and elongates the material, all such discontinuities are also flattened out and lengthened considerably. *Delaminations* resulting from centerline pipe or shrink remaining after the primary forming process will generally be located close to the center of the thickness of the rolled material, as shown in Figure 3(b).

Laminations resulting from segregation (Figure 3[c] 1 → 2) or nonmetallic inclusions (Figure 3[c] 3 → 4) may be at any depth in the rolled product. Most laminations can be detected using straight-beam ultrasonic testing, but not all laminations are continuous across their length or width, resulting in intermittent screen signals and/or a loss of backwall signal amplitude (Figure 4). On thinner sections, a *delay-line transducer* may be needed so that the near-field effects are contained in the delay line and are not introduced into the test.

Seams are elongated surface discontinuities of varying depth that usually run parallel to the steel rolling direction. They are often lengthy and sometimes very tight. Occasionally, they take the form of fissures along the grain. Being through-thickness in orientation and depending on the depth, seams may be detected using angle-beam testing. If

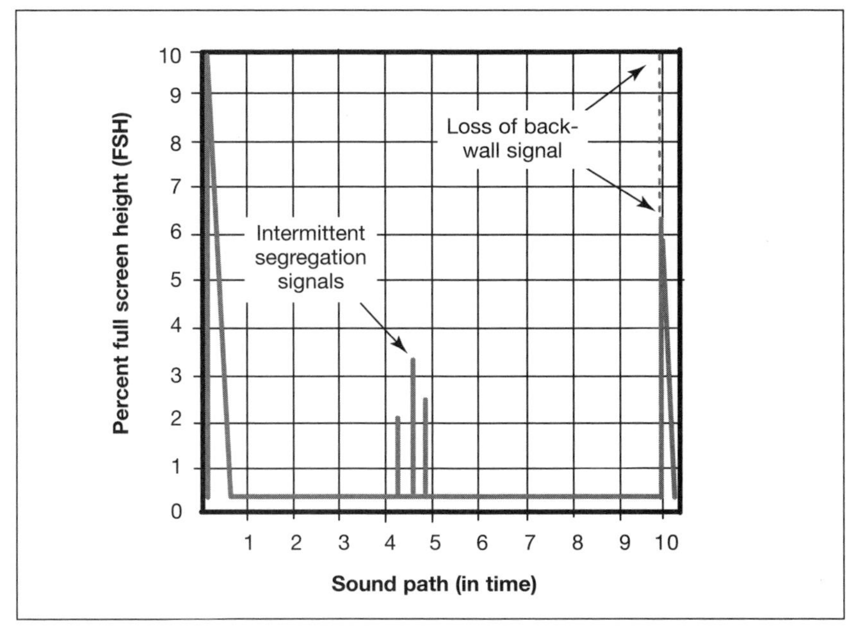

Figure 4: Intermittent lamination signals.

extremely shallow, magnetic particle testing is the preferred method, followed by ultrasonic testing to determine depth.

Bar and Rod

The most commonly used process for producing solid round stock (bar and rod) is the *rolling process*, which is much like the rolling process described for plate and sheet steel. However, since a round product is desired, the rollers in a bar or rod mill have concave contact surfaces (like shallow pulley wheels) rather than flat surfaces. Starting as a heated round ingot or pre-rolled billet, the product moves through a series of consecutively smaller-diameter paired rollers that reduce the diameter of the steel while increasing the length. Near the end of the process, some of the rollers may be oriented 90° from the previous set so that roundness is maintained. As with the sheet-rolling process, laps, seams, and laminations are the typical inherent discontinuities found in these products.

Extrusion Process for Bar and Rod

The *extrusion process* also starts with either a round ingot or a pre-rolled billet that has been heated to an appropriate temperature. The piece is then placed in an extruder, as illustrated in Figure 5. The ram forces the heated steel through a die the size of the rod or bar that is desired. As the ram advances, the metal is extruded out of the hole in the die plate, creating a rod or bar. Like the rolling process, any discontinuities in the billet will be elongated and compressed during this process. In a similar process, a hot-rolled bar or rod can be pulled or drawn through the dies instead of being pushed through. The *drawing process* is used principally in the manufacture of wire.

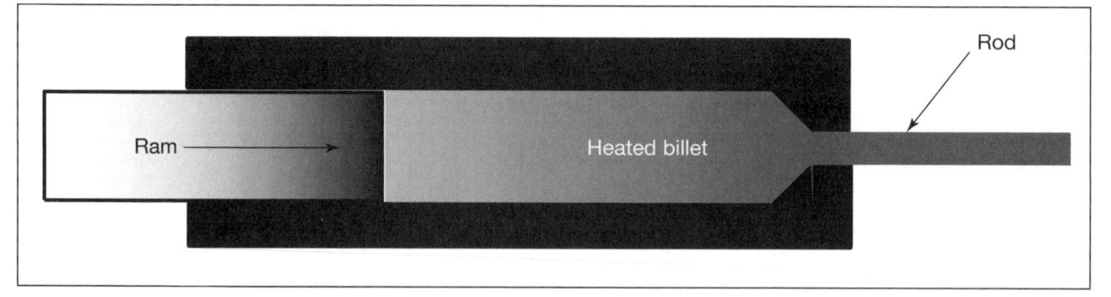

Figure 5: Extrusion process.

Ultrasonic Testing of Bar and Rod

As with plate and sheet, extruded bar and rod can have elongated discontinuities such as *laminations* from nonmetallic inclusions and segregation, and these can also be found ultrasonically. The ultrasonic testing of lengths of round stock is often done using the *immersion technique*, which involves immersing the test object in deaerated water treated with anti-corrosion chemicals.

Smaller-diameter round stock can be passed through a *water box*, as shown in Figure 6. The rod is pushed through flexible gaskets on either side of a water-filled box, which has one or more search units extending down into the water. The drive rollers spin the rod and push it through the box at a controlled speed, allowing the search units to interrogate the rod as it passes through the box, using the water in the box to couple the sound beam to the test object. Depending on the number and orientation of search units used, the test object can be tested directly through thickness (down the radius), at angles up and down the axis of the test object, and at angles around the circumference of the test object in one pass through the box.

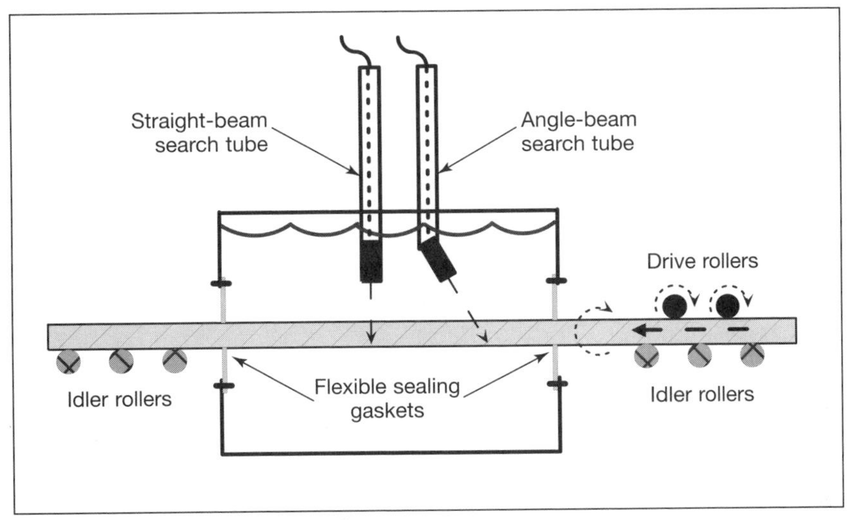

Figure 6: Rod immersion testing.

For larger-diameter round stock, a *full immersion tank* is used. This setup is similar to the water box, but the entire test object is submersed at one time. The round stock is rotated on fixed (non-moveable) rollers, and the ultrasonic instruments and search tubes are mounted on a moving assembly called a *bridge*. The bridge can be set to travel at various speeds down the length of the test object and, as described above, multiple scans can be performed at one time.

For short pieces of round stock, it may be necessary to perform the test using the *contact method*. Because the scanning surface is curved, care must be taken to ensure that the transducer is properly coupled to the test object. This can be done by using a *contoured wedge* that has been curved to match the circumference of the test object, as shown in Figure 7.

Commercially produced contoured wedges can generally be purchased for standard diameters and can be ordered for any size round stock if time is not a constraint. If necessary, acrylic can be cut to the approximate shape, then sanded to the exact shape by placing the sandpaper on a piece the same diameter as needed and sanding the wedge until it matches the circumference. *Cautionary note:* When using

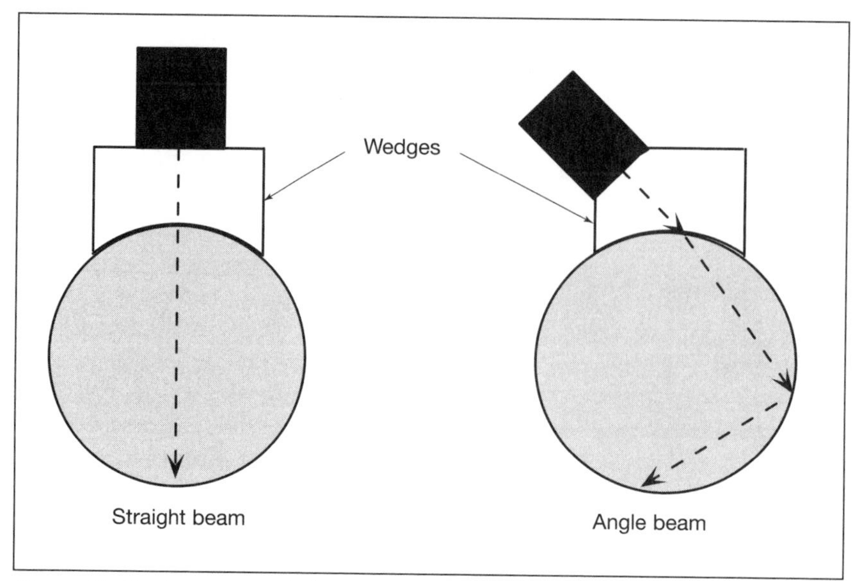

Figure 7: Contoured probes.

contoured wedges, calibration can be difficult because a calibration block matching the test object must be used so the technician knows where the sound beam is going.

Hydrogen Flakes

Hydrogen flakes, another discontinuity found in bar and rod, are fine, circular cracks located near the center of heavy steel forgings, billets, and bars that run longitudinally through the steel, as shown in Figure 8. Generally found in higher carbon and alloy steels, these flakes result when the cooling process occurs before the dissolved hydrogen can dissipate out of the steel. Straight-beam ultrasonic testing is the best method for detecting hydrogen flakes. If there is doubt about the type and location of this discontinuity, the end of the piece may be cut and magnetic particle testing can be done of the cross-section to verify the presence of the flakes.

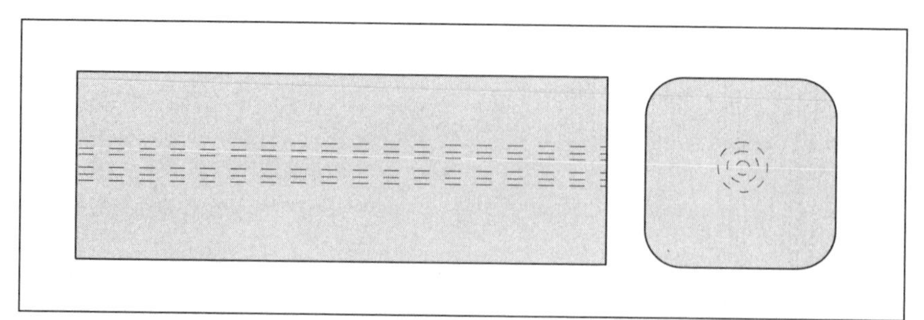

Figure 8: Hydrogen flakes.

Pipe and Tubular Products

Pipe and tube can be manufactured as seamless or welded product. *Seamless pipe and tube* in the 6 to 16 in. (152 to 406 mm) diameter range are generally manufactured in a *plug mill*. In this process, a *bloom* (large billet) is heated and pierced, then passed through a rotary elongator to form a short, thick-walled, hollow shell. A plug matching the inside diameter of the finished product is placed in the hollow shell, which is then passed through rollers that reduce the thickness, elongating the material as it reduces the thickness. Later rolling processes even out the wall thickness and bring the pipe down to its final thickness.

For seamless product in the 1 to 6 in. (25.4 to 152 mm) range, a *mandrel mill* is usually used. In this process, an ingot or billet is heated and pierced; then a mandrel is placed in the hole and the assembly is run through a rolling, or mandrel, mill. This differs from a plug mill in that the process is continuous, running between multiple pairs of curved rollers set 90° apart to elongate the material and reduce the wall thickness. The product is then reheated and rolled to final diameter.

Extrusion Process for Tubes

The extrusion process is used for small-diameter tubes. The round stock is cut to length, heated, sized, and descaled, then extruded through a steel die. The material is then run through a reducing mill to obtain the final dimensions and surface finish.

In addition to the inherent discontinuities described previously (laps, voids, laminations, and seams), *internal tears* occasionally occur during the extrusion process. These crack-like discontinuities are generally oriented around the inner diameter surface of the pipe or tube and can be found ultrasonically. Typical straight- and angle-beam tests are shown in Figure 9. *Thinning* of the pipe wall can also be found using a straight-beam thickness test. For thinner-walled product, encircling eddy current testing coils are often used instead of ultrasonic testing for discontinuity detection.

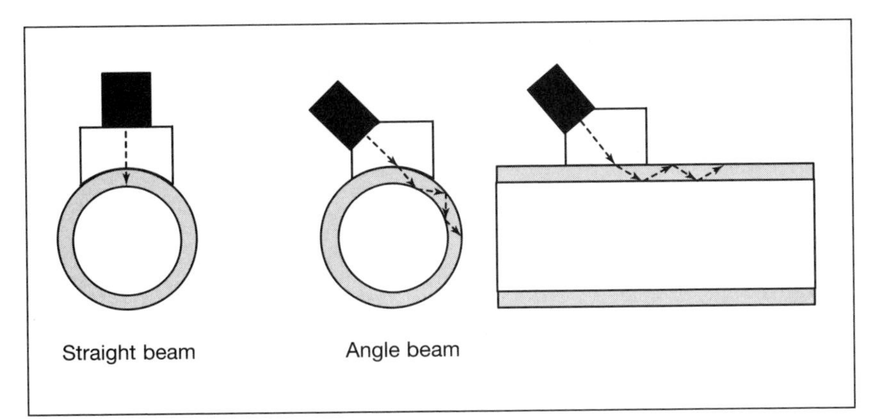

Figure 9: Contact pipe inspection.

Welded Pipe

Welded pipe is manufactured by feeding sheet or plate of the proper thickness (called *skelp*) into forming rollers or forms to create a round tube; then the edges of the tube are welded, creating a longitudinal or spiral weld seam down the length of the pipe. Weld types vary depending on the diameter, wall thickness, manufacturing process, and intended use of the finished product. More common pipe-welding processes include *electric resistance welding* (ERW), *high-frequency welding* (HFW) and *submerged arc welding* (SAW). Where submerged arc welding is performed on both the inner and outer diameter of the pipe, the process is called *double submerged arc welding* (DSAW).

Electric resistance and high-frequency welds produce a very narrow weld seam, with the most common type of discontinuity being *lack of fusion. Hook cracks* may occur near the weld line if *nonmetallic inclusions* are present at the tube edges when the weld is made. Since filler metal and flux are not used in these processes, *slag inclusions* will not be seen in electric resistance and high-frequency welds.

Ultrasonic testing of this pipe involves multiple transducers on an automated system testing from both sides of the weld to ensure full weld coverage. Submerged arc welding and double submerged arc welding discontinuities are typical of other electric arc welding processes and will be discussed in the welding section of this chapter.

Inservice Inspection of Pipe and Tube

Inservice inspection of pipe and tubular products may be done manually by the contact method or by automated scanning using a constant water-feed system for coupling. When the inspection is performed without the use of contoured wedges or shoes, the inspector must pay close attention to the contact angle of the transducer face to achieve normal (perpendicular) beam propagation into the test component. This is particularly necessary in manual scanning applications.

Forgings

The forging process uses high-pressure compressive force to cause plastic deformation of metal into a desired shape. Depending on size, shape, material type, and complexity, the test object may be heated to well above the recrystallization temperature, in a range below that temperature, or at room temperature. Pressure may be applied by a press, rollers, or repetitive blows of a hammer, depending on the type of forging. The basic forging principle is shown in Figure 10. Note the grain flow in the test object (arrows in the right-hand figure) as the metal is compressed to fill the die. As with other forming processes, inherent discontinuities are stretched and flattened in the direction in which the metal moves.

In addition to the distortion of inherent discontinuities, processing discontinuities such as *forging bursts* and *hot tears* can also occur in the forging process. Forging bursts occur when the metal cannot withstand the tensile stress that occurs during the forging process. Bursts vary in

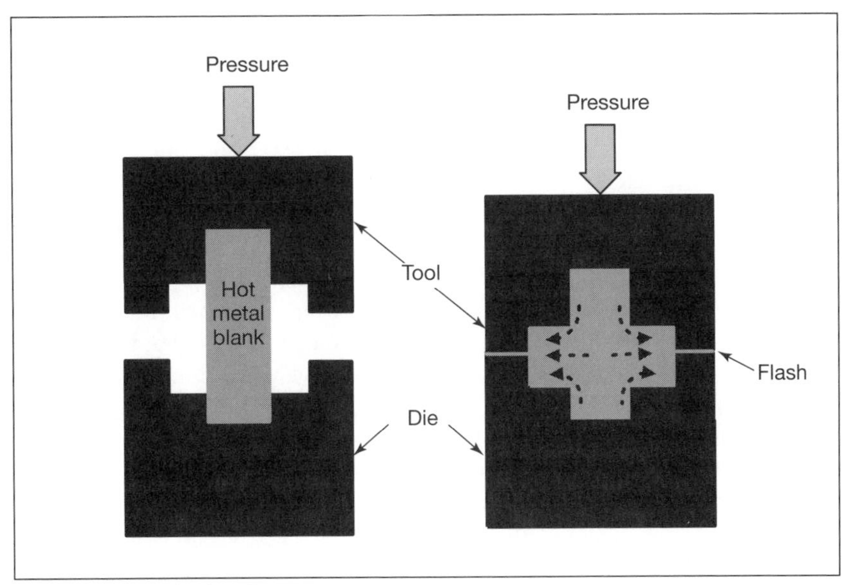

Figure 10: Basic forging process.

size, may be open cavities or similar to tight cracks, and may be oriented longitudinally or transversely, as shown in Figure 11(a). Cracking may occur when there is differential cooling at changes in thickness, as depicted in Figure 11(b). Both types of discontinuities can be found ultrasonically using either straight- or angle-beam testing, or a combination of both.

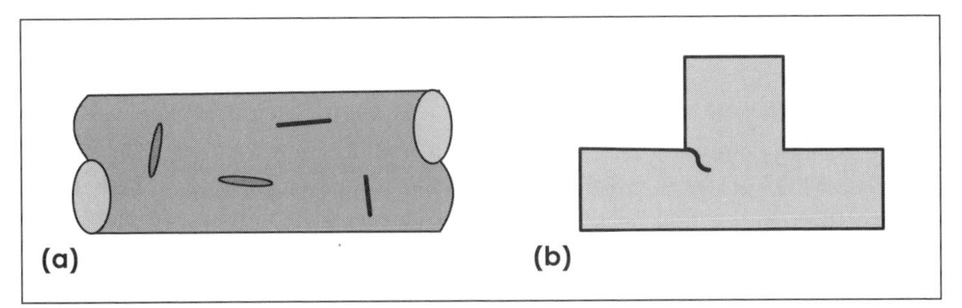

Figure 11: Forging process discontinuities: (a) bursts; (b) crack.

Ultrasonic Inspection of Forgings

Ultrasonic inspection of forgings may occur at various stages of the forging process, from the initial near-raw stage to the near-finished shape to flat-faced machined and final-stage machined forgings. Early stage inspections during the forging process are used as a screening tool to determine if the component is acceptable for further forging and/or machining processes. The penetration of ultrasound into forgings may vary with the volume of the component and the type and quality of forged material.

Applicable Codes/Standards for Forgings

The two most common specifications used to inspect forgings are AMS-STD-2154 and ASTM A-388. With some exceptions, forging discontinuities tend to be two-dimensional. As a result, most forging codes and standards require, when possible, inspection using the following parameters:

1. The part should be inspected at a point in the process before it has reached its final machined state. This requirement accounts for the zone near the surface that ultrasound normally can't resolve. When surface roughness becomes a factor, some standards will require a "UT shape" for a forging, which is when a part is machined partially on the surfaces that need to be scanned and enough material is left to account for the loss of near-surface resolution.
2. At a minimum, the part should be scanned from the surfaces where the sound propagates perpendicular to the grain-flow lines. Since the forging process flattens inherent discontinuities in the direction of the grain flow, they become larger targets for the sound beam. The inspection of some aerospace forgings even requires a flow-line diagram to determine scanning surfaces. Flow lines are determined by sectioning a sacrificial part, polishing the surface, and chemically etching the polished surface to make the grain lines visually apparent.
3. Amplitude response is correlated to a flat-bottom hole (FBH) response from a known reflector. FBHs may be drilled into an unusable section of the part being inspected, or ASTM type blocks may be used. Some specifications require the part to be inspected for intermediate echoes and loss of back reflection on parallel surfaces to account for any irregularly oriented discontinuities. Additionally, a correction factor may be added for surface roughness variations from the calibration standard to the inspection surface.

Castings

The casting process involves melting the metal and pouring or injecting it into a mold of the desired shape. Ingot casting, as discussed earlier, is one of the simpler forms of casting, but molds can be designed for extremely complex shapes and may vary from finger-sized objects up to the size of a house.

A simplified representation of the sand-casting process is shown in Figure 12. The mold is formed around a pattern in the desired shape; then molten metal is poured into the pouring cup. The metal flows through the vertical sprue into the *gating system*, filling the mold cavity. The *riser* holds additional metal so that when the metal contracts as it cools there is sufficient metal to fill the mold, preventing shrinkage cavities (described below).

Casting Discontinuities

Typical discontinuities found in castings are shown by number in Figure 13 and are defined as follows:

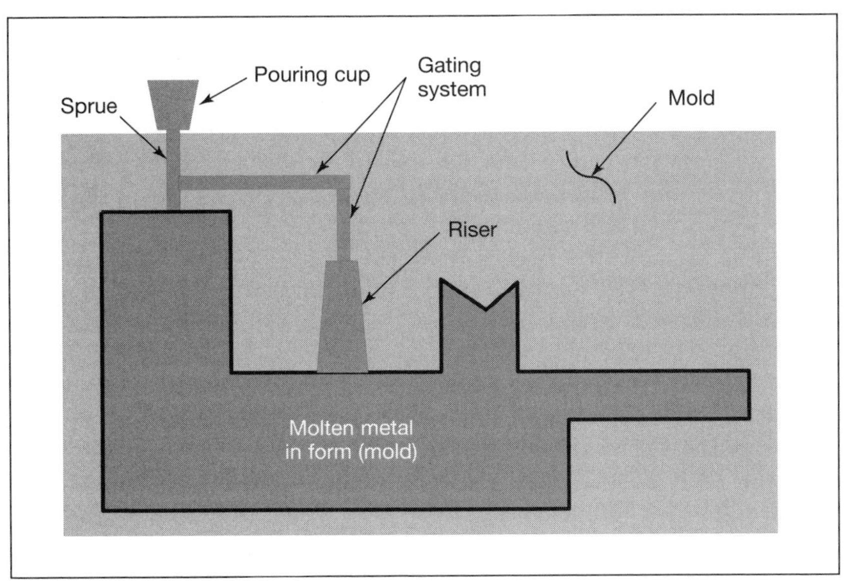

Figure 12: Basic casting process.

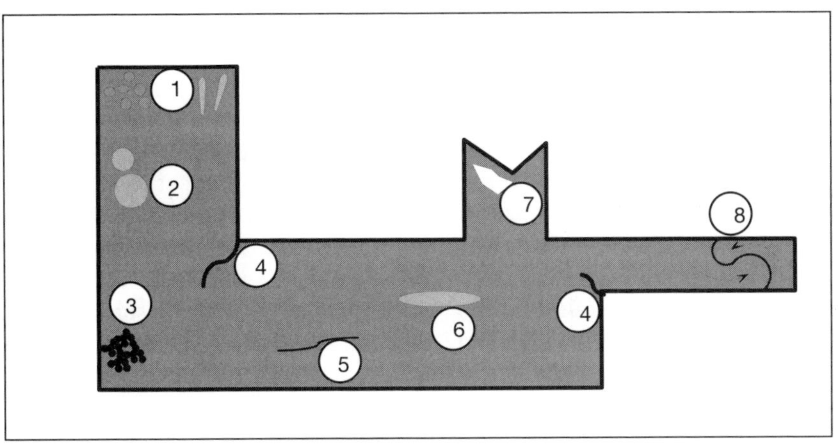

Figure 13: Casting discontinuities.

1. **Porosity** – usually caused by the release of dissolved gases as the molten metal cools, creating bubbles or pores. Pores are generally small diameter with smooth surfaces. Multiple pores in one area are called *cluster porosity*, and, if the porosity moves as the metal cools, the porosity may form an elongated void commonly called *piping* or *wormhole porosity*, as shown.
2. **Gas holes** – created in the same manner as porosity but are larger in diameter and generally tend to be isolated or limited in the number found in any one area.
3. **Inclusions** – areas where nonmetallic materials such as slag or sand are trapped in the material as the metal cools.
4. **Hot tears** – cracklike tears that occur when the material starts to contract during the initial cooling phase, just below the solidification

temperature. If the hardening material is restrained by the mold at that point, the material may tear, usually at changes in section where a stress riser already exists.

5. **Cracks** – irregularly shaped, linear discontinuities (fractures) that can be caused when internal stresses exceed the strength of the material. In the casting process, stress cracks can occur due to contraction, residual stress, and shock, or due to inservice stresses.
6. **Shrinkage cavities** – occur when the liquid metal contracts and solidifies during cooling. If there is not enough molten metal to offset the resulting contraction, the metal may pull apart, creating a void or cavity in the solidified material. These typically occur where additional molten metal cannot be fed in quickly enough to offset the contraction or where there are variations in section thickness.
7. **Air pockets** – occur when the air in the unfilled mold cannot escape as the molten metal is added. These generally are found just beneath the top surface of the object.
8. **Cold shuts** – are areas where part of the filler material solidifies before the mold cavity is completely filled. As additional molten material reaches the already cooled section of metal, it may not fuse together, forming a tight line of *disbond* (lack of fusion) between the two segments of metal.

Ultrasonic Testing of Castings

Because of the nature of the casting and cooling process, there is a tendency for the material to have larger grain sizes than materials formed in other processes. If the finished product is not subjected to additional heat-treatment processes to refine (reduce) the grain size, this can present a problem when ultrasonic testing is done. In coarser materials, such as cast iron, the grain size may be sufficiently large and coarse to cause the sound beam to reflect from the grains, resulting in the scattering of the sound beam inside the test object with a resultant loss of returned sound. In cases like this, ultrasonic testing technicians might believe that they are performing a full test when, in fact, the sound is not fully penetrating the test object. This is one of the reasons why the calibration block material is required to be as close a metallurgical match (ultrasonically equivalent) to the test object as possible.

Applicable Codes/Standards for Castings

The most common casting specification is ASTM A-609. Codes and standards for castings have to address irregularly shaped discontinuities and a larger grain structure. As a result, most codes and standards require, when possible, ultrasonic inspections using the following parameters:

1. The part is scanned for both intermediate echoes and loss of back reflection on parallel surfaces. Unlike a forging, the three-dimensional features of a casting make a poor reflector for ultrasound. A large indication may have a low-amplitude ultrasonic response and only be identifiable by loss of back reflection. Rejection

levels for loss of amplitude are normally evaluated in percent of back reflection lost due to an indication.

2. Due to the surface roughness of castings, a dB material correction factor is usually applied to account for variations between the calibration standards and the inspection surface. Since inspections for intermediate echoes typically require a calibration on larger flat-bottom holes (FBHs) than would be used for a forging, the required sensitivity is usually less in terms of gain. This is helpful when applying a correction factor since the material correction factor can require a significant amount of gain to be added.
3. Some specifications, such as EN-12680, require any indication with a 2:1 signal-to-noise ratio or greater to be evaluated in addition to other criteria. This accounts for any irregular or large-grain structure that may not give a strong ultrasonic response.

Composites (Bonded Structures)

Composites are formed by joining two or more layers (*plies*) of materials with different physical or chemical properties into one bonded assembly, as shown in Figure 14. Composites are commonly used in applications that require high-strength, lightweight materials. By combining different materials into a composite sandwich, the advantages of the properties of multiple materials can be incorporated into a single product. Composites are used in an extremely wide range of applications, varying from plywood to reinforced carbon-carbon (RCC) composites.

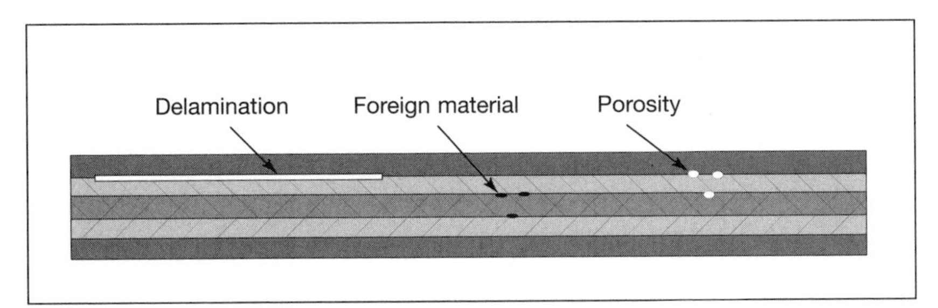

Figure 14: Composites and discontinuities.

The most common discontinuities (see Figure 14) found in composites are *delaminations*, foreign material *inclusions,* and *porosity.* Delamination, or the separation of plies, can result from shock loading, impact, or cyclic stresses. This can also result in fiber pullout where individual fibers separate from the composite matrix. The inclusion of foreign materials can occur if the composite materials are not kept clean or are mishandled during the material assembly process prior to the fusing of the base materials into one substance. Such inclusions are not only tiny areas of disbond but can create stress risers that may lead to delamination. Porosity can occur when the base materials outgas during the fusing process and all of the gases do not escape the composite before it hardens. This can also lead to weak areas that could lead to further failure.

Depending on the materials used to create a composite, ultrasonic testing can be used to test these structures. If the composite is thin, it may be necessary to use a delay line in front of the transducer or switch to an immersion technique so that the near-field effects are contained in the delay line or water path and are not introduced into the testing.

Welds

Welding is the most commonly used metals joining method in industry, and welds are the most common structural item to be ultrasonically tested under shop or field conditions. As a result, it is important that ultrasonic testing technicians have a basic knowledge of the most commonly used welding processes and that they be familiar with standard welding terminology. Prior to performing ultrasonic testing on a weld, the technician should ask which weld process was used to make the weld. Knowing this, and knowing what discontinuities can occur in the various types of weld, can prevent a technician from calling out a discontinuity that couldn't exist in the weld due to the weld process used. Avoiding miscalls of this nature can enhance the credibility of the technician.

Welding Terminology

Figure 15 shows several of the more common weld joint configurations used in industry. Welds A through E show butt welds, so named because the two pieces of base metal are butted up against each other prior to welding. The edges of the plate(s) are grooved to permit access to the bottom of the weld, which is why butt welds are often called *groove welds.* If the weld is designed to match the full thickness of the joined test objects, the weld is called a *full penetration weld.* If the weld is designed to penetrate only partway through the material thickness, as shown in weld E, the joint is called a *partial penetration weld.* Partial penetration welds are hard to test ultrasonically (if the governing code or specification permits it at all) because the ultrasonic test signal from the gap at the root of a partial penetration weld can mask discontinuities actually in the weld root.

Weld Grooves

If the groove in the base material is all from one side, the weld is designated as a *single-vee weld,* as shown in welds A, C, and D, and the root opening is at the bottom of the weld. If the joint is grooved on both sides, as shown in weld B, the weld is called a *double-vee weld* and the root is in the center of the weld thickness. Because the root is the hardest part of a weld to form, many weld discontinuities will tend to be at the root, so it is important for the ultrasonic testing technician to know the root location. Knowing the included angle of the original weld groove can aid the technician in determining which wedge angle will be best for detecting side-wall fusion discontinuities.

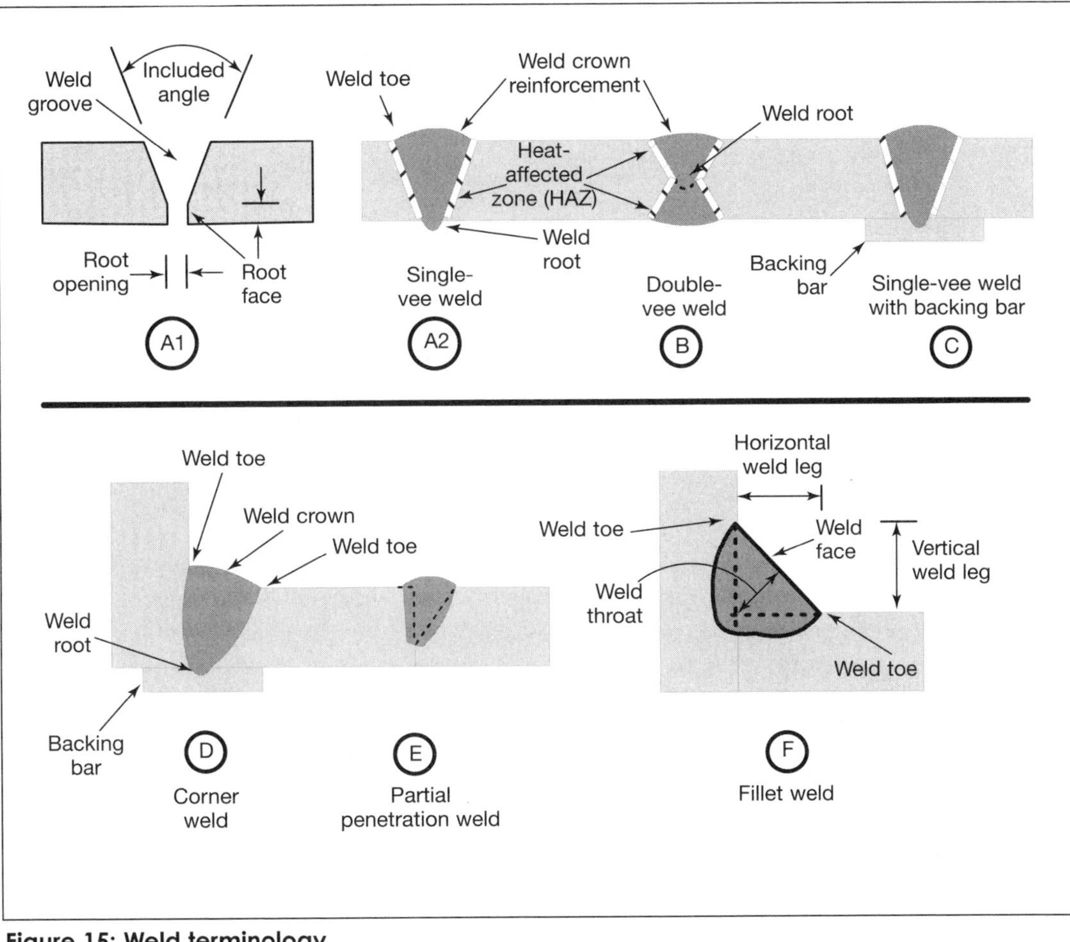

Figure 15: Weld terminology.

Weld F is a *fillet weld* that is not deposited in a groove but is placed in a corner formed by the base material. Because the majority of the weld metal is deposited above the base metal and there is an inherent gap at the root of the weld, these welds do not lend themselves well to ultrasonic testing.

Heat-Affected Zone

Along the edge of every weld is an area in the base metal called the *heat-affected zone* (HAZ). The HAZ is that area of the base material immediately adjacent to the weld that has been heated to a temperature high enough to affect the mechanical properties or change the microstructure of the metal but below the melting point. Examples of the effects of this heating are refined grain structure and changes in the hardness, ductility, or strength of the steel. The width of the HAZ varies depending on the amount of heat input into the weld, interpass temperatures, and cooling rate. Because this area is susceptible to change, most codes and specifications require that 1 in. (25.4 mm) or so of the base metal also be included in the area of interest for the ultrasonic test.

Welding Processes

In some welding processes, no filler metal is used and the weld is formed by melting the edges of the two pieces of base metal together. These are called *nonconsumable processes* since no filler metal is used. When filler metal is added to form the weld by burning off the electrode, it is considered a *consumable process*. All welds involve melting the base metal to a molten state and allowing it to join with other molten metal (or base metal) and then cooling to form a single piece. In the *electric arc welding process*, current is passed through the welding electrode to complete a circuit with the base material, resulting in a high-temperature electric arc forming between the base metal and electrode.

Shielding Gases

Because the molten metal is susceptible to contamination during the welding process, the molten metal must be shielded from atmospheric contaminants during welding. To do this, gases are released by melting various chemical elements that have been combined together to form a *flux*, the weld area is flooded with an *inert gas* (or a mixture of gases), or a combination of both techniques is used. When flux is used, the shielding gas is given off by the melting flux and the remaining melted solids cool to form a glasslike coating over the weld, called *slag*, which helps reduce the cooling rate of the weld metal. When multiple layers (passes) of weld material are required, the slag must be removed completely between passes to prevent having it remelted and mixed back into the next layer of weld or trapped between layers, creating slag inclusions.

Types of Shielding Weld Processes

Figure 16 shows examples of this shielding along with the five most common welding processes used in shop fabrication and field erection:

1. Shielded metal arc welding (SMAW).
2. Submerged arc welding (SAW).
3. Gas tungsten arc welding (GTAW).
4. Gas metal arc welding (GMAW).
5. Flux-cored arc welding (FCAW).

Shielded Metal Arc Welding

The shielded metal arc welding (SMAW) process (commonly called *stick welding*) is shown in Figure 16(a). This process uses a straight piece of welding electrode (rod), coated with chemical elements to form a flux, as described previously. Electrode length varies based on the diameter of the steel core, but the most commonly used electrode size is 14 in. (356 mm) in length. Since the electrode holder (stinger) grips the back end of the rod, not all of the rod can be consumed in the weld, with a common stub length being between 2 and 4 in. (51 and 102 mm), the length varying depending on the accessibility of the weld groove.

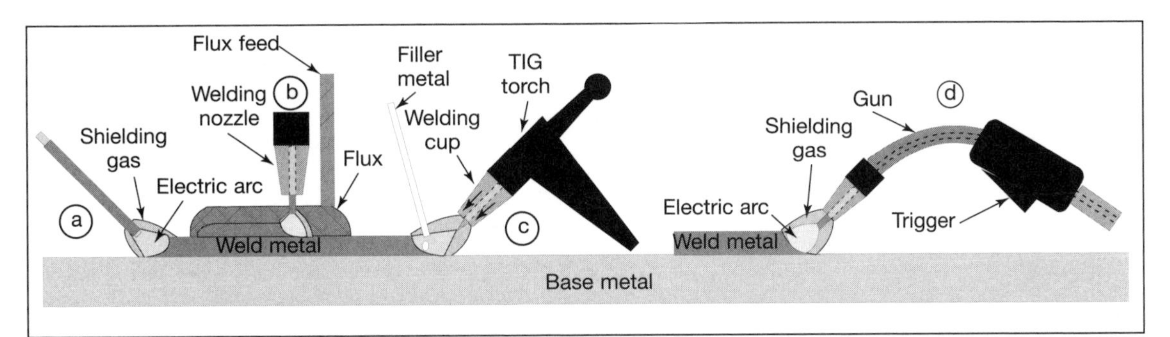

Figure 16: Basic electric arc welding processes: (a) shielded metal arc welding; (b) submerged arc welding; (c) gas tungsten arc welding; (d) gas metal arc welding and flux-cored arc welding setup.

To make a stick weld, the rod is placed in an electrode holder and the other end is scratched across the surface where the weld is wanted to create the electric arc. As the rod burns off, a pool of molten metal, or *puddle*, is formed and the welder continues to feed the electrode into the puddle and move that puddle down the weld groove to create the weld. Due to the brightness of the arc and the presence of very strong ultraviolet radiation, welders are required to protect their eyes and skin from burns.

Submerged Arc Welding

Figure 16(b) shows the submerged arc welding (SAW) process, where a solid welding wire is fed from a spool down through feed rollers and through a welding nozzle. Granular flux is fed from a flux hopper into the weld groove just ahead of the weld nozzle so that the welding wire makes contact with the base metal beneath a mound of flux. The arc is established under that flux mound, melting the flux immediately around the arc, creating the shielding gases required to protect the molten weld metal. As with the SMAW process, the melted flux cools to become slag, which must be removed between passes. Excess flux that was not melted can be recovered, reconditioned, and reused. Because the arc is fully shielded by the flux covering the weld groove, welders are not required to use eye protection if the process is operating properly. SAW is usually used in the flat position because of the need to have the flux stay on the weld. When the proper setup parameters are used, this automated welding process can produce large amounts of continuous weld. However, if the setup parameters are incorrect — for example, if the weld nozzle is misaligned with the weld groove — long lengths of bad weld may result, usually with the same discontinuity over the length of the weld.

Gas Tungsten Arc Welding

Figure 16(c) shows the gas tungsten arc welding (GTAW) process. This process was formerly called the *tungsten inert gas* (TIG) process (and still is by some welders), but since other non-inert gases are now used for shielding, this term is no longer accurate. GTAW is so named because the nonconsumable welding electrode is made of tungsten. The shielding gas comes from external gas bottles and flows through tubing to the torch handle and out through the welding cup, beside the electric lead, and back to the power source. When filler metal is required, it is usually a thin bare wire fed into the weld puddle by hand.

Gas Metal Arc Welding

Figure 16(d) shows the setup for both the gas metal arc welding (GMAW) and the *flux-cored arc welding* (FCAW) processes. These two processes use similar equipment but have different shielding processes. GMAW was formerly called *metal inert gas* (MIG) welding since the original gases used were inert. Like GTAW, other gases are now used as shielding and this term is inaccurate. (*Note:* In some countries, this process is called MIG/MAG, which denotes *metal inert gas/metal active gas* welding.)

With GMAW, the shielding gases are fed to the welding gun by tube as is done in GTAW. However, instead of having a nonconsumable electrode as in GTAW, wire is fed from an external spool through the gun and out of a nozzle in a manner similar to SAW. The wire feed speed is set at the spool controls and the welder starts both the gas and the wire feed by squeezing the trigger on the handle of the gun. When properly set, the shielding gas starts flowing just before the wire starts to feed so that the shielding gases are in place when the arc ignites.

Flux-Cored Arc Welding

Flux-cored arc welding (FCAW) also uses a gun as with GMAW, but as the name implies, the filler wire is tubular, not solid, containing a central core of fine granular flux. FCAW without shielding gas is *self-shielding* and is designated FCAW-S. If an external gas is used, the process is designated FCAW-G. With the exception of needing slightly larger wire feed drive rollers and contact tips (the copper tube inside the gun nozzle that conducts the electricity to the wire), the equipment is essentially the same as that used in GMAW.

Weld Discontinuities

Prior to performing angle-beam tests, a straight-beam test of the scanning surface is generally required by most codes and specifications. The purpose of this scan is to determine that the base metal beneath the angle-beam transducer does not contain discontinuities, particularly *laminations* that might interfere with angle-beam testing. If the base metal is laminated, the sound beam may reflect from the lamination rather than the backwall, resulting in the condition shown in Figure 17. If this occurs and is not caught prior to testing, the technician will not have any idea where the sound beam is actually going, rendering any interpretation impossible.

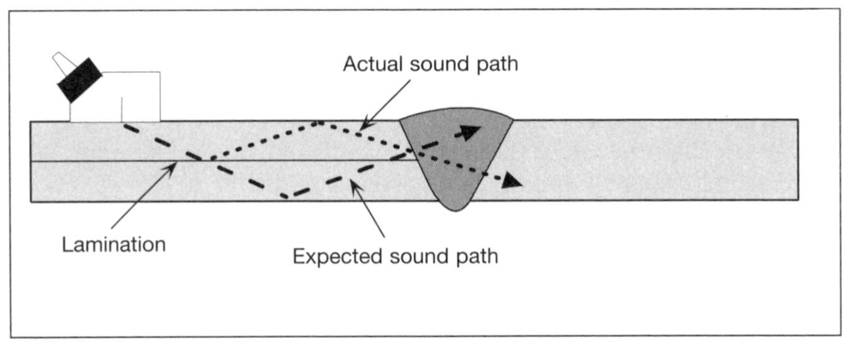

Figure 17: Scanning surface check with sound reflected from the lamination.

Knowing the kinds of discontinuities that can occur in various types of welds will help technicians understand what discontinuities to expect. Table 1 shows various discontinuities that can be found in the previously discussed weld processes.

Table 1: Welding process discontinuities.

Welding Process	Discontinuity Type						
	Cracks	Incomplete penetration	Lack of fusion	Porosity	Slag inclusions	Tungsten inclusions	Undercut
Shielded metal arc welding (SMAW)	X	X	X	X	X		X
Submerged arc welding (SAW)	X	X	X	X	X		X
Gas tungsten arc welding (GTAW)	X	X	X	X		X	X
Gas metal arc welding (GMAW)	X	X	X	X			X
Flux-cored arc welding-self shielded (FCAW-S)	X	X	X	X	X		X
Flux-cored arc welding-gas shielded (FCAW-G)	X	X	X	X	X		X

The following descriptions of various discontinuities and how they may appear during ultrasonic testing are general in nature since every discontinuity has its own individual characteristics. The screen displays shown are typical of the screen presentations of the discontinuities encountered. Actual screen displays will vary based on discontinuity size, orientation, and location. Technicians should remember that, in many cases, there may be multiple discontinuity types at the same location, such as a crack running out of a slag inclusion or slag mixed in with porosity. These conditions make it difficult, if not impossible, to state positively what discontinuity is actually being detected, which is why the term *interpretation* is used.

If the size of a discontinuity exceeds the governing acceptance criteria, it will have to be removed regardless of the discontinuity type. On the other hand, many codes and specifications state that any crack, lack of fusion or incomplete penetration is rejectable regardless of size, so under these conditions discontinuity identification can be critical. Technicians can expect to become proficient at interpretation of ultrasonic signals with experience.

Cracks

Cracks occur when stresses exceed the strength of the material, resulting in a tear or rupture in the material that is usually irregularly shaped with jagged edges that make good ultrasonic reflectors. Cracks generally initiate at a surface and propagate into the material, but if there is an internal discontinuity or stress riser, it may create a focal point for those stresses and a crack may start at that point. Figure 18 shows how a signal from a crack on the opposite of the plate will "walk" across the screen of the ultrasonic testing display.

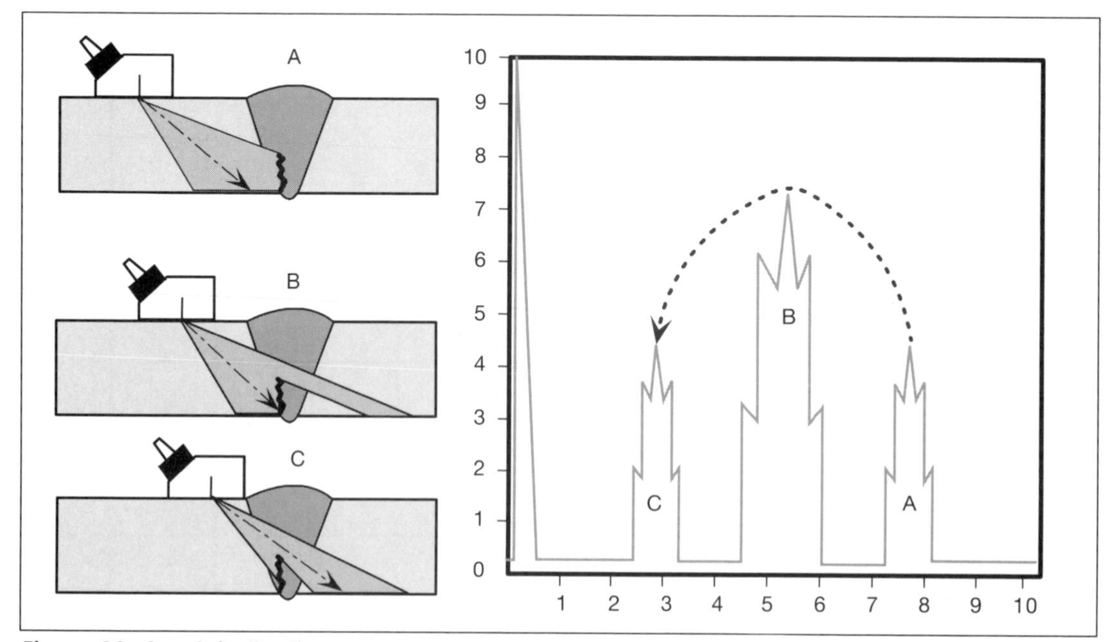

Figure 18: Crack indication.

As the sound beam approaches the crack (A), the sound beam is just beginning to hit the crack. Because the sound path from the leading edge of the sound beam is longer than the sound path along the centerline of the beam, the screen signal appears at the far right side of the screen. The signal moves to the left, gaining amplitude until the centerline of the beam hits the corner formed by the crack and the bottom of the plate (B). As the sound beam continues past the crack, the signal moves further to the left, dropping in amplitude until the sound beam clears the crack and the signal drops off the screen.

This is typical of a *crack signal*. Depending on the thickness of the test object and whether the crack signal appears in the second leg of the sound beam, this sequence may occur over a much shorter segment of the screen. The depth (height) of the crack also affects the signal amplitude. Because most cracks have jagged surfaces, the left edge of the signal may be stair-stepped as shown, creating a *steeple-shaped signal* on the screen.

Crater cracks are small shrink cracks that occur in the weld puddle (crater) at the end of a weld bead that has not been fully filled. They may be a single linear discontinuity or may have multiple cracks forming a *star-shaped indication*. These discontinuities are often shallow and, being on the top surface of the weld, are hard to detect ultrasonically due to interference from the weld's surface contour. Visual or magnetic particle testing is best for detecting this type of crack.

Incomplete Penetration

Incomplete penetration (IP) occurs when the weld metal does not fully penetrate the weld groove root area, leaving all or a portion of the original root face undisturbed, as shown in Figure 19. As the transducer is moved toward the single-vee groove weld from the left side, the forward (or upper) portion of the beam cone encounters the root face at

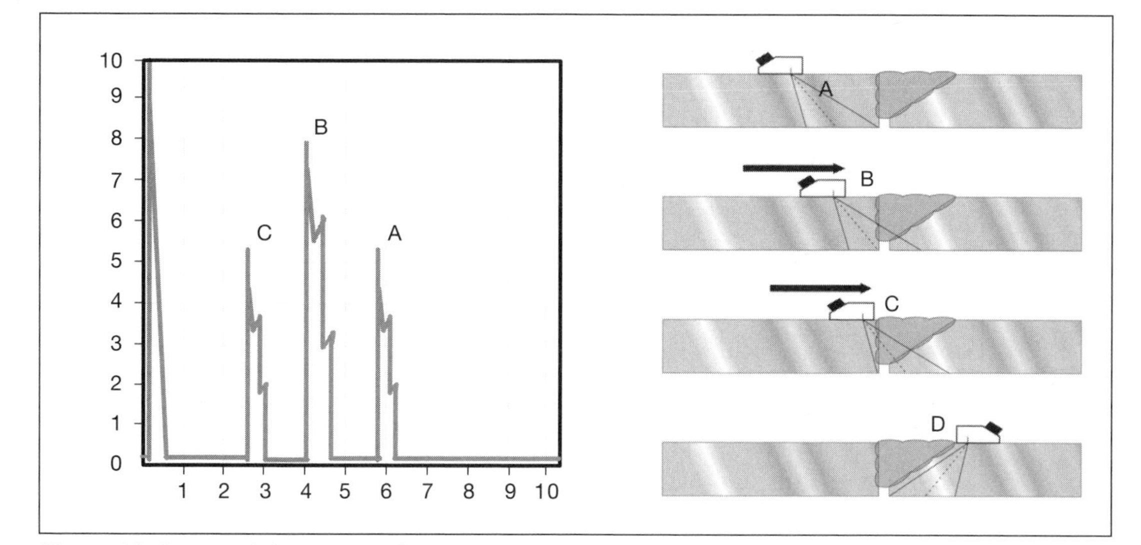

Figure 19: Incomplete penetration.

transducer position A and produces a screen deflection that matches the sound-path distance from the beam index point (BIP) of the transducer to the root face along the top edge of the beam cone (signal position A on the screen).

In the course of typical scanning, the transducer is moved closer to the weld toward transducer position B, and the signal that initiates at screen position A grows in amplitude until it maximizes at screen position B. This is in response to the increased sound energy in the center of the beam cone, which intercepts the corner reflector formed by the discontinuity. (Typically, the technician places a reference mark on the test surface at this point to indicate the maximum height of the reflection and performs the math function necessary to prove exact position of the reflector.)

As the transducer is moved closer to the weld (position C), the signal amplitude and position will decrease toward the corresponding screen position C. This is because the lower portion of the sound-beam cone is weaker than the center portion. As the movement of the transducer progresses toward position C, the beam cone centerline moves above the primary reflective surfaces of the discontinuity, thus the lower amplitude of screen signal C. The lessened sound path of position C is a measure of the distance between the BIP and the discontinuity along the lower edge of the sound-beam cone.

When approached from the other side of the single-vee weld (transducer position D), forward movement of the transducer is stopped by the weld crown, preventing full coverage of the root area. As shown, only the upper portion of the beam cone will actually contact the discontinuity in the root. In such a case, the discontinuity signal rises, but contact with the crown interferes with further evaluation unless the weld crown is ground flush or a higher-angle (70°) transducer is used.

Because incomplete penetration is caused by the original weld groove not being fully melted, the reflecting surfaces of the discontinuity are much smoother than those of a crack. Consequently, the left edge of the screen signal will tend to be more vertical instead of exhibiting the steeple shape often found with cracks.

Lack of Fusion

Lack of fusion is a discontinuity that occurs when the molten weld metal does not fuse into the base metal or previous weld layer. *Sidewall lack of fusion* occurs when the weld metal does not fuse in to the side of the weld groove, leaving a smooth, planar discontinuity along the edge of the weld groove, as shown in Figure 20(a). When molten weld metal does not tie into another weld bead, the condition is called *interbead lack of fusion*, as shown in Figure 20(b).

Sidewall lack of fusion is usually best seen ultrasonically in the second leg from the same side of the weld (transducer position A1). Because the sound beam comes up from the bottom surface, it tends to hit the lack of fusion more nearly perpendicular to the flat surface, which gives the best reflection. In the first leg (A2), the sound is more nearly parallel to the plane of the discontinuity, causing the majority of

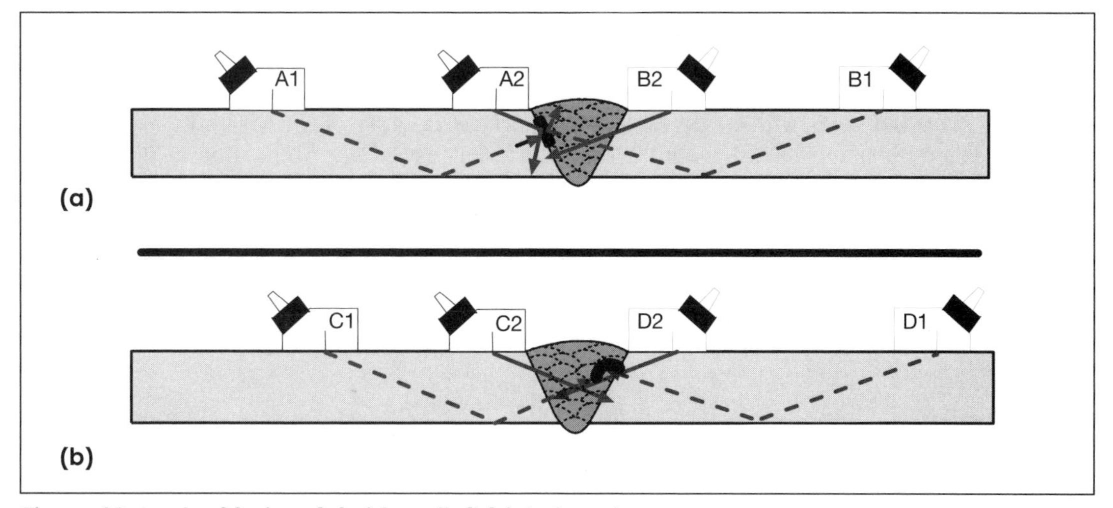

Figure 20: Lack of fusion: (a) sidewall; (b) interbead.

the sound to flow past or reflect downward from the discontinuity into the test object, away from the transducer. Some sound may return, causing a screen signal to appear, but it may have insufficient amplitude to cause the lack of fusion to be ruled rejectable.

When the weld is scrubbed from the opposite side of the weld in the second leg (B1), the sound beam is again more nearly parallel to the plane of the lack of fusion with minimal sound return. In the first leg (B2), it is possible that the transducer may bump into the weld crown preventing the sound beam from hitting the discontinuity. However, if the lack of fusion is located lower down in the weld, a very solid signal may appear since the sound beam hits the lack of fusion nearly perpendicular to the flat surface (as it does in the second leg from A1). If a strong second-leg signal indicates the probability of sidewall lack of fusion in the upper portion of the weld, the technician may need to have the weld crown ground flush so the weld can be retested from the other side in the first leg.

Interbead lack of fusion can be much harder to locate and identify because it may be in any orientation between weld beads, is usually nonplanar, and will only be as smooth as the crown of the previous weld bead. If the discontinuity is near the top of the weld, it will not be detected in the first leg of the sound beam. This is shown in Figure 20(b).

At transducer location C1, the sound beam is nearly parallel to the plane of the discontinuity and the amount of sound reflected back to the transducer is minimal. At position C2, the transducer hits the toe of the weld crown, preventing the sound beam from striking the discontinuity. At position D1, the second leg of the sound beam hits the discontinuity in such a way that it may be evaluated. However, if this indication cannot be verified from any other position, it may be necessary to grind the weld crown flush so that the indication can be evaluated in the first leg (D2).

Porosity

Porosity is defined as gas pores in the weld metal. Formed when gas is trapped in the weld before it can float to the surface, pores are generally rounded voids with a smooth internal surface. Because of their round, smooth shape, sound generally hits *small pores* as a single point contact, as shown in Figure 21. At point A, the sound beam is just coming over the pore and the sound on the edge of the beam hits the pore at a slight angle, causing that sound to reflect away from the transducer and go undetected. As the centerline of the sound beam hits the pore squarely (B), sound is reflected back and the indication appears on the screen. Then, as the sound beam moves past (C), the sound that does hit the pore reflects back behind the transducer and will not be detected. Because this occurs at a single point on a small pore, the signal is usually a single discrete vertical line that pops up at one point on the screen and then drops off without moving sideways.

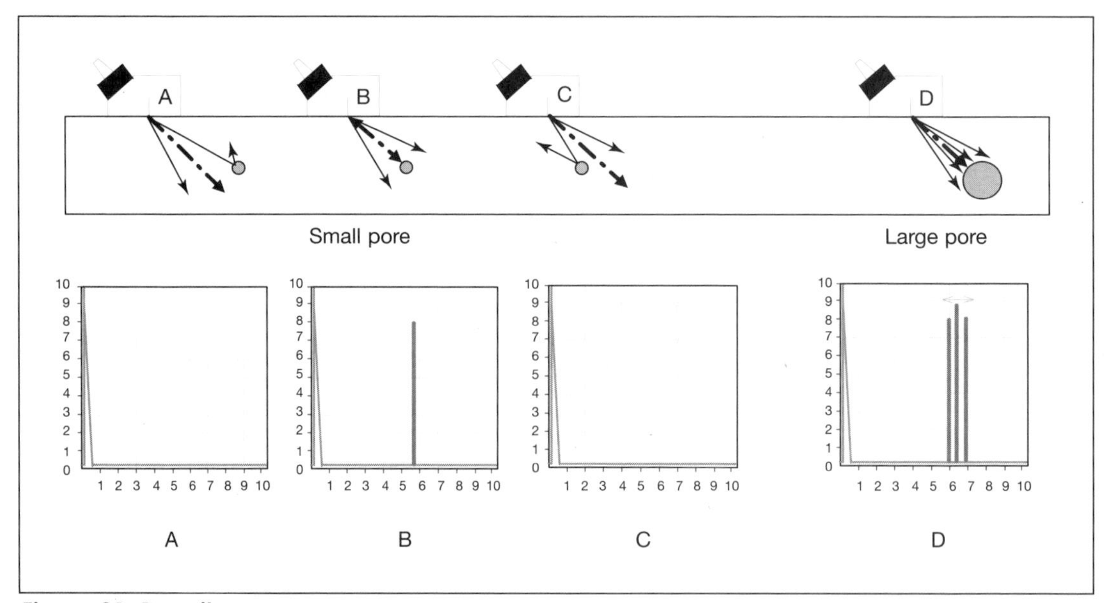

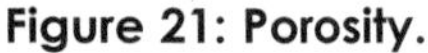
Figure 21: Porosity.

Larger gas pores produce a slightly different screen display. If the pore is sufficiently large, the surface curvature, being flatter, reflects more sound. The signal peaks as with a small pore but may also move to the left slightly as the sound beam passes over it (D). When the signal from a large pore is maximized, the single signal will “walk” back and forth sideways over a small portion of the screen with the maximum amplitude appearing at the center of this space.

Cluster porosity is just that: a group or cluster of pores near each other in the weld, as shown in Figure 22. Each pore is a discrete round discontinuity that reflects sound similar to the way a single pore does. However, since there are several discontinuities, the screen shows multiple single spikes as the sound beam passes over the cluster. If the pores are small, each signal pops up and disappears at the same point on the screen, with adjacent signals increasing or decreasing in amplitude simultaneously. The lateral spacing of the signals on the screen vary based on the individual distance from each pore to the transducer.

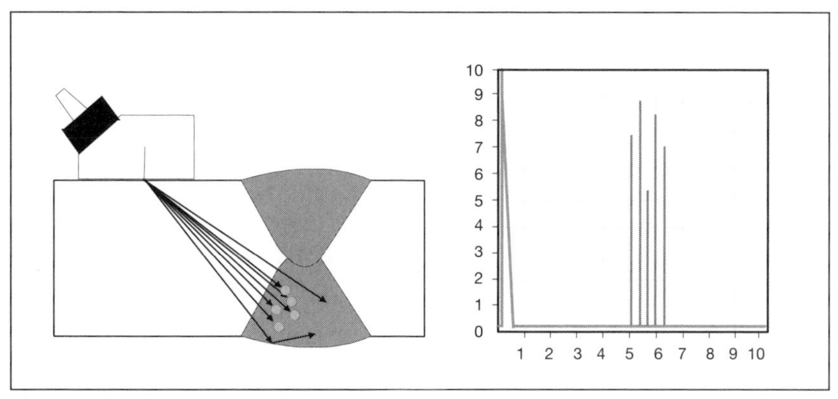

Figure 22: Cluster porosity.

Slag Inclusions

Slag inclusions come in two forms:

- **Solid slag** – left from a previous weld pass.
- **Molten slag** – trapped when the weld metal solidifies before the slag floats to the surface of the weld.

Both slag types are shown in the weld cross-section in Figure 23.

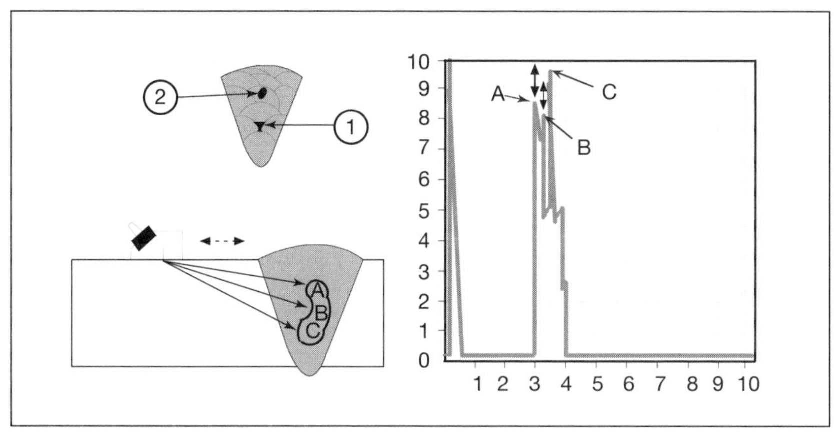

Figure 23: Slag inclusions.

Slag (1) usually occurs when the welder has not completely cleaned the earlier weld pass and then welds over that slag without remelting it, preventing it from floating up through the molten weld puddle. This type of slag may have semi-sharp edges and may be in fairly long stringers parallel to the weld length. Slag that is trapped in the cooling weld metal (2) tends to be more rounded and is often oblong or oval in shape. This type of slag is generally smooth sided (similar to a pore) but may contain gas as well as solids.

Slag signals often show up in a cluster with individual signal amplitudes varying in height as the sound beam passes over the slag. The sound reflected from the peanut-shaped slag at the bottom left of Figure 23 give the signals shown on the screen presentation. (Note: The slag has been enlarged to illustrate a typical peanut-shaped contour.) Point A, at the top of the slag, is closer to the transducer and has a convex surface facing the sound beam, so it tends to give a fairly sharp signal. The sound hitting point B hits a concave surface that is just slightly farther from the transducer. As a result, this signal tends to be focused by the curvature of the slag surface with the focal point being closer than the transducer, so less sound returns to the transducer. Being slightly lower in the weld than A, point B is farther from the transducer so that the signal falls immediately to the right of the A signal on the screen. Point C, at the bottom of the slag, is again convex, like A, so it too provides a good sound return, resulting in a higher amplitude than B. However, it is farther from the transducer than B, so that signal falls just to the right of the B signal on the screen.

As the transducer is moved forward and starts to hit the slag inclusion, the signal amplitude increases as the center of the sound beam crosses each point on the slag. Because the sound path shortens as the transducer approaches the slag, the cluster of signals "walks" across the screen from right to left until the sound beam clears the slag. As this happens, the signal height for each reflector is reduced until it drops off the screen.

Tungsten Inclusions

Tungsten inclusions are metallic inclusions that occur when the tip of the tungsten electrode melts off and drops into the weld puddle. These are usually more or less round and can give a screen signal similar to that of a gas pore, though the metal-to-metal interface does not give nearly as good a reflection as does a pore.

Undercut

Undercut is a condition that usually occurs when the welding amperage is too high, resulting in the top of the groove at the toe being burned away, leaving a depression along the edge of the weld. This condition can usually be seen visually and when ultrasonic testing is performed may result in a signal from the toe of the weld. Since undercut can mask other discontinuities at that location, if a toe signal is seen where undercut is present, the discontinuity should be removed by grinding to confirm that undercut caused the screen signal.

Nonrelevant Indications

Verification of the soundness of a weld and identification of discontinuities (if present) are the primary purposes of performing ultrasonic testing of welds. The next most important goal is to leave a good weld in place — that is, not rejecting good welds due to indications that may be caused by conditions other than relevant discontinuities. Removing and replacing good welds is an unnecessary expense for the fabricator, and making such calls undermines the credibility of the technician. Two common conditions that create nonrelevant indications in welds will be discussed here: misinterpretation of backing-bar signals and mode conversion. More generally, the presence of external reflectors and doubling will also be discussed as sources of nonrelevant indications.

Backing-Bar Signals

Backing bars are commonly used in butt welds on structural steel. The purpose of the bar is to provide a surface under the weld groove for the welder to use to lay the first bead (root pass) of the weld. A properly welded backed butt joint will result in full penetration between the sidewalls of the weld and the backing bar. As a result, sound will enter the backing bar through this weld junction and, due to geometry, may ricochet off the corners of the backing bar and then return to the transducer.

Figure 24 shows this joint configuration and how the sound beam may reflect back from a corner. Since it is below the bottom edge of the plate, the signal from a backing-bar reflector appears to be in the second leg of the sound beam. Its location in the second leg depends on which corner is causing the reflection. Because this signal occurs just into the second leg, this signal may be misidentified as a sidewall discontinuity.

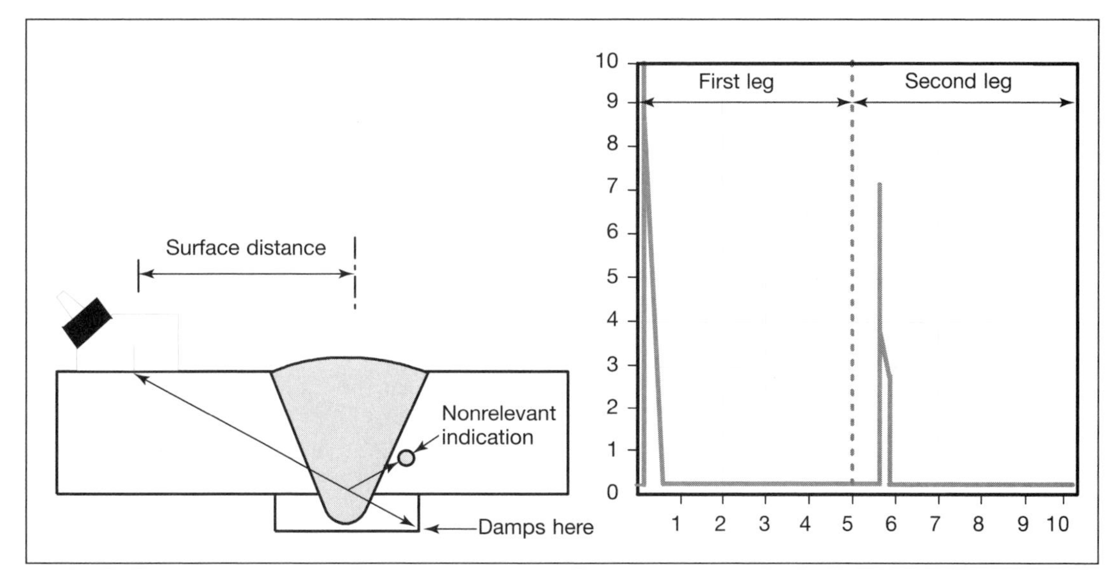

Figure 24: Backing-bar signals.

Technicians can check for this condition in three ways:

1. The weld should be tested from the opposite side. If that is not possible (for instance, with a corner weld), other means must be used.
2. If the backing bar is accessible, a technique called *damping* can be used, which involves wetting a finger with couplant, then tapping the backing-bar corner below and in front of the transducer. If the sound beam reflects from that corner, the signal amplitude will drop slightly (usually about 5% to 10% FSH) as the corner is tapped. This occurs because some of the sound enters the wet finger, causing less sound to reflect back, which decreases the signal amplitude.
3. Compare the sound path to the surface distance (as in Figure 24). If the signal is from the backing bar, this comparison will show that the surface distance is too short for the sound path and the suspected discontinuity would actually be in the base material on the far side of the weld, not in the weld.

One indicator that suggests this signal is from the backing bar is the height of the screen signal. Because a corner makes a very good reflector, the amplitude of the signal from a backing bar is usually quite high, often exceeding 100% FSH even at reference level. Under most conditions, sidewall discontinuities will not reflect nearly that amount of sound, so when such a signal is seen, the presence of a backing-bar reflector must be considered.

Mode-Converted Signals

Mode conversion is another phenomenon that can cause nonrelevant indications. Mode conversion occurs when a change in angle causes the shear wave to convert to a longitudinal wave. This occurs in a weld when the sound beam hits a reflector so oriented as to cause the wave mode to change. Two typical examples of mode conversion in welds are shown on the left-hand side of Figure 25. In the top diagram, the sound beam reflects from the gap formed by the backing bar, the weld, and the base metal. In the bottom diagram, the sound reflects from the root reinforcement.

In both cases, the change in angle is such that the shear-wave sound beam converts to a longitudinal wave, reflects up to the top weld crown, then returns to the root, converts back to a shear wave, and then returns to the transducer.

Since the velocity of a longitudinal wave is approximately twice that of a shear wave, the signal generated by the weld crown appears to be in the second leg of the sound beam at a distance of about half the thickness of the weld, as shown on the right-hand side of Figure 25. The result is a very strong screen signal that appears near the middle of the second leg. As with backing-bar signals, if technicians plot the surface distance and the sound path, they will see that this nonrelevant indication falls outside the weld zone in the base metal on the opposite side of the weld. Additionally, if the damping technique is used on the weld crown, the screen signal amplitude should change appreciably when the surface is tapped.

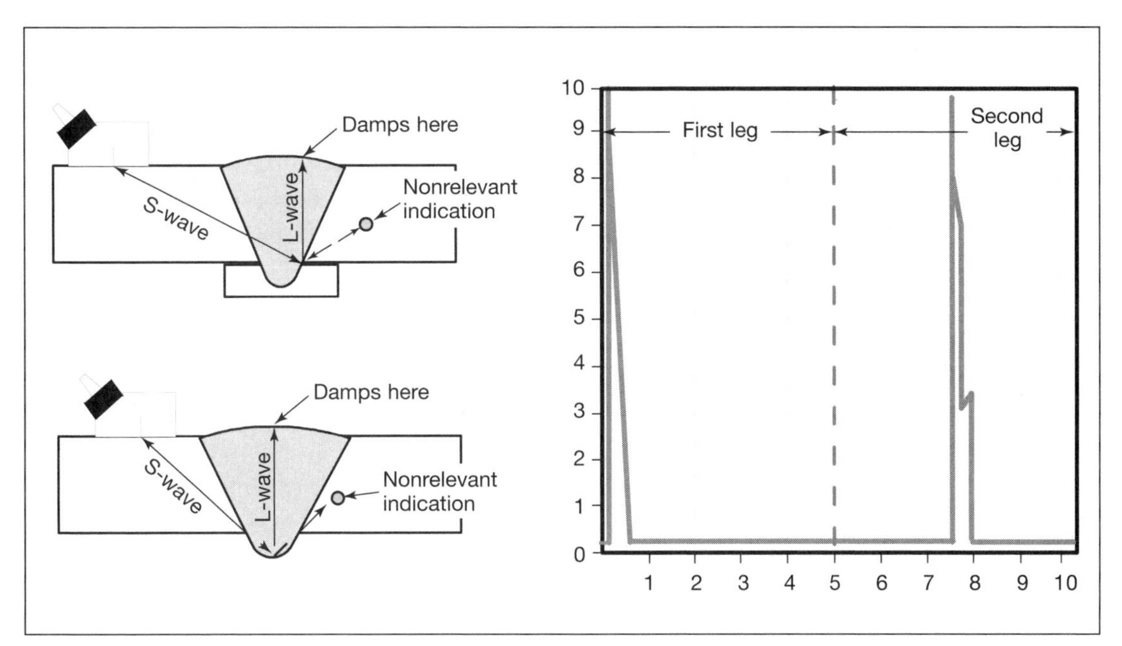

Figure 25: Mode conversion in welds.

Signals from External Attachments

External attachments are another cause of nonrelevant indications. Figure 26 shows several examples of this type of nonrelevant indication that can occur in a typical structural beam-column connection with a corner butt weld. In this case, a *gusset plate* has been fillet welded between the *column flanges* in the shop to carry the load across the gap, and moment connections were made in the field. (*Note:* A *moment connection* is a connecting joint between a beam and a column where

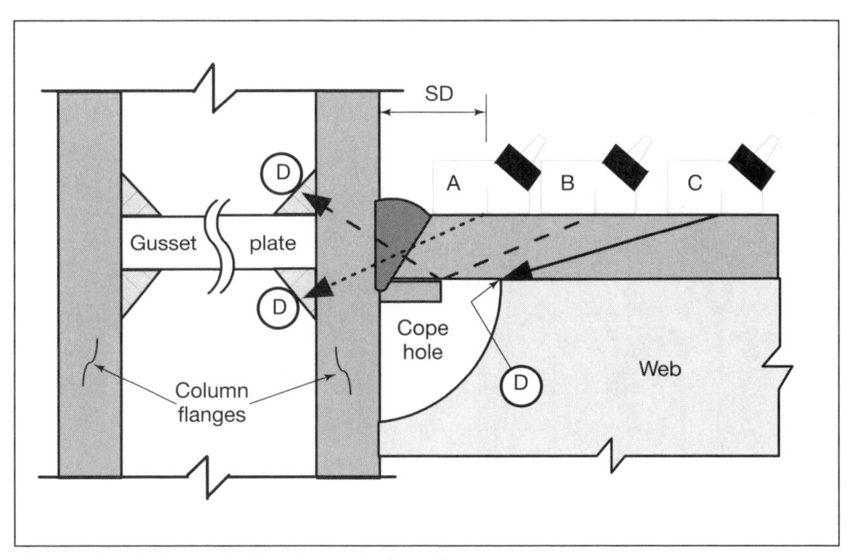

Figure 26: External attachment signals.

the end of the beam is prevented from rotating, thus creating a rigid frame without the need for cross-bracing.)

At transducer positions A and B, the sound beam passes through the weld and column flange, hitting the faces of the gusset plate fillet welds and then returns to the transducer. At transducer position C, the sound beam has hit the upper corner of the cope hole and returned to the transducer. (Note: Cutting a cope hole out of the web is a common practice to provide space to install a continuous backing bar under the weld.) All three of these indications can be damped at the locations shown by D.

At positions A and B, the surface distance from the column face is obviously much too short to have such a second-leg signal, and at C the surface distance is far too long for a first-leg signal to be coming from the weld. When signals such as these occur, technicians must consider that some outside influence is affecting the sound beam. The simplest way to determine this is to look at the back side of the test object, in this case the column flange. Similar external reflectors can occur in other applications, such as lifting lugs welded to the opposite side on the shell on an above-ground tank or attachments to the inside of pressure vessels. If the opposite side of the test object cannot be viewed by the technician, it may be necessary to check the construction drawings to determine what is causing such a signal to appear.

Doubling Signals

Doubling is a phenomenon that can occur when performing straight-beam tests, especially on materials that may be subject to excessive thinning from internal erosion or corrosion, such as pipe or tank shells. As the transducer moves onto progressively thinner material, there may be a sudden jump in thickness to approximately twice the previous reading. This is an indication that doubling has occurred.

At this point, the sound reflects from the backwall faster than the transducer can read it, so the first return signal is not detected. The sound then makes another round trip in the material and the transducer

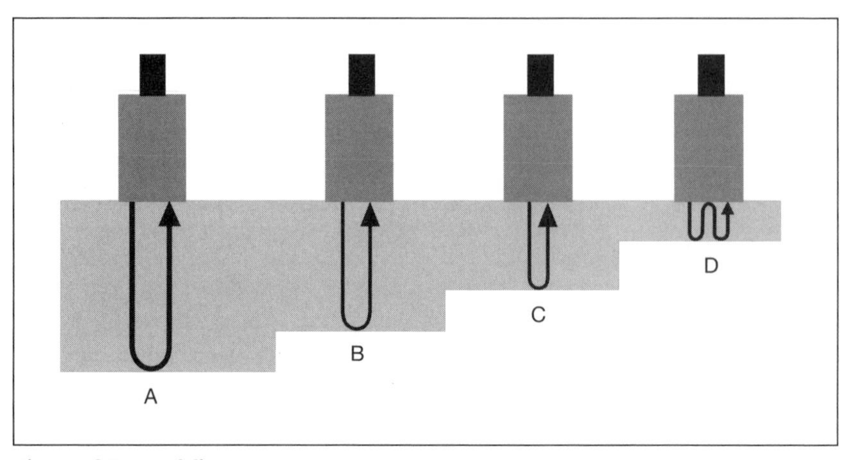

Figure 27: Doubling.

picks up the sound on the second round trip through the material, causing the reading to appear to be twice the actual thickness. A simplified example of this is shown in Figure 27, where good readings are taken at A, B, and C; then the reading doubles at D, making the material look twice as thick as it actually is.

This problem tends to occur most often when using digital thickness testers with short (or no) delay lines but occasionally occurs with A-scan units, usually when the material thickness drops to the 0.06 to 0.08 in. (1.5 to 2 mm) range. This range varies depending on the transducer type and, in some cases, the thickness tester can be tuned by the manufacturer to get lower readings. However, the best way to eliminate this problem is by using delay-line transducers to provide a longer standoff.

9

Ultrasonic Testing Applications

Introduction

This chapter is devoted to the manner by which ultrasonic techniques are used to ensure test object compliance with acceptance criteria, as carried out in several manufacturing and field service environments.

Ultrasonic tests are used for gathering information on test objects made from an array of materials in many configurations. This classroom training book emphasizes industrial and engineering applications where ultrasonic testing is used for materials characterization during manufacture and service.

During fabrication and assembly, ultrasonic testing is used to ensure that an object meets the quality criteria specified in original design specifications. These criteria often require an absence of various types of discontinuities, including cracks, inclusions, and voids in specified concentrations or sizes.

Inservice Testing

During *inservice tests*, ultrasonic testing is used, along with other nondestructive testing methods, to assess a test object's integrity. The gathered information is coupled with analytical estimates (fitness-for-service engineering analysis) of the likelihood that the test object will continue to perform its intended service in its current state. Such analysis often involves information such as wall thickness, presence of cracking, or other service-related damage that can only be gathered by use of ultrasonic testing.

Ultrasonic testing, along with most other nondestructive testing methods, provides information that, when combined with other test data, design criteria, and usage history, helps engineers judge the ability of the test object to withstand anticipated mechanical loading from applied or residual stresses. These stresses might be static or cyclical.

In most cases, nondestructive testing is mandated by safety regulations, as well as economic factors and liability exposure. Its use begins with testing of raw materials used in manufacturing or construction, continues through joining of subcomponents, becomes part of a quality assurance program and process control activities, and continues throughout the life of the test object, in the form of inservice maintenance tests.

Users of ultrasonic testing for new construction include electrical utilities, petrochemical plants and their pipeline systems, commercial buildings, and transportation sectors, such as aerospace, auto, rail, and marine. Ultrasonic testing is used in evaluating primary and secondary raw materials, formed and machined subcomponents, as well as joints created through welding, brazing, and bonding.

Uses of Ultrasonic Testing

The specifications calling for nondestructive testing of new materials and assemblies are based on the specific service environment of the test object throughout its service life. For example, discontinuities in objects exposed to static compressive load are often relatively benign in comparison to those in test objects subjected to large, cyclical stresses. The dynamic environment requires that the test object is free of crack-inducing discontinuities. These can be detected using ultrasonic nondestructive testing.

When applied to field activities, nondestructive testing is used to verify proper installation of major components and to monitor inservice degradation through regular testing cycles, in support of plant and facilities maintenance or upgrading projects. Components are retested at intervals commensurate with projected rates of degradation and support, or sometimes conservative maintenance practices.

The following sections discuss how ultrasonic testing is applied in common industrial applications. Discontinuities being sought are either planar (two-dimensional) or spatial (three-dimensional). Since planar discontinuities exhibit directional reflections, they are further subdivided into orientations parallel and perpendicular to the test surface. Different ultrasonic testing techniques are needed to effectively detect both conditions.

Test Objects with Flat Surfaces

Many objects tested with ultrasonic testing are flat with parallel surfaces. Rolled plate, bar, sheet, flat castings, extrusions, ingots, billets, forgings, and engineered materials such as composite and honeycomb panels are among the common ultrasonic test objects. Typical metal forms are wrought metals made into plates and sheet by sequential rolling. Such materials originate from billets and are rolled into strip, sheet, plate, and bar. They can contain relatively smooth and flat discontinuities that are either parallel (laminations and disbonds) or perpendicular (cracks and seams) to the major surface of the test object.

Castings, forgings, and welds may also have internal discontinuities that tend to scatter reflected sound in a random manner (gas pores, slag inclusions, forging bursts, shrinkage, chevron cracks, and intergranular cracks). Figure 1 (a through e) shows several variations of sound paths propagated in flat test objects. Figure 2 (a through e) shows the echoes received by the respective reflectors in Figure 1.

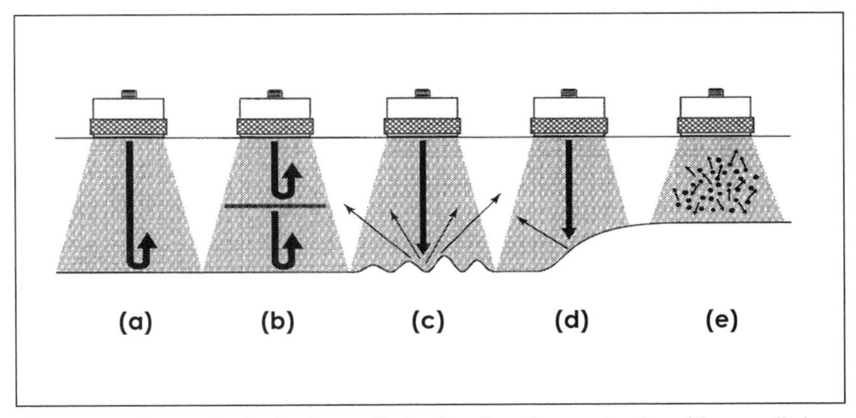

Figure 1: Ultrasonic test of parallel reflectors in products with parallel surfaces.

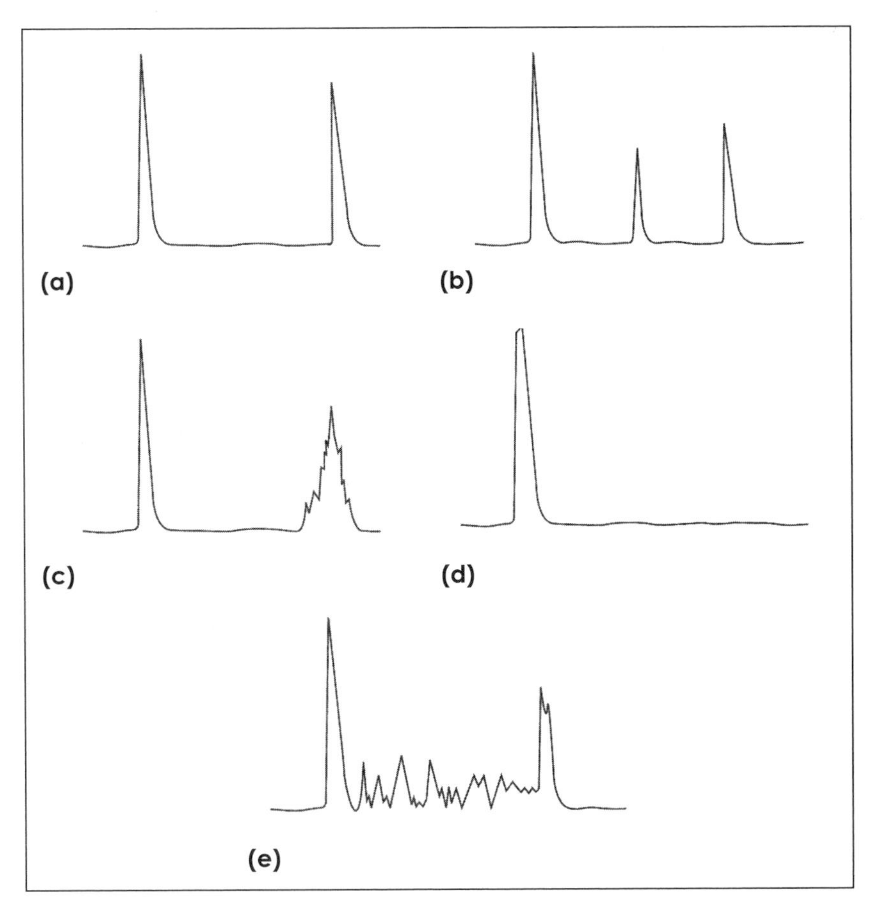

Figure 2: A-scan display for conditions shown in Figure 1.

Detecting Planar Discontinuities

Planar discontinuities act as smooth, flat reflectors that reflect a strong, clearly defined pulse. When the transducer is properly aligned with the reflected beam, the response is clear and crisp on the A-scan display. If the transducer is not closely aligned with the reflected beam, the reflected beam can be completely missed during a typical test.

Planar discontinuities often have an orientation within a test object based on the manner by which the test object was manufactured or the type of service stress to which it has been exposed. For example, cracks are usually located at the surface of a test object, propagate into the material, and may run along a plate or shaft. Similarly, seams and laminations tend to be aligned in the directions of drawing and rolling, respectively.

The strategy for detecting these conditions is to position the transducer so that it introduces the sound beam into the region of interest (surface, full volume, or corner) with a beam direction that is perpendicular to the most probable orientation of the discontinuity. Many classes of discontinuities are found using *longitudinal ultrasonic waves* sent into the test object perpendicular to the surface, so that planar discontinuities that are parallel to the beam entrance surface may be easily detected.

Discontinuities Parallel to the Entry Surface

A major concern with rolled products is the elongation of voids and inclusions into extended *laminations* or *stringers*. So-called "dirty" steel, for example, contains an excessive number of minor laminations or stringers embedded within the base material. Because of the rolling and drawing processes, these discontinuities tend to be aligned with the rolling direction. Forgings also have discontinuities that tend to be aligned with flow lines. Castings and welds, on the other hand, generally contain more symmetrical reflectors caused by gas pores, local segregation, slag inclusions, and local shrinkage.

Laminar Discontinuities

Laminar discontinuities are detected using longitudinal waves directed through the thickness of the material. This is the simplest application of pulse-echo ultrasonic testing. Strong and consistent signals are reflected from typical internal discontinuities and from the back surface. The *backwall signal* serves as a consistent time or location reference. Castings are tested with the same configurations as plates, but discontinuity signals are less pronounced and are more difficult to detect.

For applications involving a single reflector (discontinuity or backwall indications), the ultrasonic testing instrument's display is calibrated so that the front-surface indication is on the left side of the A-scan display while the backwall echo appears on the right side of the display.

This setup is the same for both contact and immersion techniques. *Note:* The *water travel time* must be removed using the time-delay control for immersion tests. In this case, the spacing between the immersion transducer and the front surface must be slightly more than one-fourth of the thickness of the test object to ensure that no multiple pulses of the water path occur between the front- and back-surface pulses from the test object.

Calibration of Horizontal and Vertical Axes

Calibration of the horizontal axis is established using multiple reflections within a known thickness of an acoustically similar material. This is done using a calibration block such as the International Institute of Welding (IIW) block or a step wedge cut into increments through the thickness range of interest. When lamination detection is performed, the horizontal location of the echo pulse defines the depth of the lamination.

Calibration of the vertical axis is very important when detecting reflectors of a specific size. The normal approach is to use blocks with precisely drilled holes. Vertical *flat-bottom holes* (FBHs) serve as disk-shaped calibration targets. Horizontal *side-drilled holes* (SDHs) reflect sound in the same way as a cylinder. In either case, the target (hole) size is mandated by procedure (or chosen by experience) so that the gain of the ultrasonic instrument is sufficient to display a pulse height of about 80% full screen height (FSH) or more when a significant discontinuity is encountered.

Thickness Measurement

When thickness is being measured, the backwall echo position defines the thickness. This is the primary method used to detect and estimate the extent of internal pipe or tank wall thinning from the outside surface. In general, the *time of arrival* of pulses within a test object is the most precise measurement an ultrasonic system can deliver.

Since the time of arrival (and not the signal amplitude) establishes the relative thickness of a test material, vertical axis calibration is somewhat arbitrary. Thickness measurements can be made as long as a strong signal is reflected from the back surface. As the back surface of a material becomes increasingly rough, the exact start point of an echo is more difficult to determine, the backwall echo becomes less distinct, and thickness measurement becomes less precise.

Discontinuities Perpendicular to the Entry Surface

Planar discontinuities, with a principal reflecting surface perpendicular to the surface of ultrasonic wave entry, are not reliably detected with conventional longitudinal wave transducers. These discontinuities include most types of surface-connected cracks, as well as lack of penetration and lack of fusion in welds. Unfavorable orientation between beam direction and reflector surface makes these tests unreliable.

Perpendicular planar reflectors are detected using sound beams traveling at relatively steep angles (shear waves) to the entry surface. Shear waves are trapped and sent back from the corners created by the crack and test-object surface. This geometry allows incident sound beams to be redirected along the same paths they traveled in reaching the locations of the corner reflectors. This is the concept behind angle-beam shear wave pulser/receiver transducers.

Crack Detection

Cracks are mostly associated with free surfaces and tend to grow inward (away from the surface) as well as along the surface. Although they may have somewhat different detailed surface morphologies, they are ideal for detection with angle-beam testing techniques.

Since cracks are mostly initiated from a surface, one might think that surface-wave ultrasonic techniques would work best for surface-breaking cracks. However, surface waves are restricted to a depth limited by the sound's wavelength. Surface waves are also very sensitive to surface conditions, such as roughness and the presence of sound damping liquids. For these reasons, surface waves tend to be used only on smooth, dry surfaces that are not flat. Since a surface wave will follow an undulating contour, they are sometimes used on gently changing shapes such as turbine blades and vanes.

Angle-Beam Technique

For materials with generally parallel surfaces, such as plate and pipe, the sound beam can be reflected from the parallel surface to redirect the beam toward the entry surface. A shear-wave transducer, as shown in Figure 3, is used for contact testing. Figure 4 shows the same concept used in the immersion technique for both plate and heavy-walled pipe. In either technique, the incident sound beam is angled within the test

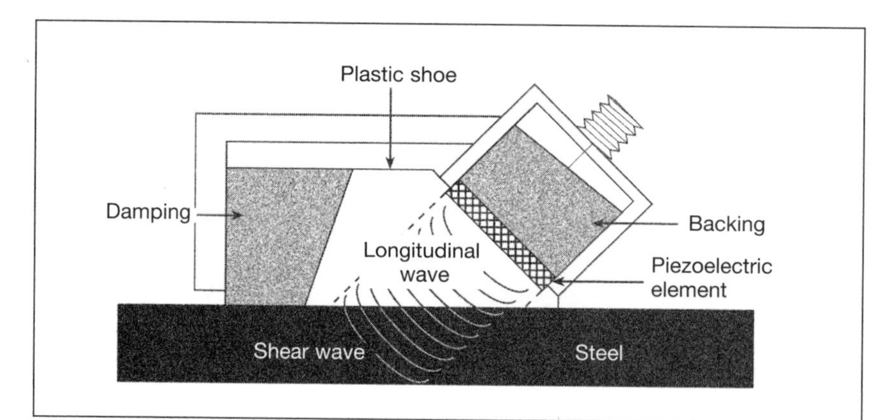

Figure 3: Shear-wave (angle-beam) transducer.

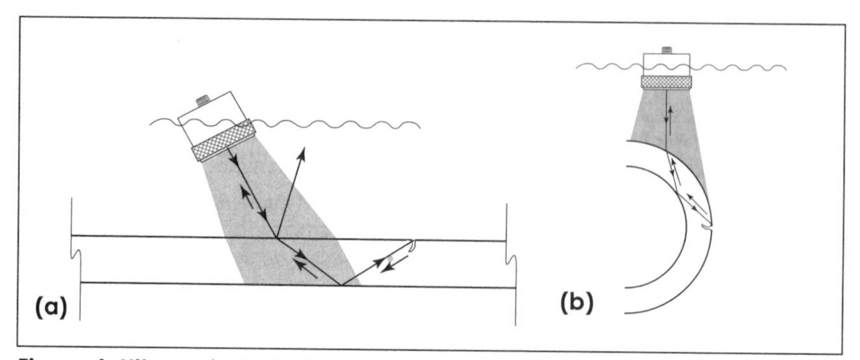

Figure 4: Ultrasonic test of perpendicular surface-connected reflectors: (a) flat plate; (b) heavy pipe.

object. Reflected echoes from surface-connected cracks travel back toward the sending transducer.

Because the reflecting cracks are at some distance from the transducer, the orientation of the transducer is critical. Rotation of the transducer by only a few degrees is enough to completely lose the echo signal, particularly if more than a single bounce is used.

This *angle-beam approach* is the primary way cracks are detected in and around welds. It does not have the convenience of the simple thickness mode (used for laminations) because no consistent back-surface reference signal is present. A signal is received only when the sound beam is reflected from a discontinuity or some other geometrical reflector, such as a corner at the plate's end or the crown or root area of the weld. The A-scan interpretation is further complicated since the location of the transducer, with respect to the weld, changes during scanning.

With no consistent reference reflector and various portions of the beam being used, the integrity of the testing process depends on a careful *calibration process*. The precise beam angle and exit (or index) point must be known and the horizontal sweep must correlate accurately with the actual sound path within the test object.

A-Scan Presentation

Figure 5 shows how echoes from surface-breaking cracks occur at different locations across the A-scan display. As the transducer is moved away from the weld, the beam passes through the center of the weld, intersects the root, and eventually encounters the crown. Signals appear on the display only when the transducer is positioned at a location where an echo pulse is reflected along the original path of the incident beam.

Since discontinuities of interest can be several millimeters or inches from the transducer, the signal falloff with distance must be considered and a *distance-amplitude correction (DAC) curve* must be incorporated into signal interpretation. The shape of the DAC curve may be drawn on the A-scan screen (either physically or electronically) to serve as a reminder of the degree to which the signal amplitude falls off with increasing distance. If the ultrasonic testing instrument is equipped with programmable gain compensation, an electronic DAC increases the gain with increased distance so that the displayed pulses appear to have the same height regardless of the reflector's distance from the transducer. This is illustrated in Figure 6.

Discontinuities Removed from the Entry Surface

Planar discontinuities that are removed from accessible surfaces include lack of sidewall fusion and incomplete penetration in double-vee welds. Such discontinuities are often difficult to detect because of their poor orientations to the pulse-echo transducer. In some cases, they can be detected based on a predetermined orientation with respect to weld geometry. For example, the double-vee weld shown in Figure 7 has its root near the mid-thickness region of the weld. If conventional angle-beam shear wave testing is used, the reflection from the discontinuity (lack of penetration) does not return to the transducer. However, a

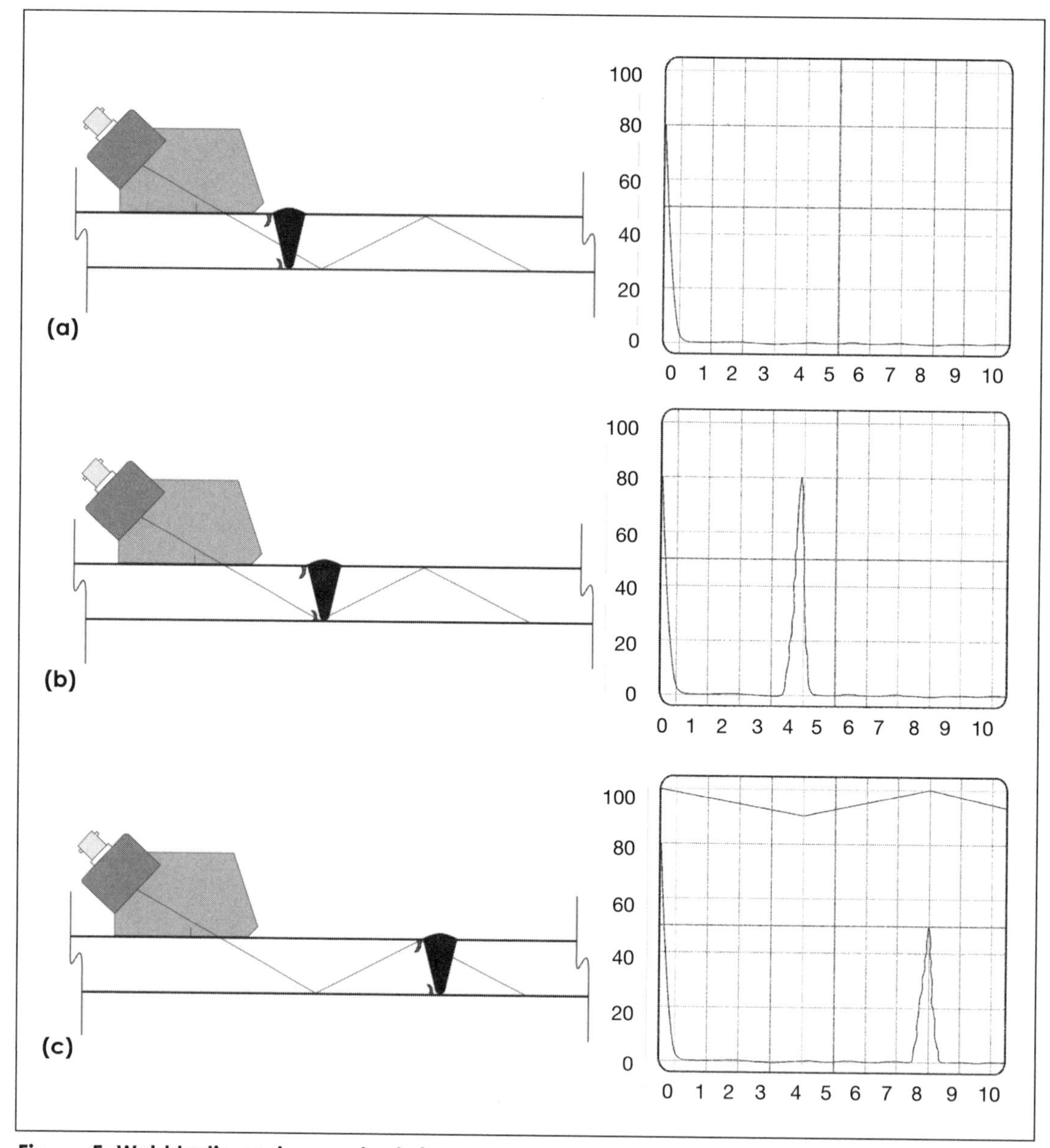

Figure 5: Weld testing using contact shear waves that intersect: (a) the weld center; (b) the weld root; (c) the weld crown.

second receiver can be used, as shown, to detect signals reflected from the face of the root preparation zone. As long as the root area is filled with weld metal, no signal is received by the receiver transducer.

Lack of sidewall fusion occurs on the right side of the weld in Figure 7. A pulse-echo transducer is able to detect this discontinuity with a beam that intersects the weld preparation surface at right angles. The incident beam must be perpendicular to the fusion line to reliably detect the lack of sidewall fusion.

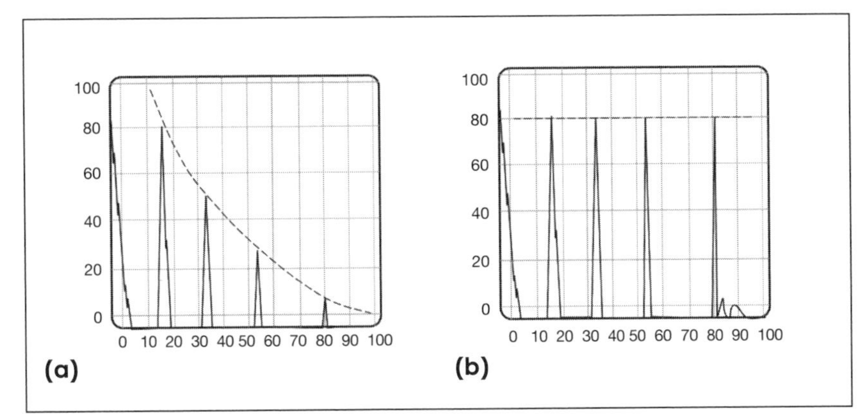

Figure 6: Distance-amplitude correction curves: (a) reference echoes; (b) distance-connected echoes.

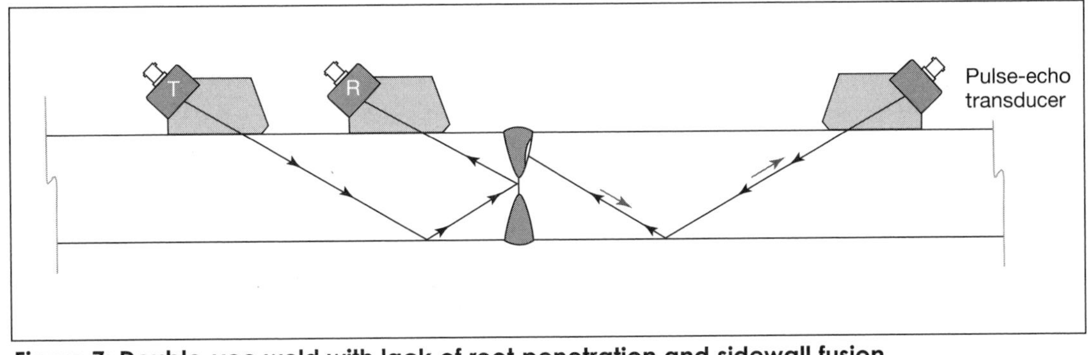

Figure 7: Double-vee weld with lack of root penetration and sidewall fusion.

Special Case of Thin Materials

Thin-gaged materials, such as sheet and composites, are usually tested with longitudinal wave transducer configurations similar to those used with plates. However, higher near-surface resolution and different interpretations of the A-scan displays are sometimes necessary. The problem with thin materials is that ultrasonic systems may not be able to clearly discriminate between the front and back surface, even when used at the instrument's best depth-resolution settings. With contact transducers, the region of interest is well within the near field and consistent results may not be possible.

One approach is to move the transducer away from the surface of the test object using a spacer such as an acrylic rod. Figure 8 illustrates a single-element probe attached to an *acrylic rod standoff*. Such a

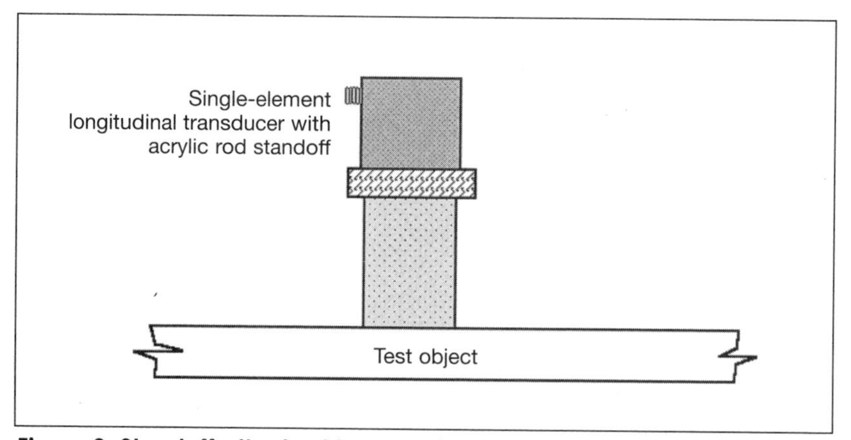

Figure 8: Standoff attached by use of threaded fitting that joins the transducer face to an acrylic rod. (Coupling agent is used between the transducer and rod, and between the rod and test object.)

delay-line transducer design positions the test material in the far field, where the sound pattern is uniform but a large interface signal still occurs at the surface of the test object.

Use of Dual-Element Transducers

On the A-scan display using a single-element transducer, multiple reflections from a thin-walled test object can make detection of a discontinuity difficult. A *dual-element transducer*, with one element serving as a transmitter and the other functioning as a receiver, provides a representation of the sound wave/material interaction that is much easier to interpret. Some dual-element transducers have the elements mounted side by side and slightly inclined toward each other. This is referred to as the *roof angle*. The region where the refracted waves intersect within the test object is a zone of higher detection sensitivity to reflectors with surfaces that are parallel to and near the surface of the test object.

As the roof angle of the transducer elements becomes steeper, the region of sensitivity moves closer to the surface. Its sensitivity also becomes more pronounced. Reflectors in this region are detected while deeper reflectors are most likely to be missed. The dual-element transducer is a setup that works well for thickness gaging within a relatively narrow range of depths. The signal response is enhanced by the absence of a strong echo from the entry surface. One problem is a small amount of leakage across the bottom of the acoustic barrier between the transmit section and the receive section, but this is minimal in most cases.

Testing of Spot Welds

For finding discontinuities parallel to the test surface in thin sheet materials, another technique uses the array of reverberations that result from sound bouncing within the homogeneous layers of the sound

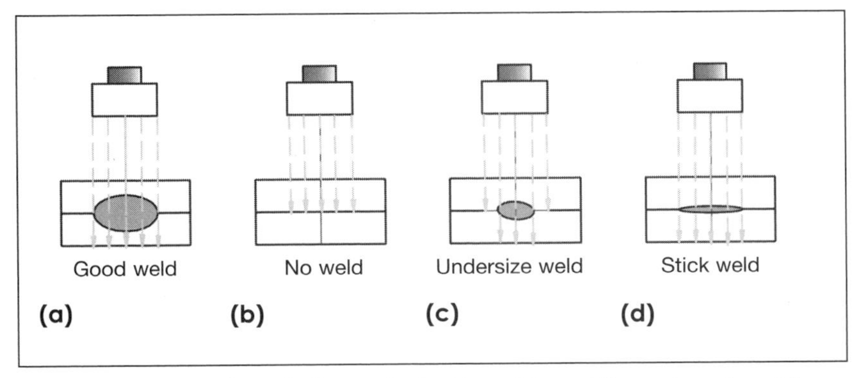

Figure 9: Schematics of ultrasonic testing of four different spot-weld coupons.

path. This is shown for four different spot-weld coupons in Figures 9 and 10. *Note:* A stick weld occurs when the metal sheets are fused but a good weld nugget is not formed because of insufficient heating.

As can be seen in Figure 10(b), an *undersize* or *unfused spot weld* produces a pattern of pulses that is spaced about half of that expected for a good weld, as shown in Figure 10(a). The general shape of the secondary (or lower amplitude) pulses in the unfused pattern tends to grow in amplitude rather than decay. This apparent doubling of pulses and partial growth are indicators the test object is not homogenous throughout its thickness.

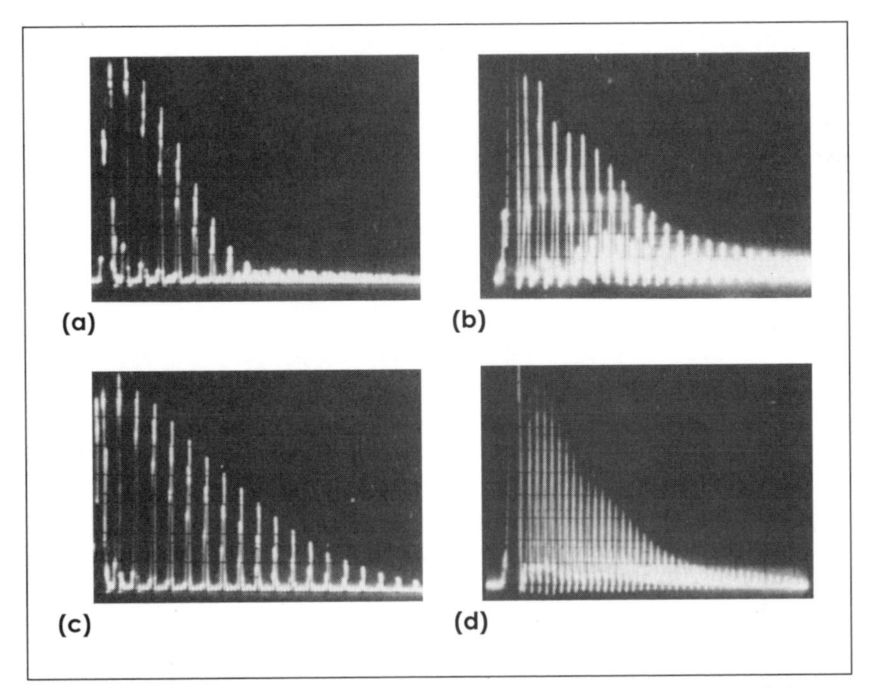

Figure 10: Ultrasonic echoes from spot-weld coupons (the principle echoes in [a], [b], and [c] are spaced out 0.48 µs apart in two layers of 0.028 in. [0.7 mm] welded steel): (a) good weld; (b) undersize weld; (c) stick weld; (d) no weld.

Bonded and Brazed Materials

This same technique is used when thin sheets of metallic materials are bonded or brazed together. The pattern indicates that the acoustic properties are not uniform throughout the thickness of the bonded region. That information alone is usually enough to cast doubt on the integrity of the bonding process. Note that no information is attainable regarding the exact depth of the disbond; however, a C-scan image will show the location of the separation. The basis for creating the C-scan relies on selection of a distinct feature of the ring-down zone that correlates with the disbonded conditions.

Testing Composites

When testing thin sheets of engineered materials such as *graphite epoxy composites*, the difficulty lies in assessing the uniformity of acoustic properties, particularly when such materials exhibit excessive scatter and absorption. Composite materials are composed of high-strength fibers encased in a weaker matrix. When tested by ultrasound, these materials produce multi-reflective interfaces that limit reverberations. Therefore, the ring-down effect, seen for metallic sheets, does not work in this case.

Composite-materials development laboratories have had success with sound that travels through the material twice. This approach doubles the system's sensitivity to sound-impeding voids or delaminations and, in the case of bonded structures, disbonded regions. This technique uses what is called a *reflector plate* on the far side of the thin materials tested with an immersion technique. Figure 11 shows the setup and a typical A-scan display. The transducer is scanned above the test object in a rectilinear pattern (X versus Y). The resulting C-scan uses the signal drop from the reflector-plate echo as the basis for plotting image density differences. When the signal drops below the gate's threshold, the intensity (or color) of the test object's image changes accordingly.

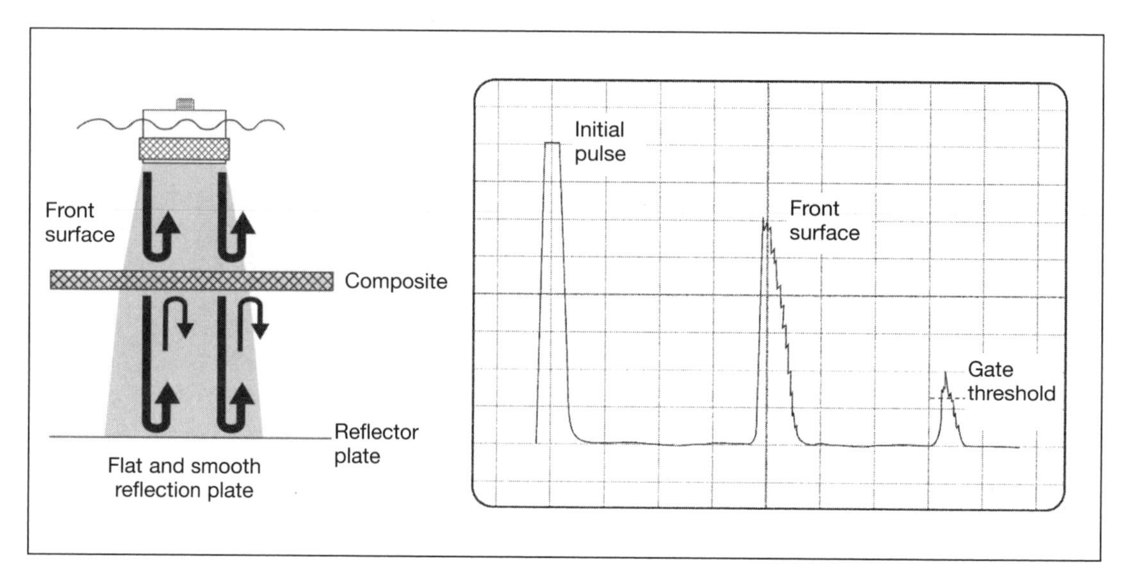

Figure 11: Reflector plate technique used with thin composite panels.

Test Objects with Curved Surfaces

Ultrasonic testing of objects with simple curved surfaces (shafts, tubes and pipes, castings, and forgings) is generally done with techniques that compensate for test-object curvature. The major problems are:

- maintaining consistent coupling,
- stabilizing transducer rocking motions while scanning, and
- compensating for the defocusing and distorted effects the curved surface creates in the sound beam.

Test objects with a small radius of curvature are more troublesome than larger-diameter test objects.

For example, a large-diameter welded pipe is tested using the same setups used for flat-plate butt joints. However, as the diameter drops below 20 in. (500 mm), the curvature of the surface causes the couplant across the face of the contact transducer to become nonuniform. The transducer is also subject to rocking during scanning. In addition, the curvature of the test object, acting as an acoustic lens, diverges the sound beam within the pipe. As the size of pipe decreases, these effects become increasingly pronounced.

To stabilize the mismatch of the flat transducer and the curved test object, a conforming plastic shoe can be used. Although this technique makes coupling uniform and controls transducer rocking, it also inhibits rotation of the transducer and does little to correct *beam divergence.*

Correction for beam divergence can be achieved by using a *contour-correcting lens* for immersion testing. In the case of contact testing, a special curved piezoelectric element is needed to serve the same purpose, with a different shoe and transducer element for each pipe diameter or curvature.

Test Objects with Irregular Surfaces

The most challenging applications for ultrasonic testing are objects with highly irregular shapes. Examples include nozzles used to join piping to heavy wall vessels, turbine and jet engine disks and blades, and large tube intersections in K or Y configurations. All of these are tested using ultrasonic techniques, but extreme care must be taken in positioning and manipulating the transducers.

Irregular surfaces often lead to internal *mode conversion* of the ultrasonic wave in objects other than welds, which were discussed previously. This complicates interpretation of the signals, as shown in Figure 12. The longitudinal transducer at the left, positioned to test the length of the axle, inadvertently creates a mode-converted shear wave at the reflection point T, caused by a fillet in the shaft. The transverse wave moves along the axle, mode converts to a longitudinal wave, and eventually returns to the sending transducer. The elapsed time would suggest that a transverse discontinuity might be located in the axle at the nonrelevant reflection site.

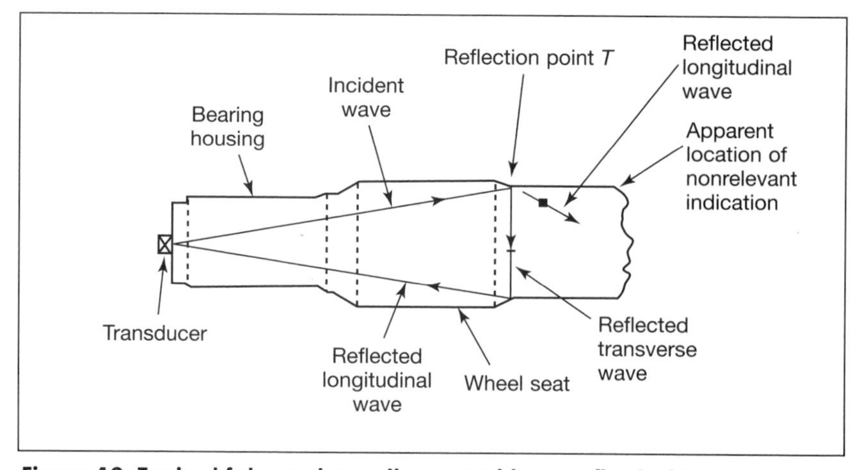

Figure 12: Typical false echo path caused by a reflected transverse wave at the axle fillet and a reflected longitudinal wave on the opposite side.

For irregularly shaped test objects, such as nozzles, ultrasonic testing is only viable when a specific local region and a specifically oriented reflector are being considered.

A near-root condition found in circumferential welds in nuclear piping systems also can create nonrelevant indications caused by test-object geometry. In some pipe welds, a *counterbore* is used to even the alignment of the two sides of the joint by grinding away enough material in the inner radius of both pipe sections to ensure proper alignment throughout the circumference of the joint. If this ground counterbore is placed too near to the root of the weld, internal reflections can be generated, including some mode-converted waves, of the type that are observed when testing for *intergranular stress corrosion cracks*. Such cracks are generally poor reflectors of ultrasound, and ultrasonic testing system sensitivity is quite high, leading to indications from stray reflections coming from the weld root area. Figure 13 shows the

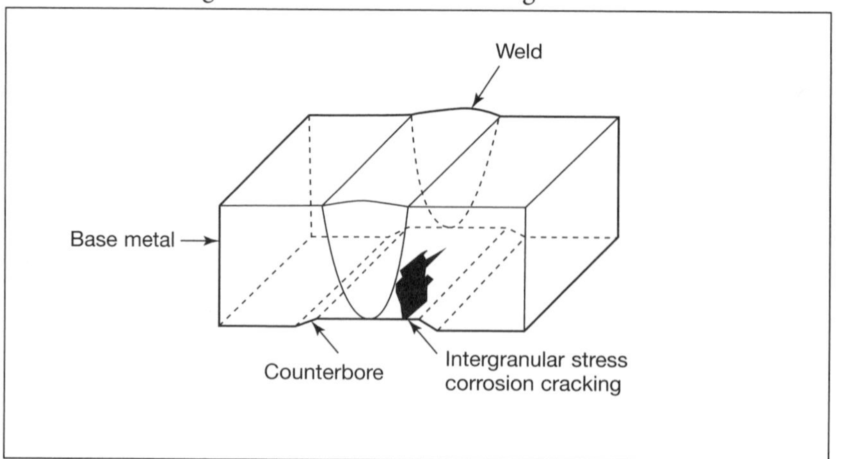

Figure 13: Typical weld configuration showing intergranular stress-corrosion cracking and counterbore.

counterbore geometry and general location of the stress cracks.

When two pipes are joined at angles other than right angles, this problem becomes even more pronounced. The Y and K connections have a weld and test geometry that changes dramatically as the technician follows the path of the fusion zone. The recommended approach for these configurations is use of a properly angled transducer in the very limited area where the beam path is traversing the region of interest. When the access position is changed, the transducer and calibration setup must be reestablished for the new test zone. Another approach demands the use of 45°, 60°, and 70° angle-beam transducers for the entire weld circumference.

Compressed Discontinuities

The physical principles of ultrasound predict that a sound beam will be reflected when it encounters a discrete change in acoustic impedance within a material. An air-filled crack within a steel plate makes an excellent reflector. However, if the crack surface is smooth and *under compressive stress*, part of the sound will pass through the interface because of the intimate contact and partial deformation of the crack's joining surfaces.

Under extreme pressures, such smooth surfaces may become transparent to an ultrasonic wave with a typical wavelength of about 0.05 in. (1.3 mm). This condition often occurs in the case of press-fit cylinders, such as bearings and retaining rings in turbine power rotors. Such a joint with a loose fit reflects an ultrasonic pulse, while the same joint under sufficient stress allows the sound to pass through.

A similar condition occurs in the case of a double-vee weld. The smooth walls in the root area of the joint preparation become abutted during the welding operation caused by compressive stresses from *shrinkage* within the bulk of the weld. When the root pass is not adequately made, the stresses can compress the faces in the root zone so tightly that a shear wave may pass through the joint undisturbed.

Compressed cracks, if detected, can cause other differences in test indications. An open crack may be detected using ultrasound, but sizing can be in error in the presence of high levels of compressed stress. Such stress may be caused by residual stresses, as in the case of the double-vee weld, or by external loading, such as a vertical column or bridge member.

Scattering Discontinuities

Planar discontinuities are noteworthy because of their directional reflectivity patterns. *Scattering discontinuities* (voluminous and globular) tend to scatter incident sound beams into many directions without the highly preferential directionality found with planar reflectors. Examples include gas pores, irregularly shaped inclusions, and shrinkage found in castings and welds, as well as bursts in forgings and chevron cracks found in drawn bar. This class of reflectors is relatively easy to detect in fine-grained metallic structures.

The scattered nature of the reflections is caused by both the overall geometry and the irregular surface of the discontinuities. Since they do not reflect a strong, single echo, their indications on an A-scan are smaller and less distinct than those obtained from properly oriented planar reflectors. However, the scattered nature of the reflections permits detection from numerous vantage points, so that sending and receiving pairs of transducers can be used for locating such scattering discontinuities. Careful alignment of the transducer is not necessary when testing for these reflectors.

Gating Applications

For a base material with many discontinuities that scatter the beam (stringers and elongated clusters of inclusions or voids), the acoustic energy reaching the back surface becomes increasingly attenuated. In extreme cases, such as in coarse-grained castings, the back-surface reflection can be totally absent from the A-scan display. In this situation, two gates are used to monitor the relative pulse heights:

- One gate monitors the bulk of the test object.
- The other gate is triggered by changes (drops) in the back-surface signal.

Discrete pulses occurring within a test object indicate the presence of single, coherent internal reflectors. A reduction in the signal received from the back surface indicates that the surface is rougher than usual, the back surface is no longer parallel to the front surface or intervening scattering reflectors exist, even if they cannot be seen as discrete pulses.

The A-scan display for flat-plate geometries identifies the location of the front surface, the back surface, and the depth of detectable intermediate reflectors. An A-scan using a gate to set a threshold for signal amplitude measurement is shown in Figure 14.

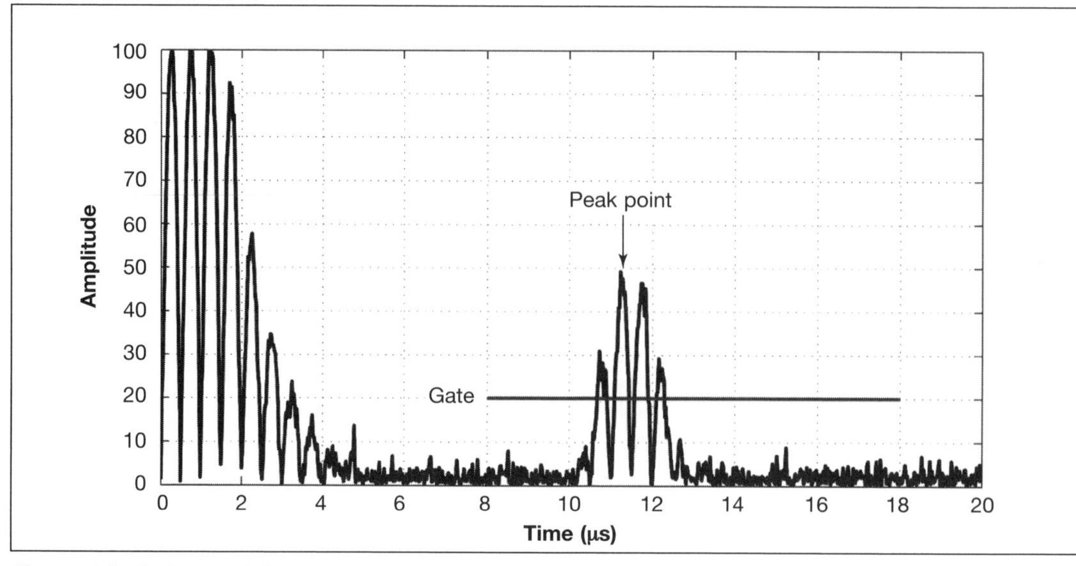

Figure 14: Gate established on an A-scan display.

When these clear-cut A-scan data are used for constructing a C-scan of the test object, the resulting images can portray the *plan view* area of internal reflectors as well as the depths at which they exist.

In the simplest case, any echo exceeding a selected threshold amplitude can be regarded as the location of a significant discontinuity. The gate used for this purpose starts just behind the front-surface indication and ends just in front of the back-surface indication. The resulting C-scan image displays, at a minimum, two levels of density, possibly represented by different colors. One density or color represents the surface areas where no reflectors are detected. The other density or color represents areas where reflectors have been detected with the threshold setting of the gate.

A more complex gate, or a system capable of advanced signal processing, captures the time delay or *time of flight* between the start of the gate and the time when the internal reflector pulse is detected. Deeper reflectors produce longer time delays. In this case, the C-scan portrays both the locations where reflectors are detected and their relative depth below the test-object surface. This depth information is portrayed by assigning a different density or color to each delay time increment. A reflector near the top surface can be made to appear dark or of a specific color on the C-scan, while a deeper reflector appears lighter or of another color.

It is important to remember that a smaller reflector located in the shadow of another larger discontinuity may not be detected at all. Depending on its size relative to the sound beam's cross-sectional area, most ultrasonic pulse energy is reflected from the first discontinuity it encounters, effectively masking other reflectors located behind it.

Another effect that may be observed is the introduction of multiple reflections between a test object's top surface and a parallel reflector near the surface. Such multiple pulses display a typical *ring-down pattern* that appears as a periodic series of indications within the body of the test object. The successive echoes are not each a new discontinuity but simply echoes of the original discontinuity. They are displayed as equally spaced striations within a B-scan (cross-section) display of the test object.

Material Characterization

The acoustic nature of a test object has a pronounced effect on how ultrasound passes through it. Fine-grained elastic materials found in many metals are considered *homogeneous* (same material throughout) and *isotropic* (same characteristics along all axes). For this class of materials, a sound beam's direction and behavior are highly predictable. These are the attributes assumed in most of the discussions related to detecting and sizing discontinuities using ultrasonic testing techniques.

When ultrasound is used on materials that deviate from these assumptions, the direction a beam takes and the rate at which its energy dissipates is largely dependent on the makeup of the material. These characteristics tend to be cumulative as a beam passes through the material, so that signal strength continues to drop as a beam travels farther.

Two conditions predominate in their effects on ultrasonic testing:

1. The size of *partial reflectors* that may exist throughout the material. Products such as castings tend to have large-grain structures, and this scatters the energy of a coherent sound wave. The effect becomes more pronounced as the average size of the grain approaches the wavelength of sound in the material. The result is an increasingly rapid decay in signal strength with distance, a behavior known as *sound-wave attenuation*.
2. Redirection of the sound path in preferential directions established by the material's *anisotropic makeup*. In metals, this condition often occurs because of preferential grain growth, particularly in cast stainless steel materials. The presence of both isotropic equiaxed and anisotropic columnar microstructures can be seen in the photomicrograph of centrifugally cast stainless steel in Figure 15.

Because ultrasound reacts to different material conditions, such reactions can be used to estimate variations in grain size, density or compactness, age-hardening, and toughness. Variables used to assess

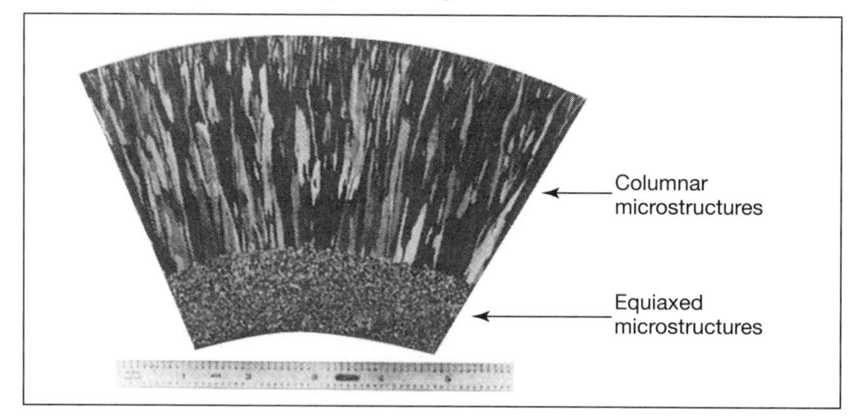

Figure 15: Photomicrograph of centrifugally cast stainless steel showing anisotropic grain structure.

these conditions are usually the velocity of ultrasonic wave propagation or sound-wave attenuation.

Limited-Access Tests

In most discussions involving ultrasonic testing, it is often assumed that access is unrestricted, permitting total freedom in the placement and angulation of transducers. In many applications, as in the case of the K and Y joints, the geometry of the test object interferes with transducer placement and alignment. For simple geometries like billets, rods, plate, sheet, and extrusions, limited access is not a problem. In complex assemblies, the testing plan may call for partial tests of components as the product is assembled because portions of the finished product will not be accessible when assembly is complete.

Limited access is a primary concern when inservice tests are planned. Thermal insulation must be removed and underground pipelines must be exposed. In addition, turbine blades at specific locations may be obscured by vanes or support structures. In some cases, complexity of a joint configuration can make traditional ultrasonic testing impossible.

Summary

This chapter addressed the detection and characterization of discontinuities in raw materials and finished components. Test objects with simple and regular geometries (plate, sheet, and billets) and curved test objects, such as pressure piping or pressure vessels with large radii of curvature, are relatively straightforward to test. Reflectors parallel to the ultrasonic testing surface are most easily detected, while planar reflectors with varying orientations to the test surface are the most difficult to detect and characterize.

It is the discontinuities—their shape, size, and orientation—in a particular material and environment that determine the technique to be used in their detection. Often, the most challenging task for the nondestructive testing technician is to determine the best technique or combination of techniques for specific test object geometries and suspected discontinuities.

>10

Phased Array

Introduction

Ultrasonic phased array (PA) testing uses multiple ultrasonic elements and electronic time delays to generate and receive ultrasound, creating beams by constructive and destructive interference. As such, phased array offers significant technical advantages over conventional single-probe ultrasonic testing: the phased array beams can be steered, scanned, swept, and focused electronically.

Terminology

Electronic scanning permits very rapid coverage of the components, typically an order of magnitude faster than a single-probe mechanical system.

Beam forming permits the selected beam angles to be optimized ultrasonically by orienting them perpendicular to the discontinuities of interest — for example, lack of fusion in welds.

Beam steering (usually called a *sectorial* or *azimuthal scan*) can be used for inspecting components with a range of appropriate angles to optimize probability of detection.

Sectorial scanning is also useful for inspections where restricted access to the test object limits conventional scanning. A sectorial scan sweeps through a selected range of angles, such as 40° to 70° shear, using the same group of elements to generate all angles.

Electronic focusing permits optimizing the beam shape and size at the expected discontinuity location, as well as probability of detection. Focusing significantly improves the signal-to-noise ratio, which also permits operating at lower pulser voltages. Overall, phased array optimizes discontinuity detection while minimizing test time.

Background

Phased arrays are widely used in medical ultrasonic imaging but had limited use in nondestructive testing in the 20th century, mainly because of the complexity and cost of the systems. As the cost of production decreased and portable computing power increased, the use of phased arrays for nondestructive testing has become more practical.

Operation

Ultrasonic phased arrays are similar in principle to phased array radar, sonar, and other wave applications. Phased arrays use an array of elements, all individually wired, pulsed, and time shifted. These elements can be a:

- linear array,
- two-dimensional matrix array,
- circular array, or
- more complex form (see Figure 1).

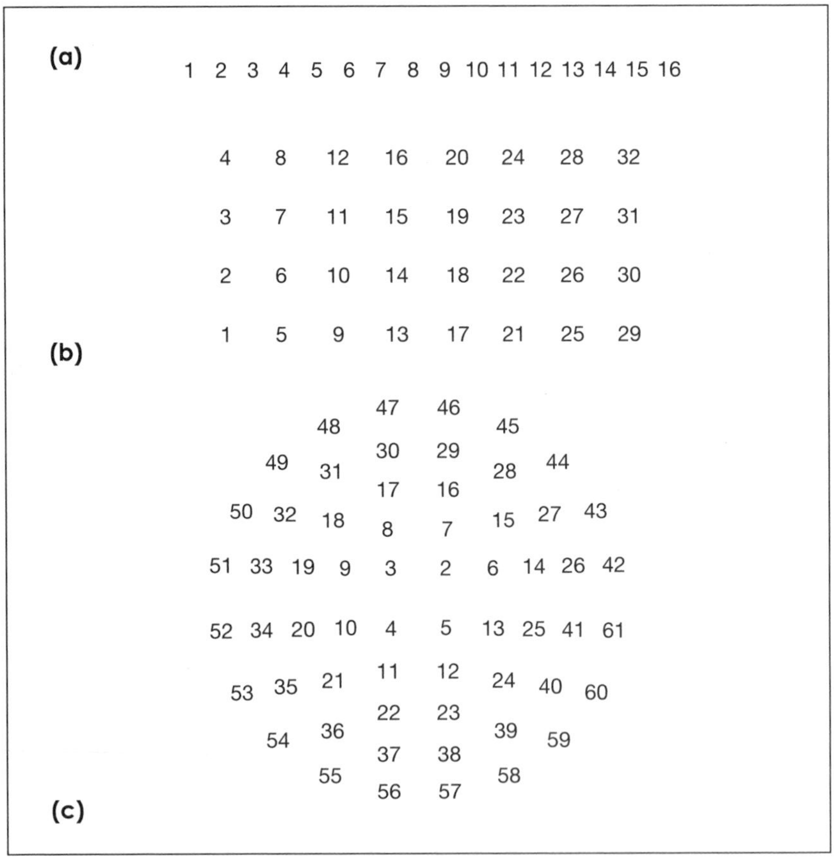

(a)

1 2 3 4 5 6 7 8 9 10 11 12 13 14 15 16

4 8 12 16 20 24 28 32
3 7 11 15 19 23 27 31
2 6 10 14 18 22 26 30
1 5 9 13 17 21 25 29

(b)

47 46
48 45
30 29
49 31 28 44
17 16
50 32 18 8 7 15 27 43
51 33 19 9 3 2 6 14 26 42
52 34 20 10 4 5 13 25 41 61
11 12
53 35 21 24 40 60
22 23
54 36 39 59
37 38
55 58
56 57

(c)

Figure 1: Array types: (a) one-dimensional linear array of 16 sensors; (b) two-dimensional matrix array of 32 sensors; (c) sectorial annular array of 61 sensors.

Most applications use *linear arrays*. These are the easiest to program and are significantly cheaper than more complex arrays because of fewer elements. As costs decline and experience increases, greater use of the more complex arrays is predicted.

The elements are ultrasonically isolated from each other and packaged in normal probe housings. The cabling usually consists of a bundle of well-shielded micro-coaxial cables. Wireless systems have also been on the increase. Commercial multiple-channel connectors are used with the instrument cabling.

Elements are typically pulsed in groups from 4 to 32, typically 16 elements for welds. With a user-friendly system, the computer and software calculate the *time delays* for a setup by using either operator input on interrogation angle, focal distance, scan pattern, and other test circumstances, or by using a predefined file (see Figure 2). The time delays are back calculated using time of flight from the focal spot and the scan assembled from individual focal laws. Time-delay circuits must be accurate to around 2 ns to provide the phasing accuracy required.

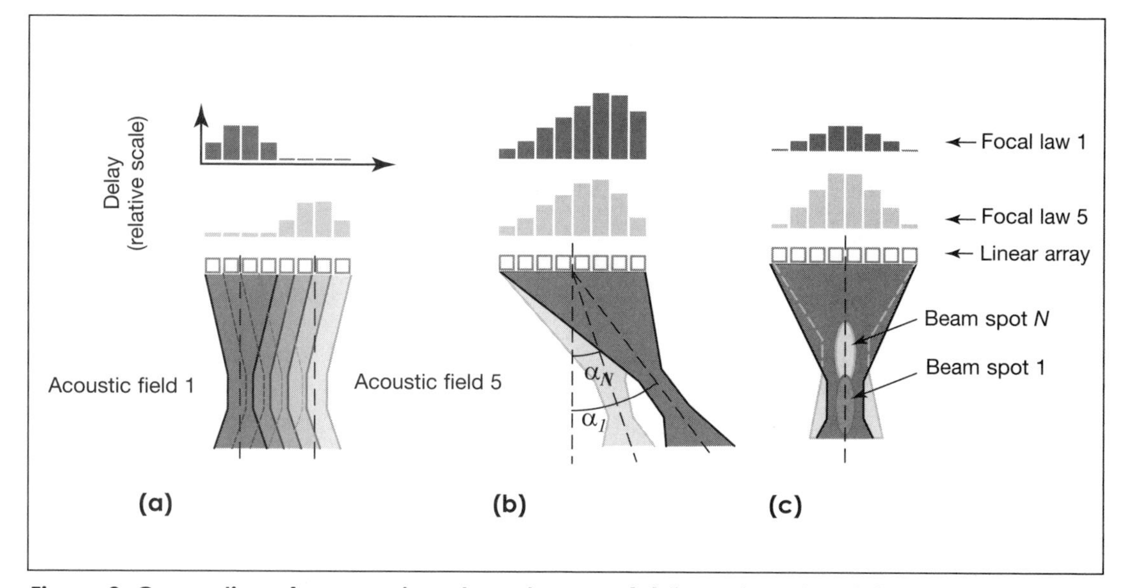

Figure 2: Generation of scans using phased arrays: (a) linear focusing; (b) sectorial focusing; (c) depth focusing.

Per ASTM E-1316, a focal law is "the entire set of hardware and software parameters affecting the acoustic sensitivity field of a phased array search unit, whether a pulse-echo or a pitch-catch configuration." Focal laws include delay mechanisms in both the transmitter and receiver.

Each element generates a beam when pulsed; these beams constructively and destructively interfere to form a wave front. The summed waveform is effectively identical to a single-channel ultrasonic instrument or discontinuity detector (referred to as a *flaw detector* in industry) using a probe with the same angle, frequency, focusing, aperture, and other settings. Figure 3 shows typical time delays for a focused normal (perpendicular) beam and reflected wave. Another sample time delay setup is shown in Figure 4.

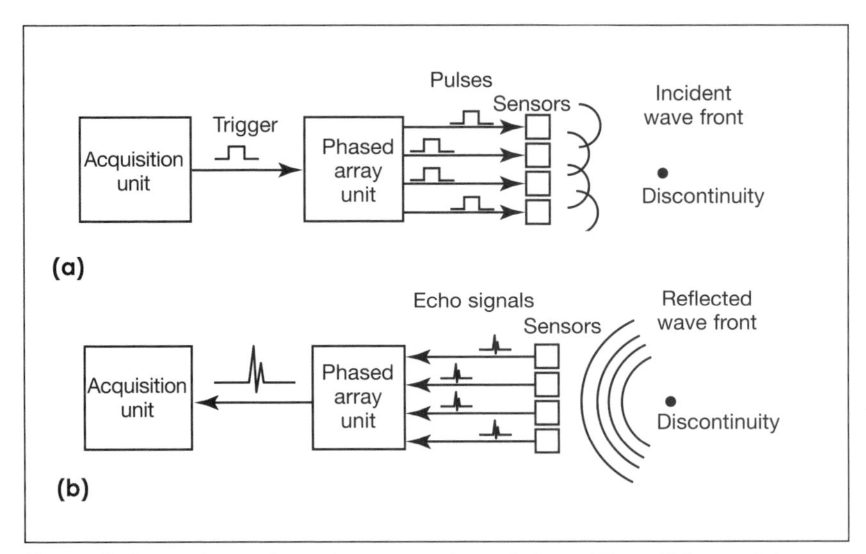

Figure 3: Beam in a phased array system: (a) emitting; (b) receiving.

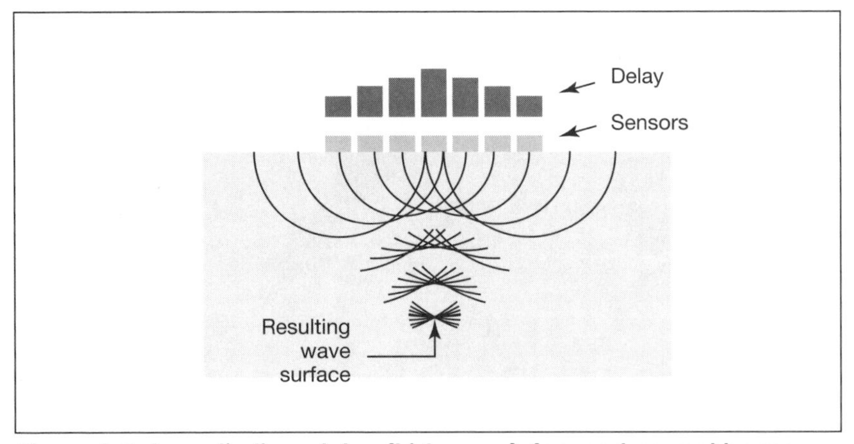

Figure 4: Schematic time delay (histogram): focused normal beam.

Implementation

From a practical viewpoint, ultrasonic phased arrays are merely a means of generating and receiving ultrasound; once the ultrasound is in the material, it is independent of generation method, whether generated by piezoelectric, electromagnetic, laser, or phased arrays. Consequently, many of the details of ultrasonic testing remain unchanged; for example, if 5 MHz is the optimum test frequency with conventional ultrasonic testing, then phased arrays would typically start by using the same frequency, aperture size, focal length, and incident angle.

While phased arrays require well-developed instrumentation, one of the key requirements is good, user-friendly software. Besides calculating the focal laws and calibrating each element in the array, the software saves and displays the results, so good data manipulation is essential. As phased arrays offer considerable application flexibility, software versatility is highly desirable. Phased array inspections can be manual, semiautomated (that is, *encoded*), or fully automated, depending on the application, speed, budget, and other considerations. Encoder capability and full data storage are usually required.

Although it can be time consuming to prepare the first setup, the information is recorded in a file and only takes seconds to reload. Also, modifying a prepared setup is quick in comparison with physically adjusting conventional instruments and probes.

Scan Types

Electronic pulsing and receiving provide significant opportunities for a variety of scan patterns.

Electronic Scans

Electronic scans are performed by multiplexing the same focal law (time delays) along an array (see Figure 5). Typical arrays have up to 128 elements. Electronic scanning permits rapid coverage with a tight focal spot. If the array is flat and linear, then the scan pattern is a simple B-scan. If the array is curved, then the scan pattern will be curved. Electronic scans are straightforward to program. For example, a phased array can be readily programmed to perform corrosion mapping, or to test a weld using 45° or 60° transverse waves, which mimics conventional manual inspections.

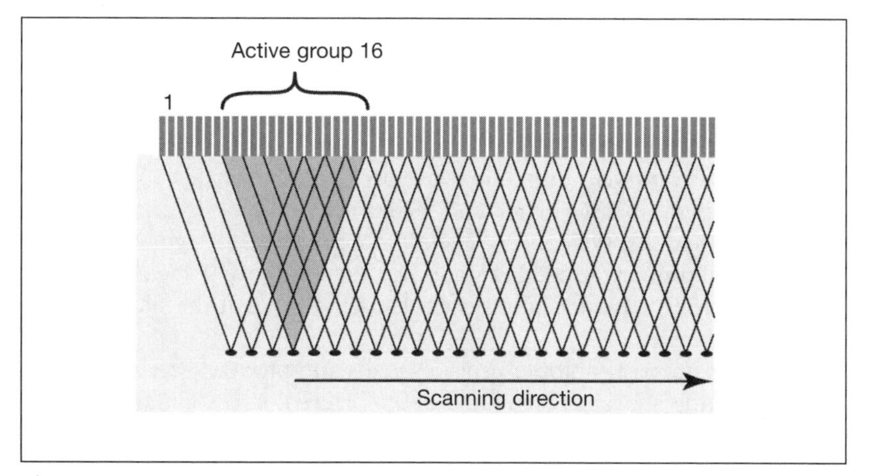

Figure 5: Electronic scanning.

Electronic scans can be used in conjunction with a two-axis scanner to perform a raster scan to cover a large area with very good resolution and sensitivity. This type of scan is often performed in aerospace or corrosion mapping applications.

Sectorial Scans (S-Scans)

Sectorial scanning is unique to phased array. Sectorial scans (S-scans) use the same set of elements but alter the time delays to sweep the beam through a series of angles (see Figure 6). Again, this is a straightforward scan to program. Applications for sectorial scanning typically involve a stationary array sweeping across a relatively inaccessible component, such as a turbine blade root, to map out features and discontinuities. Depending primarily on the array frequency and element spacing, the sweep angles can vary from ±20° up to ±80°.

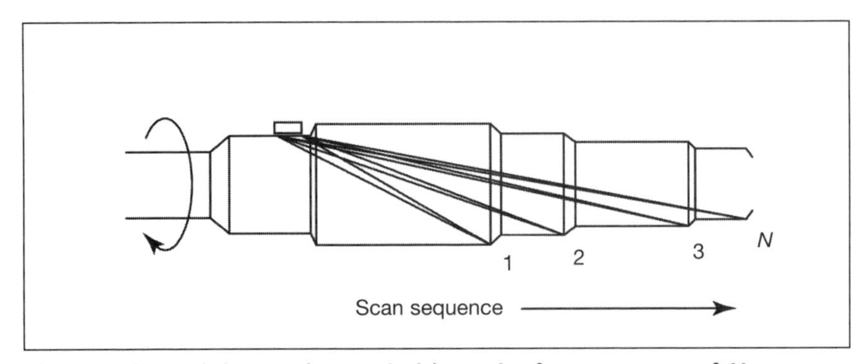

Figure 6: Sectorial scanning on turbine rotor for sequence of *N* scans.

Sectorial scanning has become popular in weld inspections for discontinuities. Such inspections often include an *encoder* so welds can be examined rapidly by performing encoded scans at multiple index positions to obtain the required coverage. Systems typically store all A-scan and position data required to make permanent records with B-scans and C-scans.

Linear Scanning of Welds

Manual ultrasonic weld inspections are performed using a single probe, which the operator *rasters* back and forth to cover the weld area. Many automated weld test systems use a similar approach (see Figure 7[a]), with a single probe scanned back and forth over the weld area. Rastering is time consuming because the system has *dead zones* at the start and finish of the raster.

In contrast, most multiple-probe systems and phased arrays use a linear scanning approach (see Figure 7[b]). Here the probe is scanned linearly around or along the weld, while each probe sweeps out a specific area of the weld. The simplest approach to linear scanning is found in pipe mills, where a limited number of probes test electric resistance welded pipe.

Phased array for linear weld tests operates on the same principle as the multiprobe approach; however, phased array offers considerably greater flexibility than conventional automated ultrasonic testing. Typically, it is much easier to change the setup electronically, either by modifying the setup or reloading another. Often it is possible to use

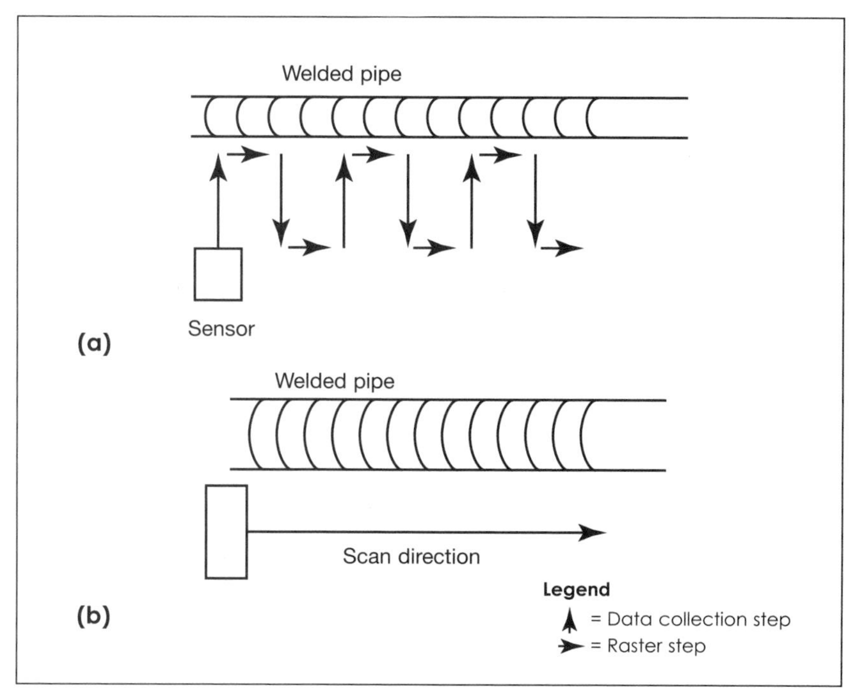

Figure 7: Phased array scanning: (a) conventional raster; (b) linear.

many more beams (equivalent to individual conventional probes) with phased array; special inspections can be implemented simply by loading a setup file.

Advantages of Phased Array

Ultrasonic phased array is flexible and used in a wide variety of industries, including aerospace, nuclear power, steel mills, pipe mills, petrochemical plants, pipeline construction, general manufacturing, and construction, plus a selection of special applications.

All of these applications take advantage of one or more of the dominant features of phased array:

- **Speed** – scanning with phased arrays is much faster than single-probe conventional mechanical systems and may provide better coverage.
- **Flexibility** – setups can be changed in a few minutes and significantly more flexibility of component dimensions is typically available.
- **Test angles** – a wide variety of test angles can be used, depending on the requirements and the array.
- **Imaging** – an image (enhanced to simulate three dimensions) of discontinuities is much easier to interpret than a waveform. The data can be saved and redisplayed as needed.

Phased array provides significant control over the shape and direction of the transmitted ultrasonic beam, thereby fulfilling two requirements for sophisticated nondestructive testing applications: dynamic focusing and real-time scanning.

Transducers with a flat face project a beam pattern that is constant in the near field and uniformly conical in the far field. Lateral resolution in the near field is limited by the diameter of the transducer. In the far field, the beam widens so that the lateral resolution of the transducer decreases. Decreasing the diameter of the transducer decreases the transition distance and increases the angle of divergence. To counter these effects, the frequency may be increased, but this decreases the wavelength, which in turn increases attenuation.

Beam Focusing

To create a smaller ultrasonic beam within the near field, the transducer can be focused by curving the transducer element or by attaching a lens to a flat transducer. A lens can cause reverberations within the piezoelectric material, so curving the transducer is preferable. The focusing ability of a transducer is described by radius of curvature and the beam width can be reduced either by increasing the diameter of the transducer or by increasing the frequency.

The amount of focusing affects the depth of beam penetration: the stronger the focusing, the shallower the focal zone. Therefore, the focused transducer is limited in possible depth and lateral resolution. These transducer focal abilities cannot be changed because they are characteristics of design and construction.

Timing System

In an array transducer system, timing of the transducer's firing can be controlled; the transmitted ultrasound from all the elements of the array combine to form an overall wave front, providing dynamic focusing. This wave front can be well controlled (shaped) by firing the outermost elements first and then firing the elements toward the interior of the transducer.

Beam Steering

Another advantage offered by phased array transducer systems is *ultrasonic beam steering*, a crucial feature in real-time ultrasonic imaging. In real-time imaging, fast-moving structures can be imaged and evaluated and the procedure can be automated to eliminate diagnostic variability caused by differing technician skill levels.

Limitations of Phased Array

Phased array nondestructive testing is relatively new and may require specific training. Phased array still requires extra setup effort, especially for complex three-dimensional applications. Two-dimensional setups are generally straightforward, provided the software is user friendly. For example, automated setup procedures have been developed for weld tests. Phased array systems are typically more costly than single-channel systems; however, the higher speed, data storage, and display, along with greater flexibility, can often offset the higher costs, especially with newer portable instruments.

Contact Modes of Phased Array

Phased array can operate in three basic contact modes: manual, semiautomated, and automated. Like other types of ultrasonic testing, phased array can also operate in immersion. The following discussion describes the three contact modes and how they are applied.

Manual Contact Phased Arrays

Normally, a portable phased array unit is used. These compact units have much of the capability of larger units. Manual phased arrays operate in a similar manner to conventional ultrasonic instruments and discontinuity (flaw) detectors but use a sector scan displayed on the screen. This allows real-time imaging with true depth positioning.

Because no encoder is used, it is not possible to generate a C-scan; however, time-generated scans and/or screen shots can be saved. Saving images reduces subjectivity, as well as giving better reporting and more repeatable scanning. Focused beams significantly improve the signal-to-noise ratio and, correspondingly, the probability of detection.

Time-Based Encoding

Most portable phased array systems allow for time-based encoding up to a specific time. This allows for pseudo C-scans without displaying the actual encoded distance — just time. This enables an operator to quickly scan areas to determine if any discontinuities require further investigation.

Encoded Linear Scans

Encoded linear scans are some of the most common phased array weld inspections. Typically, the probe is set at a predetermined distance (index position) from the weld centerline to perform a linear scan along the weld length. When performing a sectorial scan, it is very important to perform these linear scans from at least two index positions for discontinuity detection. Although plotting software may show sound passing through the entire area of interest with one index position, the sound will not be oriented correctly to detect all discontinuities. Depending on the material thickness and probe used, multiple scans may be required with an electronic scan to get coverage of the entire area of interest.

Semiautomated Contact Phased Arrays

Semiautomated tests are similar to manual tests with one major difference: the scans are encoded and all the data are stored. The simplest semiautomated system is an array with an encoder attached, but handheld scanners and belt scanners are also used for some applications (see Figure 8).

Figure 8: Typical semiautomated handscanner for piping test.

Semiautomated tests are typically used for weld inspection,

corrosion mapping, and other applications where full data storage and display are required. With these inspections, the results can be displayed as corrosion maps, A-scans, B-scans, C-scans, and D-scans (or top, side, and end views) as shown in Figure 9 or as required.

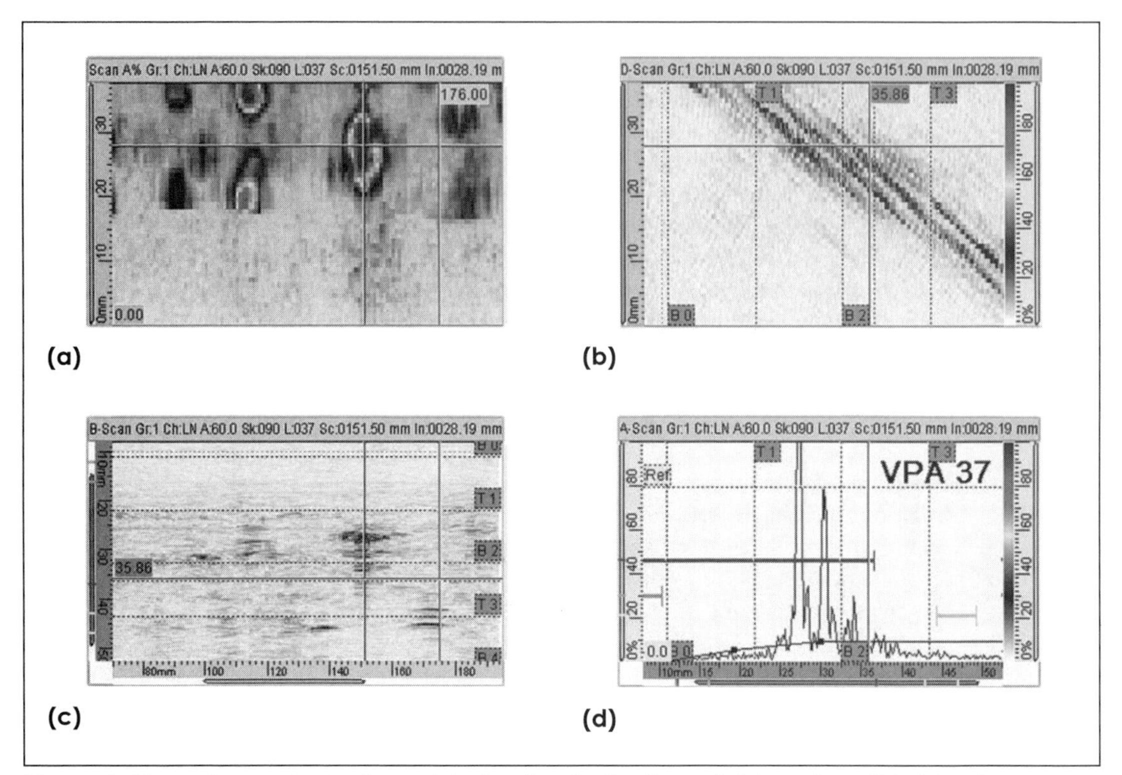

Figure 9: Phased array tests of a weld, showing indications: (a) top view; (b) side view; (c) end view; (d) waveform.

Automated Contact Phased Arrays

Fully automated test systems are totally mechanized; the operator controls the scanner from a computer and all data are collected automatically. With phased array, fully automated test systems are normally single-axis systems because the second axis is performed by electronic scanning. Typically, fully automated phased array systems are high-end products with significantly better capability than semiautomated systems. For example, the scanning speed is typically at mechanical speeds of 100 mm/s^{-1} or faster. The ultrasonic test performed may be complex, the data collection rate may be high, and the arrays may be bigger.

Discontinuity Characterization

For discontinuity characterization, there are two approaches to take with compound scanning:

1. **Discontinuity reconstruction** – by scanning with a beam width as narrow as possible. The results from all the positions are superimposed to produce a cross-sectional B-scan presentation of the discontinuity.
2. **Discontinuity classification** – by scanning with a large beam compared with discontinuity size. Figure 10 shows how the maximum echoes from each transducer position can be combined to form a compound scan amplitude locus curve.

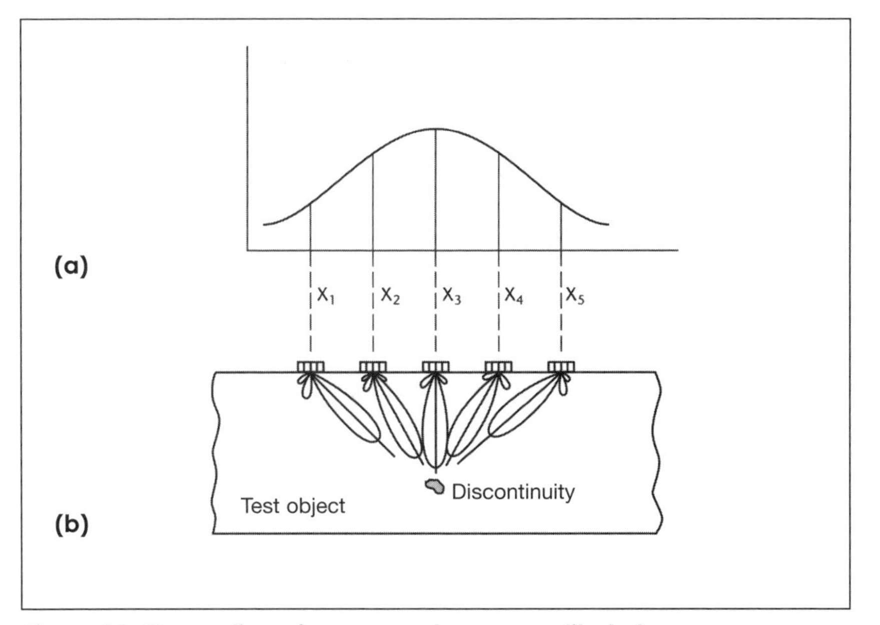

Figure 10: Generation of compound scan amplitude locus curve: (a) maximum echo amplitude; (b) beam profiles and transducer locations.

Phased Array Arrangements

Arrays are arrangements of transducer elements that offer capabilities greater than single- or multiple-transducer systems for the determination of shape, size, and orientation of discontinuities. There are three major types of arrays: linear, planar (or matrix), and annular. In phased array, a prescribed phase shift is controlled electronically and provided to each of the transducers for ultrasonic transmission.

Phased Linear Arrays

Phased linear arrays are an excellent means of implementing a real-time ultrasonic imaging system. They allow beam steering and focusing, signal processing during image formation, and a potential for parallel processing to increase data rates. A linear array can only shape or steer a beam along one axis.

Limitations of Phased Linear Arrays

Phased linear arrays have a number of limitations. For example, the response of transducer arrays is not ideal due to a decrease in the thickness-mode resonant frequency. A width-to-thickness ratio of 0.65 provides the optimum transducer sensitivity.

In addition, there are limitations to the uniform angular response of the array elements. Another problem is caused by discrete time delays that control the sequencing of transmission and reception, resulting in a jagged curve for focusing and steering. The best way to reduce this effect is to decrease the time-delay increments.

Phased Linear Array Design

The design of a phased linear array considers many critical factors, including (1) the number of elements (especially with regard to focusing), (2) whether the transducer is in contact with test material or immersed in a liquid, (3) whether the electrical excitation is burst or pulsed, and (4) control of signal transmission and reception.

Two-Dimensional Linear Arrays

Two-dimensional phased linear arrays provide the ability to steer the ultrasonic beam in multiple directions and can be used to imitate manual probe oscillation or to look for indications in front of or to the sides of the probe.

Phased Planar Arrays

A phased planar (or matrix) array is basically an extension of the two-dimensional phased linear array into the third dimension. This extension produces the planar array's major advantage: the ability to steer the ultrasonic beam. However, this comes at a high cost: a considerable increase in the complexity of electronics to control the sequencing of individual transducers. For this reason, phased planar arrays have had limited use in nondestructive testing. Control of a phased planar array is similar to that of phased linear arrays and is based on the timing of the array element's firing.

Phased Annular Arrays

Annular arrays cannot be steered, but focusing along the central axis can be enhanced by time delays in the path of the reflections detected by the array elements and then summing those results. Dynamic focusing of ultrasonic reflections is achieved by varying the time delays. In transmission mode, the ultrasonic beam may not be dynamically focused because it originates from only one ring. However, the focal length along the axial direction can be varied by changing the delays between the sequential excitation of the rings, moving from the outermost to the center.

Annular Array Design

The primary factors for the *design* of an annular array are the size and number of array elements and the frequency of transmission. The primary factors influencing the *use* of an annular array are the calculation of the focal depth and the time delays.

An annular array can be thought of as a cylindrical transducer that has been sliced into concentric rings, each forming a separate transducer. The time of transmission and reception of these rings is manipulated by electronics, thereby permitting control of the shape and the focal point of the overall wave front, always on the axis of the transducer. Reflections produced by objects closer to the transducer arrive sooner than those farther away. By changing the receiver delay lines, the focus can be changed during signal reception to concentrate on different depths along the axis.

Annular Array Applications

Nondestructive testing applications of annular arrays include inspections of turbines. For testing turbine disks, the array is segmented into quarters with randomly spaced but equal area elements. Each segment has its own channel, and the elements are randomly spaced to reduce the effects of grating lobes.

Another annular array capability is three-dimensional steering by heavily segmenting the rings. The divided ring array has 48 segments on two rings (see Figure 11). It can be steered in the range of ±45° by longitudinal-wave excitation and ±30° to ±70° by transverse-wave excitation. The system performs better than a phased linear array for discontinuity reconstruction.

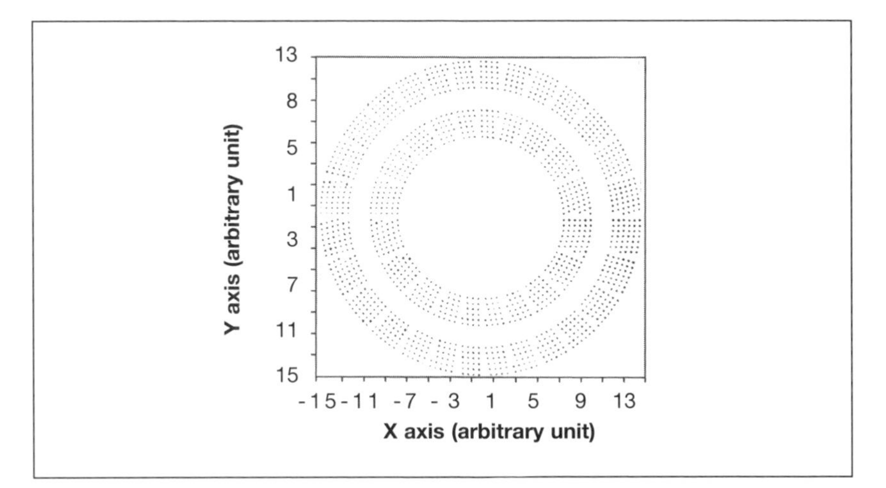

Figure 11: Optimized arrangement of divided ring array.

Applications of Phased Array Systems

Applications of phased array systems include both inspection and health monitoring. Examples include monitoring for cracks in industrial plant facilities at high temperatures and inspection of thin-walled structures for cracks using wafer-like sensors with lamb waves.

Commercial phased array systems have user-friendly software that performs calculations. For example, the operator can program a 45° transverse wave focused at 2 in. (50 mm), and the instrument calculates the time delays and focus.

Pressure Vessel Inspections

Pressure vessels normally require tests in compliance with the *ASME Boiler & Pressure Vessel Code*, mandating two separate transverse wave angles. Good practice also includes time of flight diffraction (TOFD), which can be combined in a single linear scan with phased arrays. Figure 12 shows a typical pressure vessel test using a delivery system that follows a magnetic strip.

Figure 12: Contact phased array weld test.

Results are often displayed as merged data displays, with multiple views such as top, side and end views plus TOFD (see Figure 13). The software often has special features for data analysis and full data storage. Both techniques — PA and TOFD — are allowed by *ASME Boiler and Pressure Vessel Code* to substitute UT for radiologic testing (RT) in vessels with a thickness greater than 0.5 in. (13 mm). ASME B31.3 piping code also allows for substitution of PA or TOFD for RT. Both codes give specific instructions for the use of these techniques.

Tailored Weld Inspections

Phased array is well suited for tests customized for a specific weld component or profile. An example is the automated ultrasonic testing of pipelines, which can use the *zone discrimination technique* where the

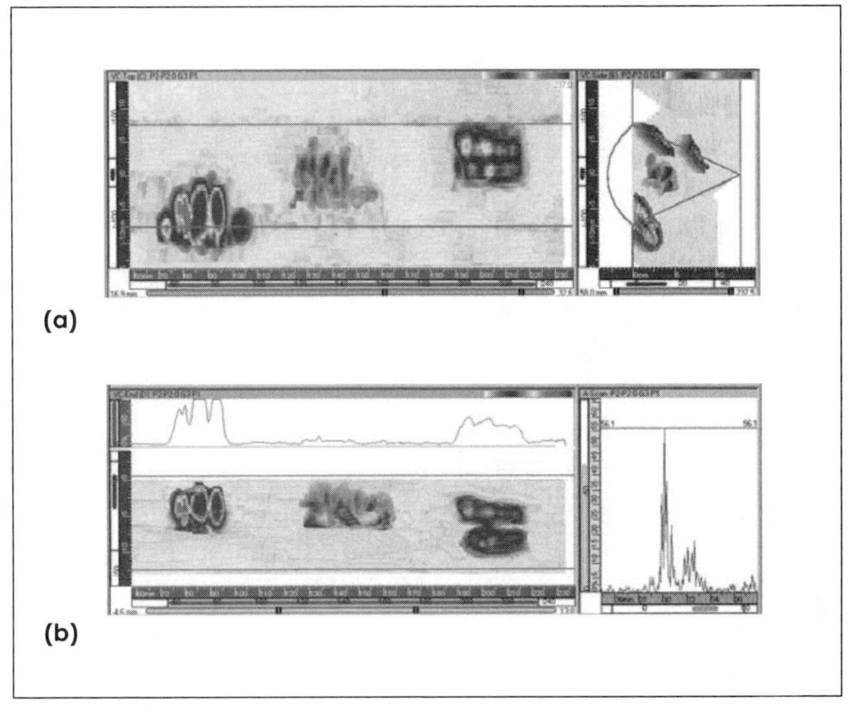

Figure 13: Phased array test of weld: (a) top view and side view; (b) end view and waveform.

weld is divided into zones and each zone is inspected using a focused, correctly angled beam. This type of test is easily performed using phased arrays and the setups can be automated.

Welding bands are used for delivery systems. Scanning speed is high, 240 in.·min^{-1} (100 mm·s^{-1}), so a 36 in. (0.9 m) pipe is scanned in under 60 s. Depending on the configuration, up to 20 MB of data per minute are saved to two separate storage locations. The data are displayed in real time so the operator can make rapid accept/reject decisions.

As with pressure vessels, the coupling is pumped liquid (water or methanol water mix). Wedges are mounted with wear pins and coupling checks are performed. This approach has been used for millions of welds.

Pipe Mills

Pipe mills are extensive users of contact ultrasonic testing, usually continuously with many different pipe diameters and wall thicknesses. Phased arrays have significant setup advantages over conventional systems, allowing fast configuration of several oblique discontinuity detection setups by simply downloading focal laws. No mechanical adjustments are needed and better coverage is obtained.

Figure 14 shows a full-body inspection system, which uses contact phased arrays to inspect for longitudinal, transverse and up to six different oblique discontinuities, measuring ±12°, ±22°, ±45°, ±67°, and ±78°. Different water wedges hold each array group; each water wedge is optimized for detection of one or two discontinuity types.

Figure 14: Phased array technique for full-body test of rotating pipe.

11

Time of Flight Diffraction

Introduction

A variation of the pitch-catch technique is the time of flight diffraction (TOFD) technique. Ultrasonic waves from a transducer are transmitted along the scanning surface and reflected from the backwall. The area between the probes is *insonified* — that is, inundated with carefully controlled sound waves — and reflectors diffract or reflect sound. The diffraction technique is therefore a hybrid of direct and indirect pitch-catch tests. Diffractions are separated in space so their reception by the receiving transducer is separated by time. This difference in time can be used to locate and size the reflector.

Basic Principle

Time of flight diffraction is an ultrasonic examination technique that can provide improved detection and sizing capabilities of discontinuities compared to standard ultrasonic pulse-echo techniques. It uses the time difference of *tip diffraction signals* from a discontinuity for sizing. Although this technique is not based on amplitude response, sufficient sensitivity is required to identify indications for evaluation.

The basic principle involves two transducers arranged in pitch-catch mode. (See Figure 1.) TOFD transducers typically have small diameters, so the sound beam has a comparably broad angle range. If there are no internal discontinuities, two wave signals exist. The first one is called a

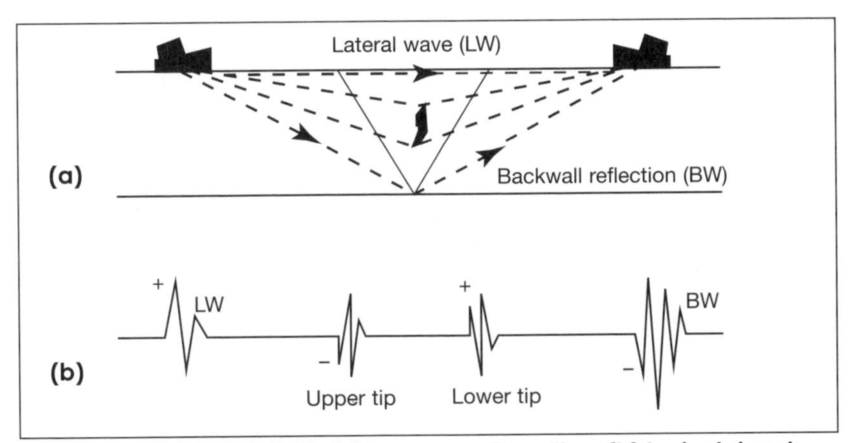

Figure 1: Principles of TOFD: (a) sensor configuration; (b) typical signals.

lateral wave. This is a longitudinal wave skimming near the surface of the test piece. The second wave is the *backwall reflection signal*.

If a mid-wall discontinuity exists in the test region, there will be two more diffracted signals, one from the top and the other from the bottom of the discontinuity. There is a phase difference for these four wave packages. The lateral wave has a positive peak, while the backwall signal has a negative peak due to reflection. The top diffracted signal has a negative peak, while the bottom diffracted signal has a positive peak.

Because phase inversions of the signals play an important role in the evaluation of TOFD results, TOFD equipment usually displays and stores radio-frequency (RF) waveforms. The screen range is often set to include additional information after the first backwall signal from the longitudinal wave. There can be another backwall signal from a composite of longitudinal and shear waves and a shear wave backwall signal, but the majority of inspection is typically performed from the lateral wave to the first backwall signal.

Common Practice

The TOFD technique is typically used to inspect welded joints in carbon steel. For other materials, TOFD may also be applicable. The technique is used in conjunction with other manual or automated weld examination techniques.

Although shear waves also exhibit the diffraction phenomenon, it is more common to use the refracted longitudinal wave mode in TOFD. This is because after the incident wave interacts with a discontinuity, it typically generates both longitudinal waves and shear waves through mode conversion.

For an incident longitudinal wave, the test can be designed such that the arrival time of the diffracted shear wave signal is behind the backwall reflection signal. In this case, all the diffracted signals from the area of interest are longitudinal waves. This makes the interpretation of the signal easier. In a longitudinal wave TOFD test, typically the signal between the lateral wave and first backwall echo signal is used for evaluation.

On the other hand, if the incident angle is beyond the first critical angle, the refracted signal from the wedge to the test material is only in shear wave mode. The lateral wave and the first backwall echo signal will still be a shear wave. However, just slightly behind the lateral wave, there will be a surface-wave mode. In addition, the mode-converted longitudinal wave from a discontinuity will be detected earlier than the first backwall echo and cause confusion in data interpretation.

TOFD has proven effective on thicknesses from 0.375 in. to 12 in. (9 mm to 300 mm). For thicknesses outside of this range, special consideration is necessary to demonstrate its usefulness for specific applications. ASTM E-2373 provides general recommendations about probe selection for different thickness ranges as listed in Table 1.

Table 1: Common practice of sensor selection in TOFD tests.

Nominal wall thickness – in. (mm)	Nominal frequency – MHz	Element size in transducer – in. (mm)	Recommended angle – degrees
<0.47 (12)	10 – 5	0.08 – 0.25 (2 – 6)	60 – 70
0.5 – 1.4 (12 – 35)	5 – 10	0.125 – 0.25 (3 – 6)	50 – 70
1.4 – 3 (35 – 75)	2 – 5	0.25 – 0.5 (6 – 12)	45 – 65
3 – 12 (75 – 300)	1 – 5	0.25 – 0.5 (6 – 12)	45 – 65

For thicknesses larger than 3 in. (76 mm), a single set of probes is most likely unable to cover the entire range with sufficient sensitivity. In this case, the test piece has to be divided into multiple test zones and each zone is covered with a set of probes.

Typically, side-drilled holes (SDHs) are used as reference discontinuities in calibration standards for TOFD. The SDHs are placed at 25% and 75% depth locations of the sample for each zone. The sizes of the SDHs are typically 0.06 in. (1.5 mm) for thicknesses below 0.4 in. (10 mm); 0.1 in. (3 mm) for thicknesses between 0.4 in. (10 mm) and 1.4 in. (35 mm); and 0.24 in. (6 mm) for thicknesses of 1.4 in. (35 mm) and above.

Applications

TOFD is used in nondestructive tests of piping and pressure vessels because of its:

- advantages over the pulse-echo technique;
- speed, objectivity, and repeatability; and
- insensitivity to weld surface conditions and discontinuity orientation.

Typically, TOFD is used for sizing after a discontinuity is detected with another ultrasonic technique. Diffraction techniques accurately determine the length and depth of surface-breaking and submerged cracks.

The technique has also been used on *nonplanar discontinuities*. The applicability of the technique may be limited because the lower crack tip may not always diffract enough energy to be detected; however, continuing improvements in developing ray-based models and evolving applications with phased array systems continue to make the technique highly useful for sizing and locating discontinuities.

TOFD is also used for detection and sizing of discontinuities in welds. The technique is sensitive for detection of weld discontinuities provided proper test parameters are used. These include transducer specifications, transducer spacing, calibration sensitivity, scanning speed, and analysis procedures.

Technique

TOFD testing typically employs two longitudinal wave angle-beam transducers arranged symmetrically opposite each other, straddling the weld or base material under test. For most weld tests, the probes are located on the parent material clear of the weld crown. One probe transmits ultrasonic energy while the other probe receives it. Transducer, pulser, and amplifier characteristics are selected to generate as broad a distribution of energy as possible over the material under test, providing full coverage on thinner welds.

For weld tests, this generally includes the weld, heat-affected zones, and adjacent parent material. Because the technique requires only a single motion axis (that is, along the weld), data acquisition requires only a simple manual scanner that can be set up and operated quickly. The scanner incorporates an encoder that records the position of the weld and enables the assembly of digital images in real time. Analysis can be performed immediately from the digital images and data are available for additional post-test reviews. Scan speeds of 20 to 80 in./min (0.5 to 2 m/min) are achievable — a major attraction of this technique.

The location of the signal origin point within the material is determined precisely using simple geometric considerations, beam angles, and the appropriate sound propagation velocity. Algorithms are built into the time of flight diffraction software system so that accurate depth, length, and through-wall dimensions can be calculated quickly while viewing the ultrasonic image.

TOFD data typically show three reference signals because of the transducer arrangement and operation in a pitch-catch mode. Reference signals are those that occur due to beam path and component geometry, and are present at the same propagation times regardless of the position within a scan along the weld length. The three signals, as shown in Figure 2, are:

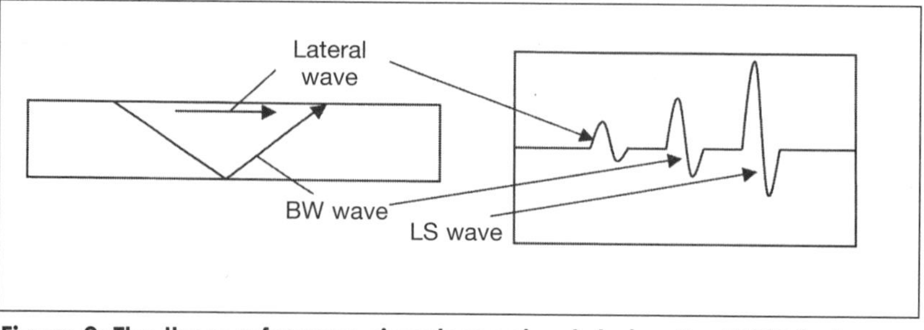

Figure 2: The three reference signals received during the TOFD test (BW = backwall reflected longitudinal wave, LS = longitudinal/shear mode-converted wave).

1. The lateral wave, caused by propagation of the sound between the transmitter and receiver in a direct path just under the test surface.
2. The primary backwall signal caused by the direct reflection of the longitudinal wave from the backwall.
3. The backwall signal created by mode conversions on the inner diameter surface (longitudinal wave to shear wave and vice versa). A shear wave to shear wave signal may also be displayed depending on how the equipment is set up.

The signals occur sequentially at increasing time in the order presented. During a normal scan, the three signals appear consistently. However, when a discontinuity is present, a signal will appear in the "time window" between the lateral wave and the reflected longitudinal signal. Knowing the probe spacing, the depth of the discontinuity can be calculated by comparing the arrival time of the discontinuity signal to the arrival time of the reflected longitudinal signal.

Discontinuity Classification

The TOFD technique can be used to detect, classify, and size many different types of discontinuities:

- A surface-breaking discontinuity produces a distorted lateral wave or backwall wave if it is deep enough to be detected.
- An embedded discontinuity produces diffracted signals distinct from the lateral wave and backwall wave.
- A point-line discontinuity has no measurable length.
- An elongated threadlike discontinuity has no measurable height.
- A planar discontinuity has measurable length and height.

Advantages of TOFD

- **Discontinuity detection** – In contrast to the pulse-echo technique, TOFD discontinuity detection does not depend on the orientation of the discontinuity. As long as there is a diffracted signal, the discontinuity should be detected.
- **Height measurement** – The TOFD technique can accurately measure the height of a discontinuity. As a result, it can be used as a method to monitor the growth of a discontinuity.
- **Sensitivity and sizing** – Compared to radiography, TOFD has better sensitivity and sizing capabilities for vertical discontinuities, higher test speed, and lower cost. It is also safer because there is no radiation.
- **Inspection data** – Inspection results are immediately available and can be permanently recorded.

Disadvantages of TOFD

- **Sensitivity** – The diffracted signal level in TOFD is usually 20 dB less than a reflected signal from a pulse-echo test. Although the amplitude of a signal is not relied on to size a discontinuity, sufficient amplitude is needed to have enough sensitivity for smaller discontinuities.

- **Dead zone** – Due to the presence of the lateral-wave and backwall signals, there is a dead zone close to the upper and lower surfaces of the test piece. Geometric conditions such as mismatch or plate curvature can compound these dead zone conditions. TOFD examinations are often supplemented with shear wave inspections to obtain coverage for surface-breaking discontinuities.
- **Sizing ability** – In order for a discontinuity to be accurately sized, two distinct diffraction signals need to be clearly identified. As a result, TOFD transducers usually require better time domain resolution than regular transducers. Another assumption behind using TOFD for sizing is that the discontinuities are vertically located at the center of the two probes. In reality, this is not always the case. For horizontally oriented discontinuities, the TOFD technique is not effective in sizing.
- **Discontinuity classification** – In some cases, small subsurface discontinuities are not easily discriminated from open-surface discontinuities.
- **Suitable applications** – The TOFD technique has limitations regarding the thickness and grain structure of the test material. Because TOFD relies on the differentiation of diffracted signals — the lateral wave and the backwall reflected signal in time — the weld thickness has to be larger than a certain number for this technique to function properly. The number given in the ASTM standard is 9 mm. In addition, TOFD has limited application for coarse-grain structures since the diffracted signal may not be easily differentiable from grain-boundary scattered signals. Thicker components may need to be inspected in zones of TOFD coverage.

Limitations

While TOFD is an attractive technique because of its speed and coverage, it does have limitations. First, the technique is limited to fine-grain materials. Another major limitation is loss of sensitivity for near-surface testing. Even as the technique detects discontinuities in welds, its surface and near-surface sensitivity is reduced by the width of the lateral-wave signal. The lateral-wave signal blocks the near-surface discontinuities. To some extent, using high-frequency, small-diameter, and highly damped transducers can overcome this limitation. Alternative surface NDT techniques should also be considered.

Surface and near-surface sensitivity also can be improved by reducing the pulse width of the lateral-wave signal. The same applies for testing of welds in thin plates — for example less than 0.4 in. (10 mm) — where the time difference between the lateral wave and reflected longitudinal wave is significantly reduced.

The simplest way to increase the time difference between the lateral-wave signal and the reflected longitudinal-wave signal is to use small-diameter transducers with short pulse widths.

Test Variables

The following variables affect the test:

- **Transducer frequency** – higher transducer frequency reduces the pulse width, thereby increasing the aperture between the lateral-wave signal and reflected longitudinal-wave signal; however, higher frequencies reduce ultrasound penetration.
- **Transducer diameter** – a smaller diameter decreases the pulse width of the refracted signal; however, a smaller transducer means lower sensitivity or a lower signal-to-noise ratio.
- **Increased damping** – increased transducer damping reduces pulse width. Typical pulse width for time of flight diffraction transducers should be approximately 1-1/2 cycles; however, increased damping reduces sensitivity.
- **Probe separation distance** – smaller probe separation increases the time difference between the lateral wave and reflected longitudinal wave signals. Probe separation is normally set so that the two beams intersect at a depth of two-thirds of the material thickness.

Data Display

Typically, a TOFD test should be equipped with a positional encoder that is synchronized to ultrasonic pulsing so the test results can be recorded with position information. During the testing, the set of probes moves together parallel to the axis of the weld. The display is usually a combination of B-scan and A-scan signals.

Figure 3 shows TOFD testing of reheat line girth welds. The inspectors watch the time of flight diffraction display as the weld is scanned manually with a single axis scanner. Battery-powered integrated equipment is used, making the system portable and easy for field tests.

Figure 3: TOFD testing of cold reheat line girth welds. Testing is done using 5 MHz, 60° longitudinal wave, 0.25 in. (6.3 mm) diameter transducers.

During inspection, the A-scan display is the current signal. In data-review mode, the A-scan display is typically related to the current cursor position. The B-scan display used in TOFD is usually a grayscale image of all of the radio-frequency (RF) A-scan signals at different positions stacked together. Therefore, it is also called a *stacked A-scan.*

In the grayscale image, white corresponds to a large positive value and black corresponds to a large negative value. Although it is a common consensus that grayscale images have better visual differentiation for different values, a color display may also be used for the B-scan.

Figure 4 shows a typical TOFD display with an RF waveform A-scan and B-scan. A sketch of the notched block that was scanned to produce the image is inset. In the upper left image, the lateral/longitudinal (LL) and longitudinal/shear (LS) waves are evident. The four notches that are evident as the scan progresses are at 0.10 in. (2.54 mm) intervals (with an equal increase in height). The notches are at 20%, 40%, 60%, and 80% throughwall. At the right edge, there is a 90% throughwall ID notch.

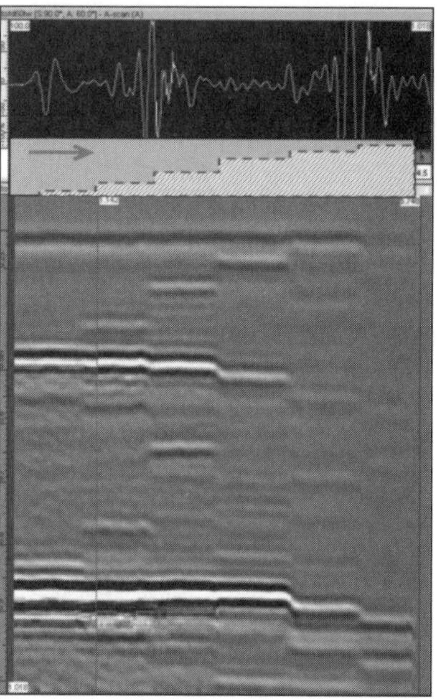

Figure 4: TOFD with A- and B-scans.

Figure 5(a) is an example of TOFD data on porosity in a weld. A radiograph of weld porosity is shown in Figure 5(b) for comparison.

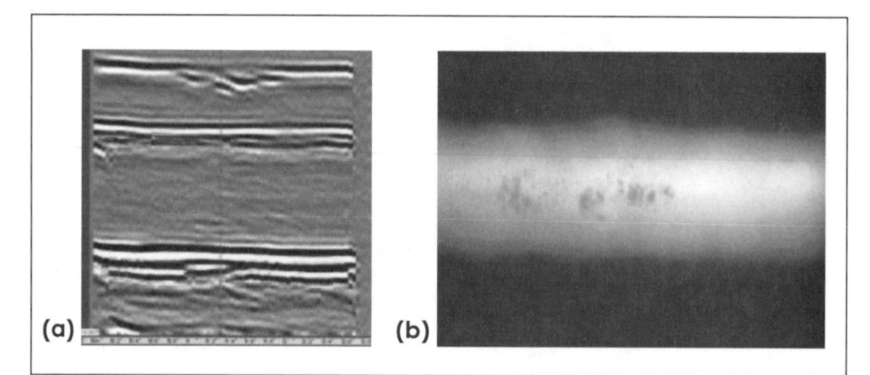

Figure 5: Porosity in a weld: (a) TOFD display; (b) radiograph.

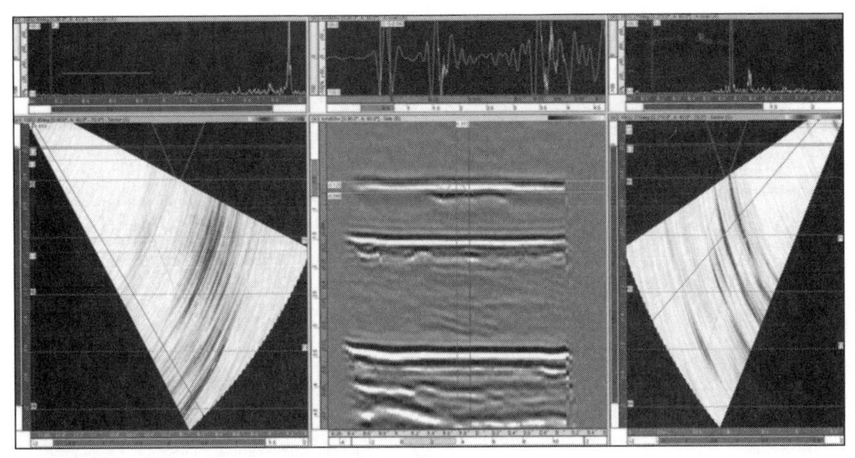

Figure 6: Combination PA and TOFD scans.

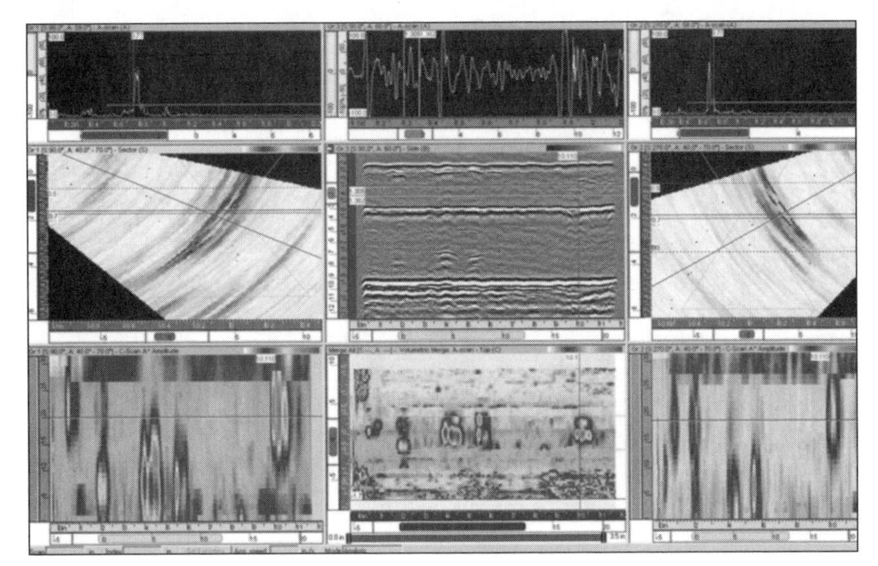

Figure 7: Combination PA sectorial and TOFD scans.

Figure 6 is an example of a combination phased array and TOFD scan. A phased array ultrasonic probe is placed on each side of the weld along with a TOFD probe on either side. The indication is of sidewall lack of fusion in the weld.

Figure 7 is a combined scan with a phased array ultrasonic probe performing a sectorial scan on each side in conjunction with a TOFD scan.

Lastly, Figure 8 shows the image of a weld with various indications.

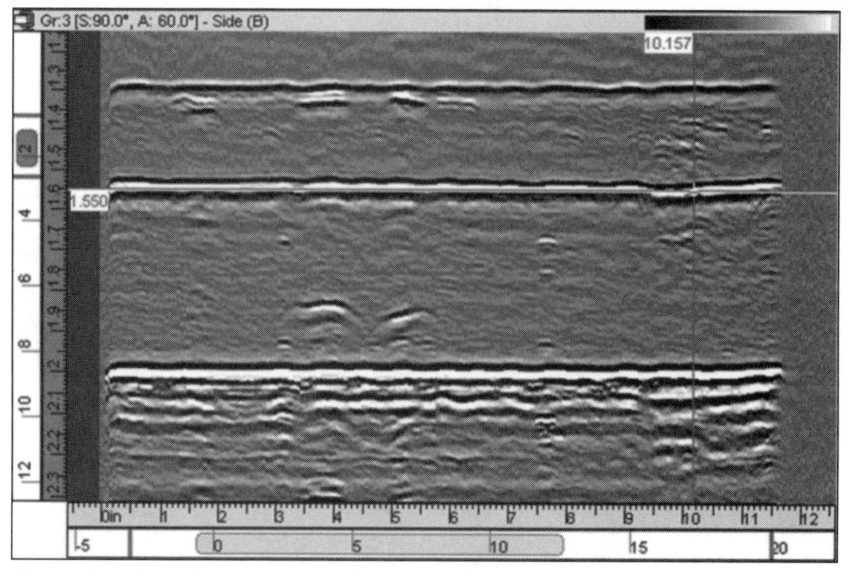

Figure 8: TOFD display of weld indications.

12

Guided Wave Method

Introduction

Guided wave is a nondestructive testing method in its own right, as presented in *Recommended Practice No. SNT-TC-1A: Personnel Qualification and Certification in Nondestructive Testing* (2011). Compared to ultrasonic bulk waves that travel in infinite media with no boundary influence, guided waves require a structural boundary for propagation. By definition, "guided wave" is a general term used to describe the wave propagation phenomenon where the guidance of a boundary plays a very important role. The structure in which a guided wave may propagate is called a *waveguide.*

Basic Principle

For situations where reflection and refraction are neither sufficient nor convenient to describe the wave interaction with the boundary, guided wave interpretation can be used to simplify the description of the wave-propagation phenomenon. As shown in Figure 1, if a wave propagating from position A to position B in a plate is analyzed, describing it with bulk-wave reflection and mode conversion becomes almost impossible since hundreds of reflections must be considered. As an alternative method, wave propagation may be described as possible wave modes in the plate. Now it is considered a guided wave that may be as simple to analyze as a single mode of propagation.

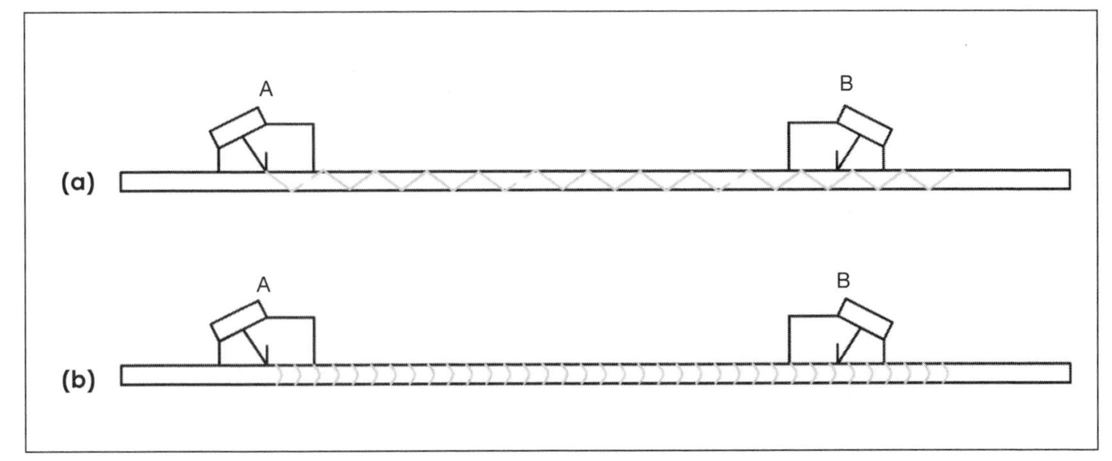

Figure 1: Wave propagation: (a) bulk waves; (b) guided waves.

Waveguides

Two guided wave possibilities are illustrated in Figure 2 for a rayleigh (surface) wave and a lamb (plate) wave.

There are many other guided wave possibilities, as long as a boundary on either one or two sides of the wave is considered. Natural waveguides include:

- plates (such as aircraft skin),
- rods (rails, cylinders, square rods),
- hollow cylinders (pipes, tubing),
- multilayered structures,
- curved or flat surfaces on a half space, and
- one or more layers on a half space.

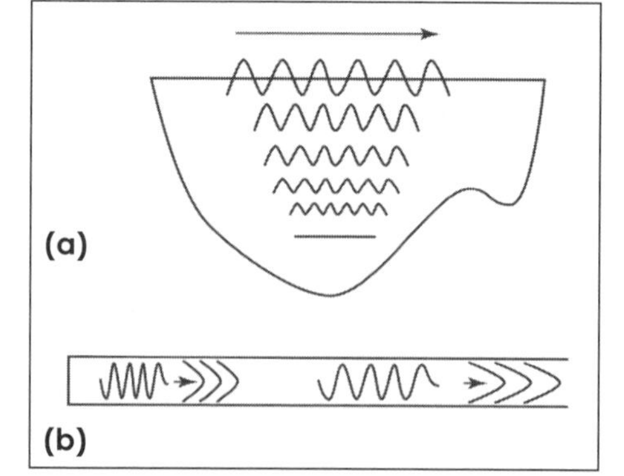

Figure 2: Guided wave types: (a) rayleigh (surface) waves; (b) lamb (plate) waves.

Most structures are natural waveguides provided the wavelengths are large enough with respect to dimensions in the waveguide. If the wavelengths are very small, then bulk-wave propagation can be considered — those waves used traditionally in ultrasonic nondestructive pulse-echo and through-transmission testing.

One difference, of many, associated with guided waves is that many different wave velocity values can be obtained as a *function* of frequency, whereas, for most practical bulk-wave propagation, wave velocity is *independent* of frequency.

To get some idea of how guided waves are developed in a waveguide, imagine many bulk waves bouncing back and forth inside a waveguide with mode conversions between longitudinal and transverse constantly taking place at each boundary. The resulting superimposed waveform traveling along the waveguide is just a sum of all of these waves, including amplitude and phase information.

The outcome strongly depends on frequency and introductory wave angles of propagation inside the structure. The strongly superimposed results are actually points that end up on the *phase-velocity dispersion curve* for the structure.

Advantages and Limitations of Guided Wave

Advantages

The principal benefits of guided wave can be summarized as follows:

1. Inspection over long distances from a single probe position is possible, giving complete wide-area or volumetric coverage of the test object (for flat or curved plate, tubing, piping, multilayer structures, or other natural waveguides).
2. There is no need for scanning; all of the data are acquired from a single probe position. Test setup is easily implemented due to a leave-in-place probe. For base material inspection, the raster scan can be

eliminated or the pitch of the raster can be increased because of the longer range of coverage.
3. Often, greater sensitivity than that obtained in conventional straight-beam ultrasonic testing or other nondestructive techniques can be obtained, even with low-frequency guided wave testing.
4. There is also an ability to inspect hidden structures; structures under water, coatings or insulation; concrete; and multilayered structures because of the ability to test from a single probe position via wave-structure change and controlled mode sensitivity along with the ability to propagate over long distances. Other examples are the area under pipe support, pipe sections inside a wall, or pipes buried in soil.
5. Guided wave is able to establish appropriate wave resonances and excellent overall discontinuity detection and sizing potential through proper mode and frequency selection or tuning.
6. Guided wave is especially suitable for the inspection of thin materials, which are difficult to inspect with conventional ultrasonic testing methods. As a result, guided wave testing is a very good complement for a traditional bulk-wave test.
7. There is also a cost effectiveness associated with guided wave because of the test simplicity and speed (often less than 1/20 of the cost of standard ultrasonic testing techniques).

Limitations

The major challenge of guided wave testing is that it is an emerging technology in the process of development. The wave mechanics are still not fully understood in some complex applications. Thus, guided wave techniques are used as a screening tool. Other challenges include:

- Discontinuity sizing capability is still in a research and development stage and has not been fully developed. In some situations, the return signal amplitude can be used as basic information for length and depth sizing. In other situations, guided waves can only be incident on a discontinuity from limited angles. As a result, this limitation makes it fundamentally impossible to reconstruct detailed discontinuity shape and size.
- The applications of guided wave for relatively thick structures are limited. For thicker structures, guided wave operation frequencies are typically much lower than for conventional bulk-wave techniques. When the frequency used is only in the 10 kHz to 100 kHz range, the sensitivity of inspection will significantly be reduced compared to localized testing.

Propagation Distance

Because there are many types of guided waves, a commonly asked question is, “How far can guided waves propagate?” However, it is difficult to give a definite number. Guided wave propagation range may vary from several fractions of an inch (millimeters) to hundreds of yards (meters) depending on structure geometry, material attenuation, surrounding material, and test mode. Other factors include the frequency selected, instrument power level, instrument receiver capability, the targeted discontinuity size, and so on.

Depending on the application, guided wave operating frequencies may also vary from tens of kilohertz to the megahertz range. If it is desired, a guided wave test may operate below 20 kHz, in which case it is not an ultrasonic wave in a strict sense.

Types of Guided Waves

Several types of guided waves are used in nondestructive testing, as described below.

Surface Waves

A surface wave is a special type of guided wave that is guided with a single surface. A surface wave is also called a *surface acoustic wave* (SAW) or rayleigh wave.

Guided Waves in Plates

Guided waves in plate structures can be further classified as lamb waves and shear horizontal (SH) guided waves.

- **Lamb waves** – Lamb waves were first described theoretically by British mathematician Horace Lamb. In a strict sense, a lamb wave refers to a guided wave in a single-layer plate that has particle motion in the wave propagation direction and thickness direction. Similar waves in more complex structures, such as multiple layers or curved plates, can be referred to as lamb-type guided wave modes. Lamb waves can be further classified as *symmetric* and *asymmetric* based on their displacement fields, as discussed in Chapter 2.
- **Shear horizontal (SH) guided waves** – An SH guided wave has particle motion only in the direction that is perpendicular to the wave propagation direction and parallel to the surface in a plate.

Wave Modes in Tubular Structures

There are two basic categories of guided wave propagation in tubular structures: one for wave propagation in the *axial direction*, as shown in Figure 3(a), and the other for waves propagating in the *circumferential direction* of the pipe, as depicted in Figure 3(b). It is important to note that both the thickness and diameter of the structure are essential for specifying guided waves in a tubular structure.

Axial Direction

There are three types of guided wave modes for axial guided waves in pipes:

1. **Longitudinal mode** – when the wave field distribution is symmetrical about the axis, or *axisymmetric*, and the particle motion is in the radial direction and axial direction.
2. **Torsional mode** – when the wave field distribution is axisymmetric and the particle motion is in the circumferential direction.
3. **Flexural mode** – when the wave field is not axisymmetric.

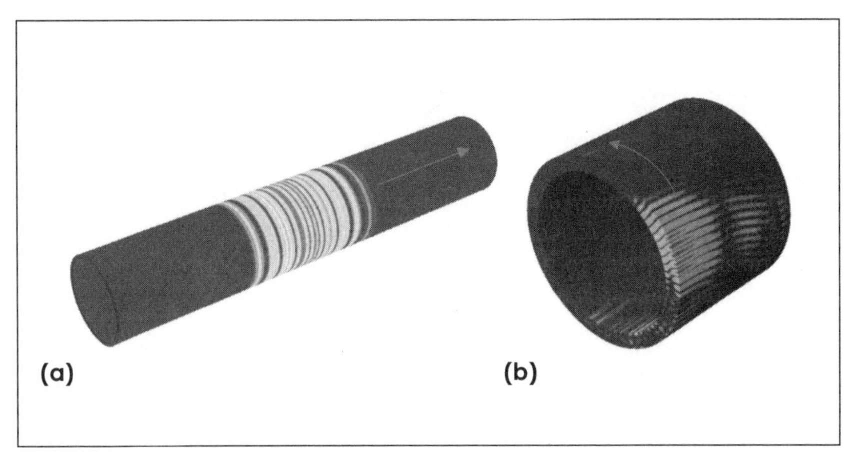

Figure 3: Guided waves in pipe: (a) axial direction; (b) circumferential direction.

Circumferential Direction

There are two basic types of guided wave propagation along the circumference of a tubular structure:

- **Lamb-type mode** – particle motion in the circumferential and radial direction.
- **SH-type mode** – particle motion in the axial direction.

Dispersion

Dispersion Curves

Dispersion curves are used to describe and predict the relationship between frequency, phase velocity and group velocity, mode, and thickness in guided wave testing. Fundamental to the understanding of guided wave analysis in NDT is the generation or utilization of phase velocity, group velocity, and attenuation dispersion curves.

Understanding Dispersion Curves

As noted, *dispersion* means the wave velocity is a function of frequency. Although this appears to be in conflict with our understanding of the constant velocities of bulk waves, it is a very important feature of guided wave analysis. Because of boundary constraints, many guided wave modes may exist in a plate. Each mode is represented with a curve showing the relationship between wave velocity and frequency. These curves can be obtained from theoretical simulation or experiment.

Figure 4 shows an example of dispersive and nondispersive guided wave propagation. The modes are labeled as *antisymmetric* A0, A1, and so on, or *symmetric* S0, S1, and so on. For nondispersive wave propagation, the pulse duration remains constant as the wave travels through the structure. On the other hand, for dispersive wave propagation, because wave velocity is a function of frequency, the pulse duration changes from point to point inside the structure. The change is because each harmonic of the particular input pulse packet travels at a different wave velocity. There is a decrease in amplitude of the waveform and an increase in pulse duration, but energy is still conserved for most materials.

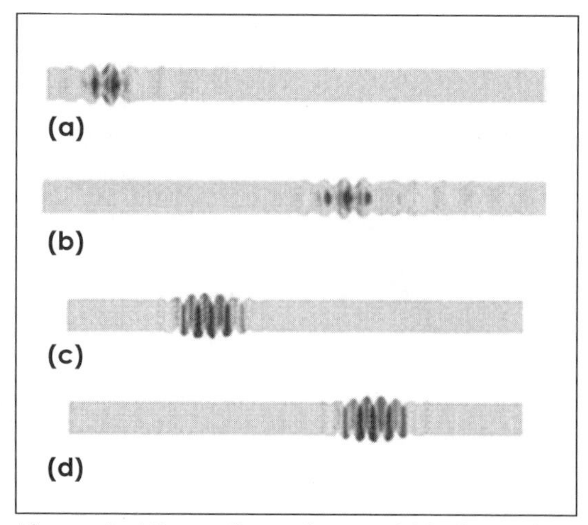

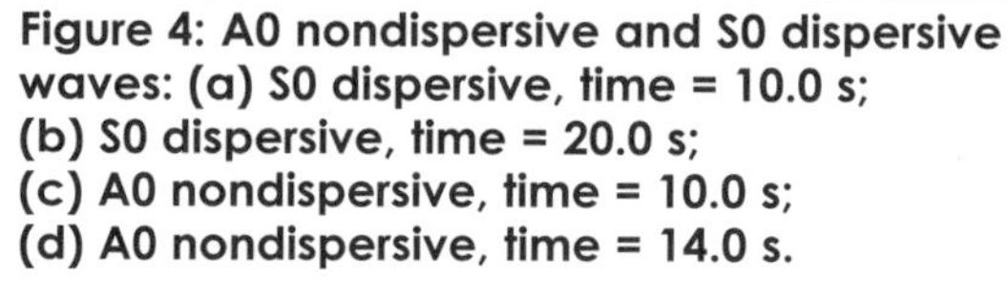

Figure 4: A0 nondispersive and S0 dispersive waves: (a) S0 dispersive, time = 10.0 s; (b) S0 dispersive, time = 20.0 s; (c) A0 nondispersive, time = 10.0 s; (d) A0 nondispersive, time = 14.0 s.

Figure 5 shows the phase velocity dispersion curves and group velocity dispersion curves for a particular traction-free aluminum plate. The particular limits in the diagram as plate velocity, surface-wave velocity, transverse-wave velocity, and cutoff frequencies are all shown.

Phase and Group Velocity

The set of curves of possible guided wave modes plotted together is called a *dispersion curve plot*. Dispersion curves for a given material can be plotted to show the relationship of velocity to frequency and test-object thickness. Here, velocity can be either phase velocity or group velocity:

- **Phase velocity** – the speed at which a specific point or phase on the wave propagates through a test object.
- **Group velocity** – the velocity measured from the propagation of the entire wave package.

For bulk waves in isotropic media, "velocity" is the term commonly used, and there is no difference between phase velocity and group velocity. In more complicated systems, phase velocity and group velocity are different. The difference between phase velocity and group velocity is extremely important for the understanding of guided waves.

Derivable from the phase velocity dispersion curves are sets of group velocity dispersion curves. The values of the group velocity dispersion curves depend on the ordinate and slope values of the phase velocity dispersion curves. As mentioned, the group velocity is defined as the

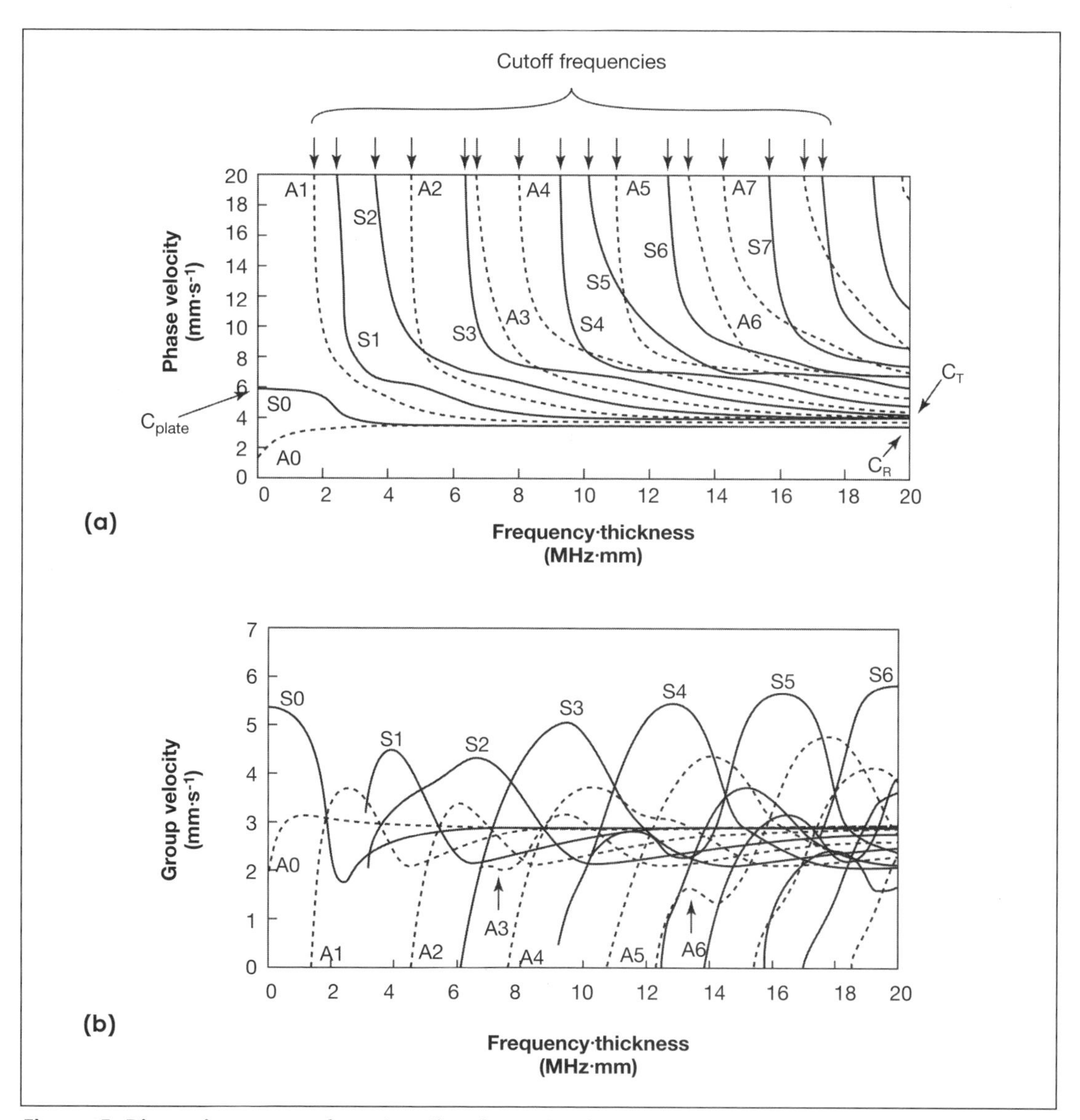

Figure 5: Dispersion curves for a traction-free aluminum plate: (a) phase velocity dispersion curves; (b) group velocity dispersion curves.

velocity measured in a waveguide of a packet of waves of similar frequency. This group velocity is what is actually measured in an experiment.

The waves formed by throwing a stone into water can help explain the difference between phase and group velocity. The velocity of a particular wave in the packet of waves that are propagating is the phase velocity and the group velocity is the packet velocity. Dispersion curves can be generated for all types of structures including plates, rods, tubes, multilayer structures, rails, or any waveguide, whether isotropic or anisotropic.

All guided wave problems have associated with them the development of appropriate dispersion curves and corresponding wave structures. Of thousands of points on a dispersion curve, only certain ones lead to a valid test — for example, those with:

- greatest penetration power;
- maximum displacement on the outer, center, or inner surface;
- only in-plane vibration on the surface to avoid leakage into a fluid; or
- minimum power at an interface between a pipe and a coating.

Guided Wave Transducers

Since there are many different types of guided waves and their frequencies range from kilohertz to megahertz, the corresponding instruments and sensors also vary from application to application. The following are a few of the transducers used to generate and receive guided waves:

- Conventional straight-beam ultrasonic.
- Conventional angle-beam ultrasonic.
- Mechanically clamped-on piezoelectric.
- Air-coupled piezoelectric.
- Adhesively bonded piezoelectric.
- Adhesively bonded or mechanically clamped-on magnetostrictive.
- Laser ultrasound.
- Electromagnetic acoustic transducers (EMATs).

Electromagnetic Acoustic Transducers

An electromagnetic acoustic transducer (EMAT) is a device for the excitation and detection of ultrasonic waves in conductive or magnetic materials. No physical contact is required with the test object because the coupling occurs through electromagnetic forces. The working distances are typically less than a millimeter, and the probe often is allowed to rest on the surface of the test object. This ability to provide reproducible signals with no couplant is often more important than noncontact operation.

Advantages of EMATs

The major motivation for using EMATs is their ability to operate without couplant or contact. Important consequences of this include operation on moving objects, in remote or hazardous locations, at elevated temperatures, in a vacuum, and on oily or rough surfaces. Moreover, alignment problems may be reduced because the direction in which the wave is launched is primarily determined by the orientation of the test-object surface rather than the probe. Finally, EMATs have the ability to conveniently excite horizontally polarized transverse waves or other special wave types that provide test advantages in certain applications.

Limitations of EMATs

The downside of EMATs is a relatively low operating efficiency. However, this inefficiency may be overcome by high transmitter currents, low noise receivers, and careful electrical matching. In ferromagnetic materials, the magnetization or magnetostrictive mechanisms of coupling can often be used to enhance signal levels.

EMAT Probe Configurations

As shown in Figure 6, an EMAT is essentially a coil of wire excited by an alternating current and placed in a magnetic field near the surface of an electrically conductive or ferromagnetic material. Practical electromagnetic probes consist of much more than a single wire, however. It is usually necessary to wind a coil and design a bias magnet structure so that the distribution of forces couples to a particular wave type.

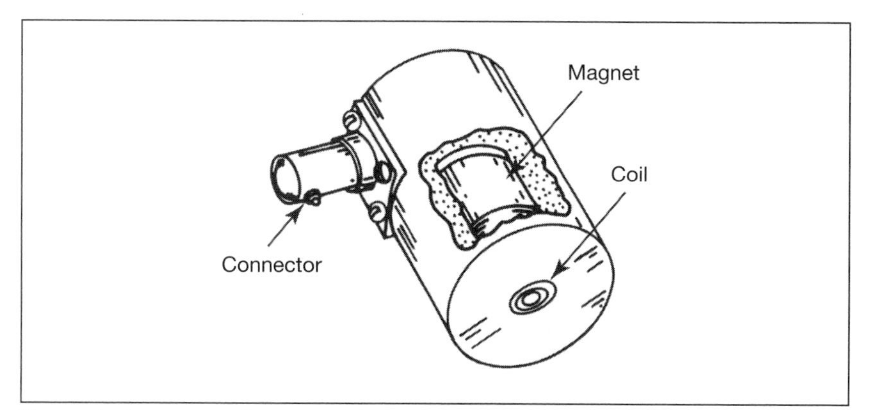

Figure 6: Permanent magnet transverse-wave EMAT.

Physical Mechanisms of EMATs

EMAT testing uses two mechanisms to generate sound waves through the interaction of magnetic fields:

- **Lorentz force** – When the material is conductive, the alternating current (AC) in the spiral electric coil of the EMAT generates eddy currents on the surface of the material, as shown in Figure 7. The distribution of eddy currents is only at a very thin layer of the material, called *skin depth*, and is influenced by the *lorentz force* — the force exerted by a magnetic field on a moving electric charge. The lorentz force, in turn, is controlled by the design of the magnet and electric coil, the properties of the test material, the relative position

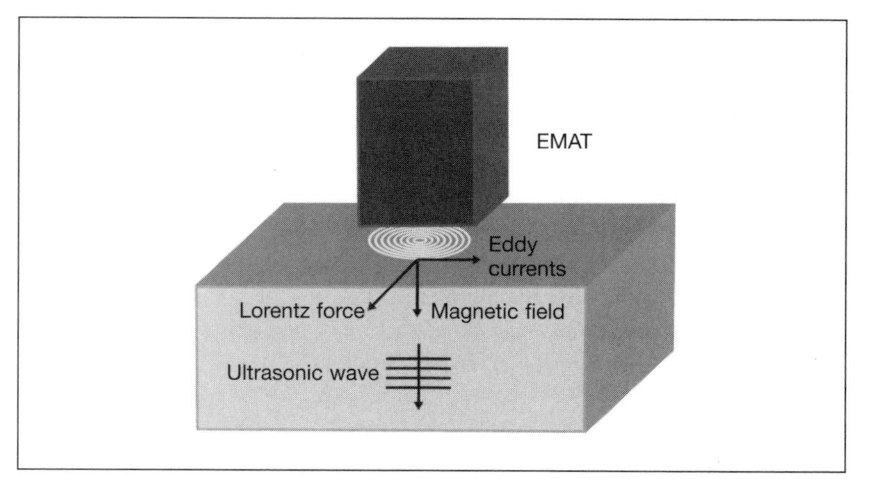

Figure 7: Principle of wave excitation using an EMAT.

between the transducer and the test part, and the excitation signal of the transducer. The forces on the test object alternate at the frequency of the driving current and act as a source of ultrasonic waves.

- **Magnetostriction** – This occurs when ferromagnetic material undergoes a dimensional change when an external magnetic field is applied. The AC in the electric coil induces an AC magnetic field that produces magnetostriction at ultrasonic frequencies in the material. This disturbance then propagates in the material as an ultrasonic wave, as shown in Figure 8.

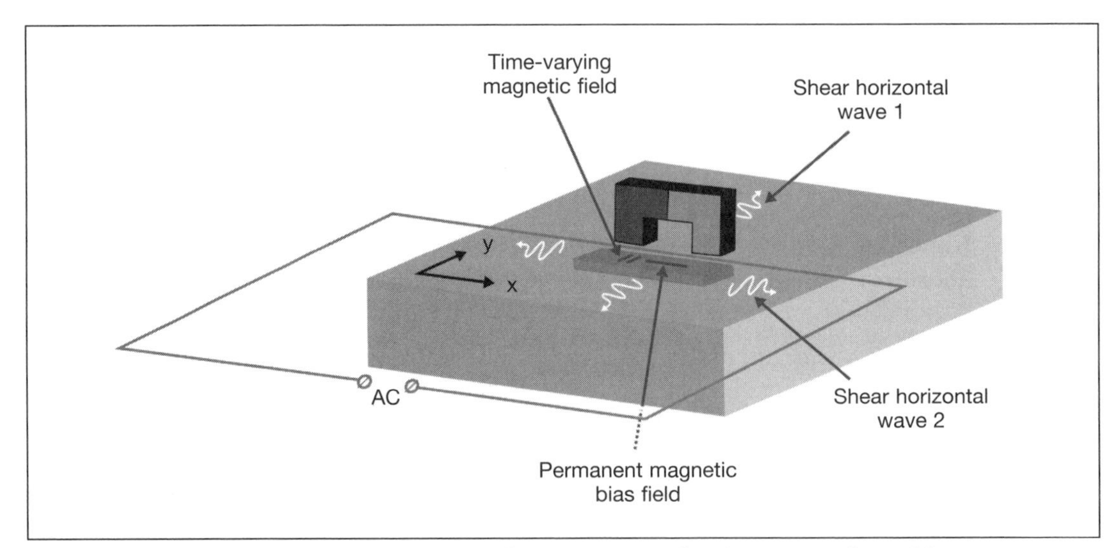

Figure 8: Configuration of a magnetostrictive EMAT used for the generation of transverse vibrations in a plate.

Sensor Arrays

Special guided wave instruments and transducers have also been developed for pipeline inspection. Instead of using the conventional concept of scanning, these transducers are operated by mechanically clamping or bonding a ring of sensor arrays around the pipe. At a single transducer location, the inspection range can be from a few meters up to a few hundred meters depending on the surrounding material of the pipeline. The sensor rings can be made of piezoelectric transducers or magnetostrictive transducers, as shown in Figure 9.

A piezoelectric transducer ring is made of individual piezoelectric elements, varying in number from 4 to 64 or more based on the particular design. The elements may be connected together so that all of the elements are active at the same time. The elements may also be divided into groups with each group controlled independently and working as a phased array. The magnetostrictive sensor can be a single ring or a group of segments (perhaps 8) that cover the entire circumference.

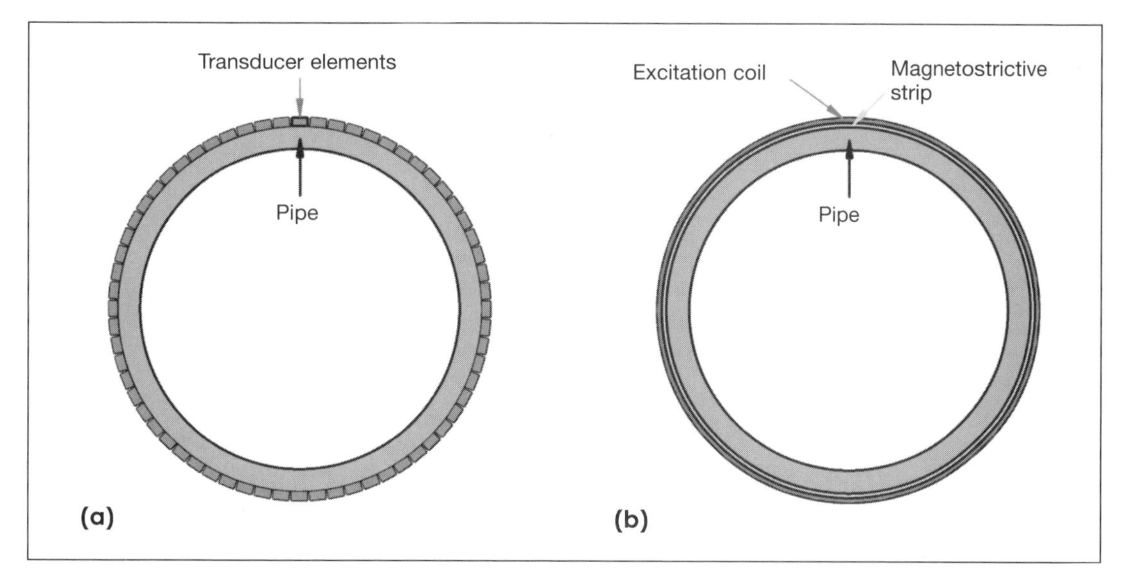

Figure 9: Schematics of guided wave pipe inspection sensors: (a) piezoelectric sensor array; (b) magnetostrictive sensor.

Applications of Guided Wave

Pipeline Inspection

Guided wave inspection of pipelines is useful because a large area can be tested from a single transducer position. Some of the initial work done in this area was for steam generator tube testing. It was discovered that these waves could go far and still be able to evaluate discontinuities at a long distance from the transducer position. Beam focusing is possible, although a different computation technique to achieve focusing is necessary than that required in phased array for bulk-wave focusing.

A sample configuration of pipeline testing with a wrap-around guided wave sensor is illustrated in Figure 10. There are a number of arrangements for this application via straight-beam sensors, angle-beam sensors, electromagnetic acoustic transducers, magnetostrictive sensors,

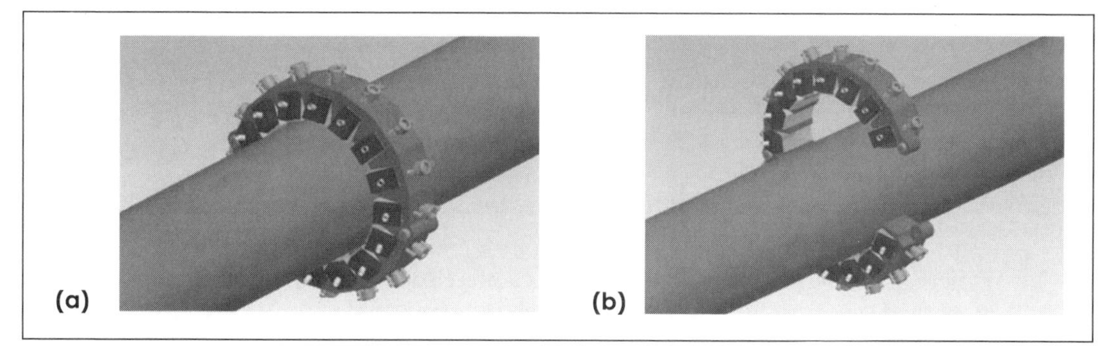

Figure 10: Representative wrap-around ultrasonic guided wave array for long-range ultrasonic guided wave inspection of piping: (a) attached; (b) detached.

and others at frequencies ranging from 20 to 800 kHz, depending on the distance of propagation and the discontinuities sought. Typically, low-frequency test systems find discontinuities that have a 5% cross-sectional area or more. Higher frequencies can go down to 1% cross-sectional area or less.

Aircraft Inspection

Aircraft skins are well suited to guided wave testing. Note in Figure 11 a possibility of guided wave testing. In Figure 11(a), if ultrasonic energy can be passed from a transmitter to a receiver across a lap splice joint, the integrity of the bond can be evaluated. However, the wave structure must be adjusted with reference to a phase velocity dispersion curve to have sufficient energy at the interface to allow propagation into the second medium.

Once the technique is developed, tools can be used as illustrated in Figure 11(b). In this figure, the double spring-hopping probe can be placed on a material quite easily and, at the appropriate mode and frequency, can evaluate the integrity of the lap splice joint.

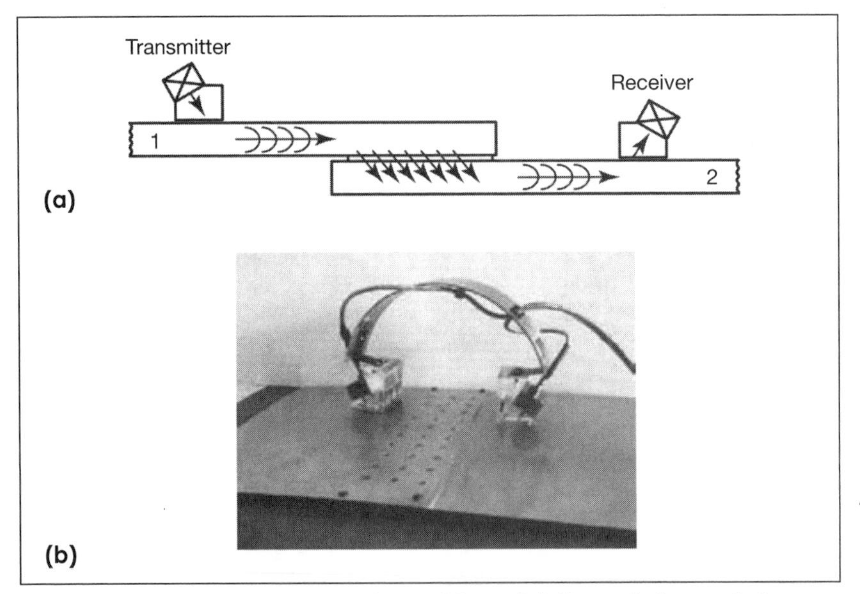

Figure 11: Lap splice test sample problem: (a) through-transmission; (b) double-spring hopping probe.

Closing

Because of tremendous advances in the understanding of guided wave propagation and the computational ability by mathematical and finite element analysis, guided wave testing is a practical test option. The method can be used to solve many problems using guided wave analysis in nondestructive testing and structural health monitoring.

›13

Evaluation Standards

The Role of Standards in Industry

Standardized ways for making and assembling mass-produced products came into prominence at the start of the Industrial Revolution. With the transition from handmade tools to objects featuring interchangeable parts, the stage was set for creating standardized approaches to most industrial activities. Safety concerns also motivated the development of standards, especially after 1900 when catastrophic explosions were common with boilers used in riverboats and public building heating units. Standardization in the United States continued to gain support with the federal government's control of large construction and manufacturing contracts.

ASTM Standards

In 1898, the American Society for Testing and Materials (ASTM International) created a set of standards that addressed the safe construction and use of industrially significant materials including most metals in various grades, ceramics, chemicals, concrete, graphite, paint, textiles, tires, and wood. The practices used in nondestructive testing are covered in Volume 03.03, devoted to test methods and analytical procedures. References to these practices can be found throughout the entire set of 72 ASTM volumes.

ASME Code

In response to the failures of boilers and pressure vessels, the American Society of Mechanical Engineers (ASME) created the first *ASME Boiler and Pressure Vessel Code* in 1911. As the importance of material quality and integrity of welded joints became evident, the use of nondestructive testing became increasingly prominent in the requirements of the ASME code. Use of the code for construction and testing of nuclear power generation facilities relies heavily on the application of nondestructive testing to detect and evaluate the size of discontinuities.

API Standards

The American Petroleum Institute (API) was founded in 1919 to standardize engineering specifications for drilling and production equipment. Today, API standards set the criteria for conducting nondestructive testing of piping and storage facilities as well as long-distance transmission lines.

AWS Codes

The first edition of the *Code for Fusion Welding and Gas Cutting in Building Construction* was published by the American Welding Society (AWS) in 1928. The first bridge welding specification was published separately in 1936. These basic documents have evolved into AWS D1.1, *Structural Welding Code Steel,* and AASHTO/AWS D1.5, *Bridge Welding Code*, created to address the specific requirements of state and federal transportation departments.

Use of Standards and Codes

Such codes and standards are written with a rigorous consensus process using technically competent individuals representing all concerned parties. Codes and standards are regularly upgraded to reflect the evolution of technology and the changing needs of user communities. Standards become legally binding when referenced in government regulations or cited in a contract. Purchasers and sellers incorporate standards into contracts; scientists and engineers use them in laboratories; architects and designers use them in plans; government agencies reference them in codes, regulations, and laws; and many other organizations and companies refer to standards for guidance.

Typical Approaches

Ultrasonic tests in a critical or well-regulated industry are often covered by multiple documents. For example, the nuclear power generation industry uses procedures written in accordance with the *ASME Boiler and Pressure Vessel Code*. This code, in turn, is supported by published ASTM standards. Sometimes these are augmented by company, customer, or Nuclear Regulatory Commission (NRC) guidelines. To meet the intent of these documents, as well as their stated requirements, testing personnel must assure an employer that ultrasonic testing activities, documented in straightforward procedures, are in compliance with the entire spectrum of applicable codes and standards.

Requirements are stated in codes and standards in ways that differ from document to document. ASTM standards tend to emphasize the way tests are conducted but leave the issue of acceptance criteria to be decided by the buyer and the service organization. In this way, the actual testing procedures are determined by senior technical personnel, who must agree on an appropriate set of acceptance criteria and related operational issues.

Section V, *Nondestructive Examination*, of the ASME code sets the ground rules for performing nondestructive testing. However, the extent of coverage, acceptance criteria, and interpretation schemas are indicated in other sections, such as those devoted to new construction of power boilers (Section I), pressure vessels (Section VIII), and nuclear components (Section III), as well as inservice tests of nuclear components (Section XI). Details for testing specific materials are often referred to as *ASTM standards*. To address ultrasonic testing requirements, all applicable sections of the ASME code, including supplemental code cases that clarify specific issues, must be considered.

Safety Issues

The issue of safety is so important that most states and provinces within the United States and Canada have written boiler and pressure vessel laws that incorporate ASME codes through direct reference. In these cases, adherence to ASME code is not just a matter of an agreement between buyers and sellers but is enforced by the chief technician of the state or province. This legal connection has made ASME code one of the most powerful agents for incorporating nondestructive testing practices into the construction of electric power and processing plants.

Acceptance Criteria

In the cases of industry standards such as API and ASTM, some latitude is given to the user for establishing acceptance criteria. The basis for final acceptance is usually reflected in the procurement documents, but the specific criteria can be altered, provided agreement is reached between the technical representatives of the buyer and the seller. The *AWS Structural Welding Code* also contains such a provision. However, the AWS code is different from the others in that its cited practices are quite prescriptive, while the others tend to rely more on technician judgment.

The AWS code prescribes transducer sizes, propagation angles, and regions within the weld where each transducer is applicable. It sets the compensation for distance in accordance with prescribed near-field and beam-spread parameters. It prescribes layout markings and protocols for reporting ultrasonic indications. Furthermore, it defines the classification of indications based on a lookup table that is applicable for either static or dynamic loading.

When still in use, *military standards* and *maintenance technical orders* are characterized by their structured approaches based on specific test object configurations and material types. In these cases, the approach to testing is keyed to the particular region in a tested system, with acceptance decisions based on accept/reject criteria.

Standards and codes may call for interpretation and their levels of detail may vary considerably. In many organizations, implementation issues are resolved by a team of knowledgeable technical managers who make up what is sometimes called a *materials review board.* It is the task of this board to decide how specific test-object conditions are to be processed in compliance with the spirit and directives of an applicable standard or code.

Structure of Standards

Ultrasonic standards tend to identify the approaches allowed for certain tests. They identify how transducers are selected; how scanning is done; when and how calibrations are performed; how to address special situations, such as curved test objects and transfer of calibration data; what acceptance criteria are used; and administrative issues, such as personnel certification, and report creation and retention. An ultrasonic test, as cited in some requirements, must address the following items:

1. Instrumentation (selection, operating ranges).
2. Calibration (link to test objects).
3. Search unit type, size, and frequency (wave geometry).
4. Screen settings (metal path).
5. Area to be scanned (coverage intensity).
6. Scanning technique (manual, coupling, automatic).
7. Indications to be recorded (minimum sensitivity).
8. Data record format (forms to be followed).
9. Accept/reject criteria (basis or specification reference).
10. Personnel qualifications (certifications).

The degree to which these and other items are controlled usually depends on the criticality of the application. Nuclear and aerospace criteria tend to be most demanding, while testing of raw materials is less demanding.

Sample Specifications

Outlined below are excerpts from commercial and military specifications. They are given here to provide an overview of their content. These excerpts are not complete and should not be considered as replacements for the original issue of a standard. Note that some grammatical and typographical changes have been made for this Personnel Training Publication. Contrary to ASNT publications department style, SI units have not been included, as they are not used in the original versions of the following sample outlines.

ASTM Standard

ASTM standards define nondestructive tests in an orderly and technically sound manner, often for specific test objects. The standards are intended for use in many different situations, and the details of operational practice are often left to supplemental contractual agreements between the buyer and seller of the test services. Some of the requirements serve as recommendations or as candidates for specific actions. Alternates may be agreed to by the buying and selling participants.

Following is an excerpt from ASTM A-609, *Standard Practice for Castings, Carbon, Low-Alloy, and Martensitic Stainless Steel, Ultrasonic Examination Thereof.*[1] It defines a system of reference blocks with flat-bottom holes that can be used to develop distance-amplitude corrections as well as establish a reference sensitivity for straight-beam tests of cast steel components. The standard further defines conditions under which tests are to occur (material conditions, scan rates, reporting requirements) but does not give specific information about recalibration intervals, quality levels, or personnel certification. The buyer must include these specifics as supplemental requirements.

ASTM A-609 has been adapted for this Personnel Training Publication with permission.

Excerpt from ASTM A-609

1. Scope.

1.1. This specification covers the standards and procedures for the pulse echo ultrasonic testing of heat-treated carbon and low alloy steel casting by the longitudinal-beam technique.

2. Basis of purchase.

2.1. When this specification is to be applied to an inquiry, contract or order, the purchaser shall furnish the following information.

2.1.1. Quality levels for the entire casting or portions thereof.

2.1.2. Sections of castings requiring testing.

2.1.3. Any additional requirements to the provisions of this specification.

3. Equipment.

3.1. Electronic apparatus: Pulse echo, 1 to 5 MHz, linear ±5% for 75% of screen height.

3.2. Transducers: longitudinal wave, 1 to 1-1/8 in. diameter, 1 in. square; prefer 1 MHz beyond 2 in. depth.

3.3. Reference blocks: flat-bottom holes, number 16, distance-amplitude curve: 1 to 10 in., cast materials that have a metallurgical structure similar to the castings being tested. Other blocks may be used provided they are proven to be acoustically equivalent to the cast steel. The hole bottom shall be cleaned and plugged. Each block identified. Block specifications: 32 rms, flat/parallel to within 0.001 in., hole diameter 1/4 ±0.002 in., perpendicular within 0.5 h.

4. Personnel requirements.

4.1. The seller shall be responsible for assigning qualified personnel. A qualification record shall be available on request.

5. Casting conditions.

5.1. Heat-treat before ultrasonic testing.

5.2. Surfaces shall be free of interference.

6. Test conditions.

6.1. Each pass of transducer to overlap.

6.2. Rate less than 6 in. per second.

7. Procedure.

7.1. Adjust sweep to put backwall at least halfway across the cathode-ray tube.

7.2. Mark the flat-bottom hole indication height for each of the applicable blocks on the cathode-ray tube screen. Draw line through indication marks. Set peak at three-fourth screen height. This is the amplitude reference line.

7.3. Use transfer mechanism to compensate for surface roughness differences. Use backwall reflection from block and casting in same thickness and conditions.

7.4. Attenuator-only control that can be changed during testing. Signals may be increased for visibility, but returned to base level for signal evaluation. Calibration should be rechecked periodically using transfer block as basic reflector.

7.5. Regions having parallel walls and exhibiting loss of back reflection shall be rechecked and treated as questionable until the cause is resolved using other techniques.

8. Data reporting.

8.1. Total number, location, amplitude and area of all indications equal to or greater than 100% amplitude reference line, questionable areas, testing parameters and sketch showing untested areas and location and sizes of reportable indications.

9. Acceptance standards.

9.1. Criteria for individual castings should be based on a realistic appraisal of service requirements and the quality that can normally be obtained in production of the particular type of casting.

9.2. Acceptance quality levels shall be established between purchaser and manufacturer.

9.3. Other means may be used to establish the validity of a rejection based on ultrasonic testing.

ASME Standard

ASME has structured its nondestructive testing requirements as part of the *ASME Boiler and Pressure Vessel Code*. This comprehensive set of rules defines allowable design practices, materials, construction practices, testing approaches, and documentation. The code ensures consistent construction of new boilers, pressure vessels, and ancillary components including piping, containment, and support systems.

The ASME code is subdivided into sections devoted to specific classes of components (pressure vessels, boilers, piping) and supporting technologies (welding, nondestructive testing, materials). Test objects constructed in accordance with ASME code often satisfy a multitude of requirements. What follows are brief excerpts from Section V, *Nondestructive Testing*, Article 5: *Ultrasonic Examination Methods for Materials*.[2] Examples of how the referencing section of the *ASME Boiler and Pressure Vessel Code* is used for the introduction of specific requirements are also presented. The subject of ultrasonic testing of ferritic cast materials was chosen to compare with the ASTM specification and a modified set of requirements of Sections III and V.

The important area of weld testing is included to highlight the use of special-purpose calibration blocks (not commercial calibration blocks) and to describe methods of verifying instrument linearity and accommodating test-object curvatures.

Excerpt from Article 5

This outline describes or references requirements that are to be used in selecting and developing ultrasonic testing procedures for welds, objects, components, materials, and thickness determinations. It has been adapted for this Personnel Training Publication with permission.

T-510: Scope

When testing to any part of this article is a requirement of a referencing code section, that referencing code section should be consulted for specific requirements for the following:

1. Personnel qualification and certifications.
2. Procedure requirements and techniques.
3. Testing system characteristics.
4. Retention and control of calibration blocks.
5. Acceptance standards for evaluation.
6. Extent and retention of records.
7. Report requirements.
8. Extent of testing and volume to be scanned.

T-522: Written Procedure Requirements

Ultrasonic testing shall be performed in accordance with a written procedure. Each procedure shall include at least the following information, as applicable:

1. **T-523.1: Test coverage.**
   - 1.2. 10% overlap of piezoelectric element.
   - 1.3. Rate ≤ 6 in. per second unless calibrated otherwise.
2. **T-530: Equipment and supplies.**
   - 2.1. Frequency: 1 to 5 MHz.
   - 2.2. Screen linearity: ±5% in 20 to 80% range.
   - 2.3. Control linearity: ±20% amplitude ratio.
   - 2.4. Check calibration at beginning, end, personnel change and at suspected malfunction.
3. **T-540: Applications.**
4. **T-541: Material product forms.**
   - 4.1. Plate, forgings, bars and tubular products.
5. **T-541.1: Castings.**
   - 5.1. When ultrasonic testing of ferritic castings is required by the referencing code section, all sections, regardless of thickness, shall be examined in accordance with SA-609; supplemented by T-510, T-520, as well as T-541.4.1, T-541.4.2 and T-541.4.3.
6. **T-541.4.1: Equipment.**
   - 6.1. Transducer shall be 1.13 in. diameter, 1 in.^{2}, 1 MHz, (others allowed if sensitivity acceptable).

7. **T-541.4.2: Calibration.**
   - 7.1. Blocks: same material specification, grade, product form, heat-treatment and thickness ±25%. Surface representative.
   - 7.2. Longitudinal wave: per SA-609.
   - 7.3. Method.
     - 7.3.1 Straight beam per SA-609.
     - 7.3.2 Angle beam 80% peak, side-drilled hole distance-amplitude curve from block.
8. **T-541.4.3: Testing.**
   - 8.1. Refer to SA-609.
   - 8.2. A supplementary angle-beam test shall be performed on castings or areas of castings where a back reflection cannot be maintained during the straight-beam testing or where the angle between the front and back surfaces of the castings exceeds 15°.
   - 8.3. The requirements for extent of testing and acceptance criteria shall be as required by the referencing code section.
9. **T-541.5: Bolting material.**
10. **T-542: Welds.**
    - 10.1. Requirements for ultrasonic testing of full-penetration welds in wrought and cast materials including detection, location and evaluation of reflectors within the weld, heat-affected zone and adjacent material. Covers ferritic products and pipe. Austenitic and high-nickel alloy welds covered in T-542.8.5.
11. **T-542.2: Calibration.**
    - 11.1. Basic calibration block.
    - 11.2. Material: same product form and material specification or equivalent P number grouping. P numbers 1, 3, 4 and 5 are considered equivalent for ultrasonic testing. Test with straight beam.
    - 11.3. Clad: same welding procedure as the production part. Surface representative.
    - 11.4. Heat-treatment: at least minimum tempering treatment of material specification for the type and grade and postweld heat-treatment of at least 2 h.
    - 11.5. Curvature: >20 in. diameter considered flat to <20 in. diameter.
    - 11.6. System calibration.
      - 11.6.1. Angle beam (refer to Article 4, Appendix B).
      - 11.6.2. Sweep range: 10% or 5% full sweep.
      - 11.6.3. Distance-amplitude correction: 20% per 2 dB. Echo from surface notch.

11.6.4. Straight beam (refer to Article 4, Appendix C).

11.6.5. Sweep range: 10% or 5% full sweep.

11.6.6. Distance-amplitude correction: 20% per 2 dB.

11.7. Frequency.

11.7.1. Change of system component before the end of the test (series), every 4 h and at personnel change.

12. T-542.6: Welds in cast ferritic products.

12.1. Nominal frequency is 2.25 MHz, unless material requires the use of other frequencies. Angle selected as appropriate for configuration.

12.2. Distance-amplitude curve is not required in first one-half V-path in material less than 1 in. thick.

13. T-542.7: Testing of welds.

13.1. Base metal should be free of surface irregularities.

13.2. Scan with longitudinal wave for laminations at two times sensitivity.

13.3. Manipulate and rotate longitudinal reflectors perpendicular to weld axis at two times sensitivity over reference level.

13.4. Manipulate transverse reflectors along weld at two times from both directions.

14. T-542.7.2.5: Evaluation.

14.1. An indication in excess of 20% distance-amplitude curve shall be investigated to the extent that it can be evaluated in terms of the acceptance standards of the referencing code section.

15. T-542.8.5: Austenitic and high-nickel alloy welds.

15.1. Ultrasonic testing is more difficult than in ferritic materials because of variations in acoustic properties of austenitic and high-nickel alloy welds, even those in alloys of the same composition, product form and heat-treatment. It may, therefore, be necessary to modify and/or supplement the provisions of this article in accordance with T-110(c) when examining such welds.

16. T-580: Evaluation.

16.1. With distance-amplitude curves, any reflector that causes an indication in excess of 20% of the distance-amplitude curve should be investigated to criteria of referencing code.

17. T-580: Reports and records.

17.1. A report shall be made indicating welds tested, locations of records of calibrations (instrument, system, calibration block identification) shall also be included.

Military Standard

Military standards tend to use highly specific instructions for their requirements, including the design and use of calibration blocks, methods of system performance analysis, and other operating instructions. Below are adapted excerpts from MIL-STD-2154, which standardizes the process for using ultrasonic testing on wrought metals and products greater than 0.25 in. (0.64 cm) thick.

This military standard is applicable to the testing of forgings, rolled billets, or plate, extruded or rolled bars, extruded or rolled shapes, and test objects made from them. It does not address nonmetals, welds, castings, or sandwich structures. It addresses both immersion (Type I) and contact (Type II) methods for testing wrought aluminum (7075-T6, 2024), magnesium (ZK60A), titanium (Ti-6Al-4V annealed) and low-alloy steel products (4130, 4330, 4340), using five acceptance classes. Note that MIL-STD-2154 has been superseded by SAE-AMS-STD-2154.

Excerpt from MIL-STD-2154

1. **Scope:** detection of discontinuities in wrought metals having cross-section thickness equal to 0.25 in. or greater.
2. **Requirements.**
   - 2.1. Orders shall specify type of testing and quality class in drawings including identification of directions of maximum stresses.
   - 2.2. Personnel shall be Level II or Level III.
   - 2.3. Detailed procedure to be prepared for each test object and type of test. It shall cover all of the specific information required to set up and perform the test.
3. **Detail requirements.**
   - 3.1. Couplants.
     - 3.1.1. Immersion (Type I), free of visible air bubbles, use preapproved additives, such as inhibitors or wetting agents.
     - 3.1.2. Contact (Type II), viscosity and surface wetting sufficient to maintain good energy transmission.
4. **Standard reference block materials:** listed alloys or from the same alloy as the test object, free from spurious indications. To be tested to class AA using immersion, longitudinal wave.
5. **Equipment.**
   - 5.1. Frequency: 2.25 to 10 MHz, refer to ASTM E-317.
   - 5.2. Gain: ±5% full screen height over full range.
   - 5.3. Alarm: front-surface synchronization.

5.4. Transducers.

5.4.1. Longitudinal wave, 0.38 to 0.75 in. diameter.

5.4.2. Shear wave, 0.25 to 1 in. diameter or length.

5.5. Manipulators.

5.5.1. Angular adjustment: ±1°.

5.5.2. Linear accuracy: ±0.1 in.

6. Reference standards.

6.1. Flat surface: Number 2, 3, 5, 8 flat-bottom hole per ASTM E-127.

6.2. Curved surface: R <4 in., special block.

6.3. Angle beam: IIW, for transducer exit/angle side-drilled hole block, rectangular-beam hollow-cylinder block, pipes.

6.4. Verification: drawings/radiographs, comparison amplitude plots, linearity plots, surface finish, material certifications.

7. Testing procedures.

7.1. Scan parallel to grain flow up to speeds that found reflectors in base materials and at reference amplitude, angulate to maximize, check high-stress regions.

7.2. Near-surface resolution limit for 2:1 signal-to-noise ratio: 0.13 in. for 1 in. range through 0.5 in. for 15 in. range. If failure experienced, test from both sides.

8. Immersion.

8.1. Water path: ±0.25 in. of standardization, maximize water-to-metal interface signal, develop distance-amplitude curve if needed, angle transducer 23° ±4° to get shear wave from 45° to 70° in aluminum, steel and titanium. Set primary reference response at 80% full screen height. Set scan index between 50 and 80% of the half-amplitude response distance from reference standard.

8.2. Establish for each transducer used. Establish transfer factor using four points from different locations based on back-surface reflections or notches, but only if the response is more or less than the comparable signal from the reference standard, allowable range between 60 and 160% or ±4 dB.

Acceptance Criteria

Discontinuities are evaluated with gain set for 80% full screen height (FSH) on a reference block with a hole diameter equal to the smallest acceptable for the applicable class and with a metal travel distance equal to the reflector depth within ±10%.

For longitudinal-wave tests, loss of back reflection exceeding 50% shall be cause for rejection unless caused by nonparallelism or surface roughness. Linear discontinuity length is measured using the 50% drop method.

Figure 1 illustrates the evaluation technique. MIL-STD 2154, paragraph 5.4.16.2, provides the directions for application of this procedure. It reads:

> **Linear discontinuities:** Estimate the length of linear discontinuities having a signal amplitude, corrected by the transfer technique, which are greater than 30% of the primary reference response or 50% of the distance-amplitude curve. Position the transducer over the extremity of the discontinuity where signal amplitude is reduced to 50% of the primary reference response or distance-amplitude curve. Move the transducer toward the opposite extremity of the discontinuity until the signal amplitude is again reduced to 50%. The distance between these two positions indicates stringer length. Reject any material or test object with linear discontinuities longer than the maximum allowed in the applicable class.

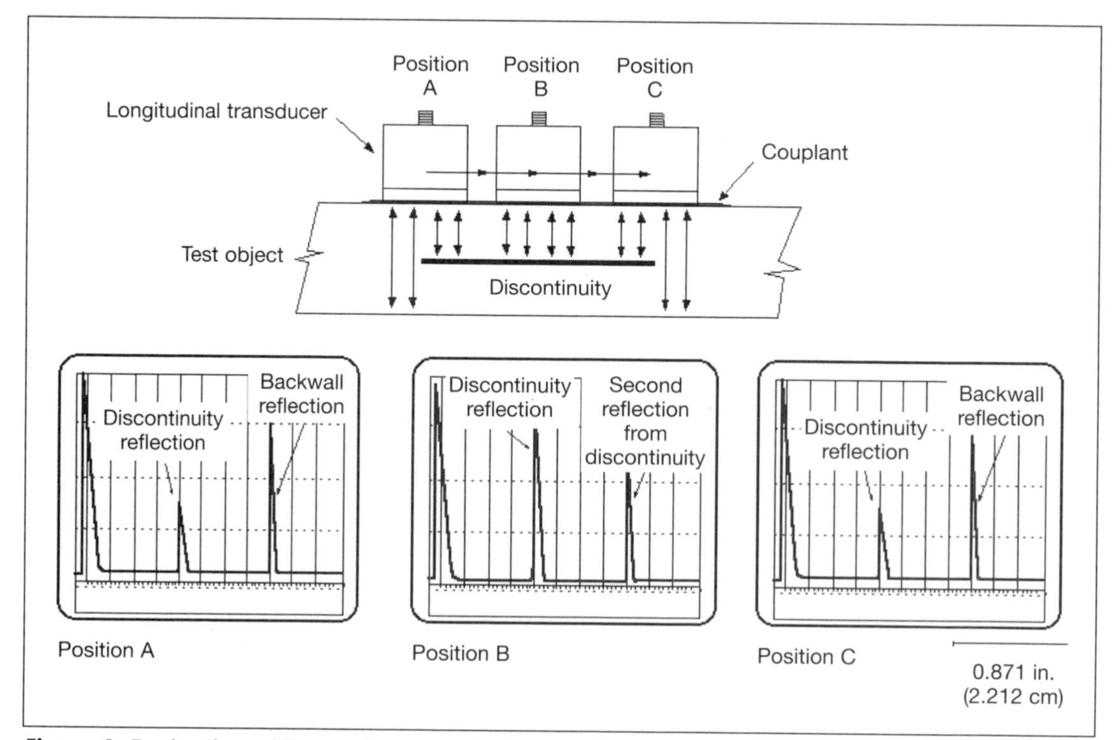

Figure 1: Evaluation of linear discontinuity for length.

Quality Assurance Provisions

Regarding quality assurance, the standard reads:

> System performance to be checked before testing, at 2 h intervals during continuous testing, at instrument setting changes or modules and after testing. Distance-amplitude curve setups are to be checked daily for the thickness range of material being tested.
>
> Data records shall be kept on file in accordance with the contract. Location and general shape (size) of rejectable indications are to be recorded. Indications in excess of acceptance criteria are permitted if they will be subsequently removed by machining. A C-scan will be made showing the location and size (by discontinuity grade) with respect to the material being scanned.

Construction Standards

Nondestructive testing requirements are often included in the detailed requirements for construction of welded structures that are stressed under static loads (buildings), cyclical loads (bridges), or tubular structures (drilling platforms). Different acceptance criteria are used, based on the purpose of the structure and the types of service to which it is exposed. The base metals are mostly the carbon and low-alloy steels commonly found in steel structures.

The criteria listed below are typical for static loading structures. Included are the criteria for rejection, based on different discontinuity classes. Severity is determined by the degree to which the discontinuity indication exceeds a reference level, as modified by sound-path attenuation, weld thickness, and search-unit angle. The classes and reject criteria range from large sizes that are all rejectable to minor discontinuities that are all acceptable.

The presence of more than one class in close proximity is addressed in special notes, as is the treatment of primary tensile stress welds and electroslag welds.

The following sections are representative of a building test code:

1. **Personnel qualification**: personnel performing nondestructive testing, other than visual testing, shall be qualified in accordance with the current edition of the American Society for Nondestructive Testing *Recommended Practice No. SNT-TC-1A*. Only individuals qualified for Level I and working under the Level II or Level III technician or individuals qualified for Level II or Level III may perform nondestructive testing.

2. **Extent of testing**: information furnished to the bidders shall clearly identify the extent of nondestructive testing (types, categories, or location) of welds to be tested.

Additional Considerations for Evaluation Standards

Application of Results of Other NDT Methods

When comparing ultrasonic data to that derived from other NDT methods, a working knowledge of the limitations of each method will aid in using those methods to either confirm or exclude indications. For example, UT results can indicate lack of fusion in a weld that may not be evident in a radiograph. In this particular case, understanding that a radiograph finds discontinuities based upon loss of material, which can be minimal in lack of fusion, radiography cannot be used to exclude the possibility of lack of fusion from the weld. For this reason, the technician must be careful not to exclude discontinuities simply because the item under inspection was accepted when tested by another NDT method unless specifically allowed in the evaluation standard.

Types and Locations of Discontinuities

Codes and standards require characterization of the type of discontinuities as well as their respective location, length, width, and depth. Some standards may even require reporting of acceptable discontinuities above a given threshold. Even if the item being inspected is rejected, this information can provide useful information when trying to prevent a failure from recurring. The ability to map discontinuities in multiple planes provides much added value to using ultrasonic testing as an inspection method and at times can provide discrete information.

Intended Use of the Part

When no code or standard exists for an item being inspected, criteria may be determined by evaluating the intended use of the part and the minimum discontinuity size requirements that are specified in a related or similar code. From this information, an applicable inspection standard can be used or a new inspection technique setup. Additionally, appropriate inspection zones can be established to ensure coverage of critical areas most likely to fail.

Summary

Standards are important for ensuring consistent testing quality in critical industry segments. Their intent is to set a nondestructive testing approach that meets the minimum safety expectations of the user community yet maintains sufficient flexibility to be effective for many specific conditions. This level of flexibility is often achieved by letting the supplier and user compromise on specific elements of the standards that apply in a given situation.

When nondestructive testing standards are part of legal requirements for construction and manufacturing, they are often identified in, and used to support, broader-based codes. Codes mandate the features of a standard that must be followed and may even be more restrictive than the original standard. The best example of this approach is in the *ASME Boiler and Pressure Vessel Code*, where the product sections (Section VIII for pressure vessels, for example) identify required acceptance criteria, yet testing procedures are found in a separate section (Section V for nondestructive testing).

Many codes reference another set of standards (ASME adopts specific ASTM standards, for instance) or a technical society may reference someone else's code as part of its standard approach to nondestructive testing (API references Section V of the ASME code). Although this approach effectively uses the technical expertise of other organizations, the administration and development of operating procedures for a given company can become complicated. It can be time consuming to compile nondestructive testing application requirements within many of these documents for a particular design configuration. In most standards and codes, the document is set up to first fit material, design, and welding needs. Nondestructive testing applications are presented throughout the text as the primary needs are addressed.

Conclusion

The complexity and expense of today's machines and fabricated structures dictate the use of many testing methods and procedures that ensure longer life and function of these machines and structures, as well as the life and health of those who will be working on or close to them. For example, the traveling public is protected every moment of the day by intensive nondestructive testing applications applied throughout the body, wing, and engine assemblies of all aircraft. Even motor vehicles are extensively evaluated throughout their assembly by use of various methods of nondestructive testing.

The concepts and techniques that a student and trainee have encountered in this book mark the beginning of an important transition between the introduction to ultrasonic testing techniques and the future of additional instruction, hands-on training in various ultrasonic testing applications, and, most important, on-the-job experience. Important decisions are made daily based on ultrasonic tests performed by competent technicians, all of whom began their careers as ultrasonic testing students.

With the development of computer-interfaced ultrasonic applications, many facets of ultrasonic testing have been made better and easier to use. Yet human understanding and intuition are still key elements in using the test systems to generate accurate, trustworthy results.

---

[1]ASTM A-609, *Standard Practice for Castings, Carbon, Low-Alloy, and Martensitic Stainless Steel, Ultrasonic Examination Thereof.* West Conshohoken, PA: American Society for Testing and Materials International. 2000. Reprinted with permission.

[2]*ASME Boiler and Pressure Vessel Code:* Section V, *Nondestructive Examination*, Article 5: *Ultrasonic Examination Methods for Materials.* New York, NY: American Society of Mechanical Engineers. 2001. Reprinted with permission.

References

The following publications are training references for further study of ultrasonic testing and guided wave as recommended in *ANSI/ASNT CP-105: ASNT Standard Topical Outlines for Qualification of Nondestructive Testing Personnel* (2011).

Ultrasonic Testing

ASNT Level II Study Guide: Ultrasonic Testing Method. Columbus, OH: The American Society for Nondestructive Testing, Inc. Latest edition.*

ASNT Level III Study Guide: Ultrasonic Method. Columbus, OH: The American Society for Nondestructive Testing, Inc. Latest edition.*

ASNT Questions & Answers Book: Ultrasonic Testing Method. Columbus, OH: The American Society for Nondestructive Testing, Inc. Latest edition.*

Dubé, N., ed. *Introduction to Phased Array Ultrasonic Technology Applications: R/D Tech Guideline.* Waltham, MA: Olympus NDT. 2004.

Workman, G.L. and D. Kishoni, tech. eds., P.O. Moore, ed. *Nondestructive Testing Handbook,* third edition: Volume 7, *Ultrasonic Testing.* Columbus, OH: The American Society for Nondestructive Testing, Inc. 2007.*

Guided Wave Testing

Achenbach, J.D. *Wave Propagation in Elastic Solids.* New York: North Holland. 1987.

Alleyne, D.N., B. Pavlakovic, M.J.S. Lowe, and P. Cawley. "Rapid Long-Range Inspection of Chemical Plant Pipework Using Guided Waves." *Insight* 43 (2001): 93–96.

Puchot, A., C. Duffer, A. Cobb and G. Light. "Use of Magnetostrictive Sensor Technology for Testing Tank Bottom Floors." *Materials Evaluation* 68.6 (2010): 603-607.*

Rose, J.L. "Standing on the Shoulders of Giants: An Example of Guided Wave Inspection." *Materials Evaluation* 60.1 (2002): 53–59.*

Rose, J.L. *Ultrasonic Waves in Solid Media.* Cambridge, UK: Cambridge University Press. 1999.

*Available from the American Society for Nondestructive Testing, Inc., Columbus, OH.

Figure Sources

All figures derive from sources published by The American Society for Nondestructive Testing, Inc., except for the following used with permission:

Chapter 1

Figures 3 & 4 – Gilbert Torres, Jr., Apex NDT Training Services

Chapter 3

Figure 20 – Vladimir Genis, Drexel University

Chapter 5

Figure 8 – Phillip W. Trach, Laboratory Testing, Inc.

Chapter 6

Figures 21 & 22 – Vladimir Genis, Drexel University

Chapter 11

Figure 1 – Reprinted, with permission, from ASTM E-2373, *Standard Practice for Use of the Ultrasonic Time of Flight Diffraction (TOFD) Technique*, copyright ASTM International, 100 Barr Harbor Drive, West Conshohocken, PA 19428. A copy of the complete standard may be obtained from ASTM, www.astm.org.

Figures 4–8 – James B. Elder III, Savannah River National Laboratory

Chapter 12

Figure 7 – Adapted from figure submitted by Huidong Gao, Innerspec Technologies, Inc.

Figure 8 – Adapted from figure submitted by Glenn Light, Southwest Research Institute

Glossary

A-scan display: A cathode-ray tube or flat-panel liquid crystal display in which the received signal is displayed as a vertical height or pip from the horizontal sweep time trace, while the horizontal distance between any two signals represents the material distance (or time of travel) between the two conditions causing the signals.

Acoustic impedance: The factor that greatly influences the propagation of an ultrasonic wave at a boundary interface. It is the product of the material density and the longitudinal-wave velocity within the material.

Amplifier: A device to increase or amplify electrical impulses.

Amplitude, echo: The vertical height of an A-scan received signal, measured from base to peak or peak to peak.

Angle of incidence: The angle between the direction of the transmitted wave and the perpendicular to the boundary interface at the point of incidence.

Angle of reflection: The angle between the direction of the reflected wave and the perpendicular to the boundary interface at the point of incidence. The angle of reflection is equal to the angle of incidence.

Angle of refraction: The angle between the refracted rays of an ultrasonic beam and the perpendicular to the refracting surface.

Angle testing: A testing method in which transmission is at an angle to one test surface.

Angle transducer: A transducer that transmits or receives the acoustic energy at an acute angle to the surface to achieve a special effect, such as the setting up of shear or surface waves in the test object.

Attenuation: The loss in acoustic energy that occurs between any two points of travel. This loss may be caused by absorption, reflection, and so on.

Attenuator: A device for measuring attenuation, usually calibrated in decibels (dB).

B-scan display: A screen display in which the received signal is displayed as an illuminated spot. The face of the display screen represents the area of a vertical plane through the material. The display shows the location of a discontinuity as it would appear in a vertical section view through the thickness of the material.

Back reflection: The signal received from the back surface of a test object.

Background noise: Extraneous signals caused by signal sources within the ultrasonic testing system, including the test material.

Barium titanate (polycrystalline barium titanate): A ceramic transducer material composed of many individual crystals fired together and polarized by the application of a direct-current field.

Beam spread: The divergence of the sound beam as it travels through a medium.

Boundary echo: A reflection of an ultrasonic wave from an interface.

C-scan: A data presentation method yielding a plan view through the scanned surface of the test object. Through gating, only echoes arising from the interior of the test object are indicated. In the C-scan, no indication is given of the signal depth.

Collimator: A lens assembly attachment designed to reduce the ultrasonic beam spread.

Compensator: An electrical matching network to compensate for circuit impedance differences.

Compression wave: A wave in which the particle motion or vibration is in the same direction as the propagated wave. Also known as *longitudinal wave*.

Contact testing: A method of testing in which the transducer contacts the test surface, either directly or through a thin layer of couplant.

Contact transducer: A transducer that is coupled to a test surface either directly or through a thin film of couplant.

Contracted sweep: A contraction of the horizontal sweep on the viewing screen of the ultrasonic instrument. Contraction of this sweep permits viewing reflections occurring over a greater depth of material or duration of time.

Couplant: A substance used between the face of the transducer and test surface to permit or improve transmission of ultrasonic energy across this boundary or interface.

Critical angle: The incident angle of the sound beam beyond which a specific refracted mode of vibration no longer exists.

Cross-talk: An unwanted condition in which acoustic energy is coupled from the transmitting crystal to the receiving crystal without propagating along the intended path through the material.

Damping (ultrasonics): Decrease or decay of ultrasonic wave amplitude with respect to time.

Damping (transducer): Limiting the duration of vibration in the search unit by either electrical or mechanical means.

Dead zone: The distance in a material from the surface to the nearest testable depth.

Decibel (dB): The logarithmic expression of a ratio of two amplitudes or intensities of acoustic energy.

Delayed sweep: A means of delaying the start of a horizontal sweep, thereby eliminating the presentation of early response data.

Delta effect: Acoustic energy reradiated by a discontinuity.

Diffraction: The deflection of a wave front when passing the edges of an obstacle.

Diffuse reflection: Scattered, incoherent reflections caused by rough surfaces or associated interface reflection of ultrasonic waves from irregularities of the same order of magnitude or greater than the wavelength.

Discontinuity reflection: The screen display presentation of the energy returned by a discontinuity in the material.

Dispersion, sound: Scattering of an ultrasonic beam as a result of diffuse reflection from a highly irregular incident surface.

Divergence: Spreading of ultrasonic waves after leaving the search unit; a function of material velocity, plus crystal diameter and frequency.

Double-crystal method: The method of ultrasonic testing using two transducers with one acting as the transmitter and one as the receiver.

Echo: See **Boundary echo**.

Effective penetration: The maximum depth in a material at which the ultrasonic transmission is sufficient for proper detection of discontinuities.

Electrical noise: Extraneous signals caused by externally radiated electrical signals or from electrical interferences within the ultrasonic instrumentation.

Far field: The region beyond the near field in which intervals of high and low acoustic transmission intensity cease to occur. Also known as *fraunhofer zone*.

Focused transducer: A transducer with a concave face that converges the acoustic beam to a focal point or line at a definite distance from the face.

Focusing: Concentration or convergence of energy into a smaller beam.

Fraunhofer zone: See **Far field**.

Frequency: Number of complete cycles of a wave motion passing a given point in a unit time (1 s); number of times a vibration is repeated at the same point in the same direction per unit time (usually per second).

Fresnel zone: See **Near field**.

Gate: An electronic means to monitor an associated segment of time, distance, or impulse.

Ghost: False indication caused by wraparound due to high pulse repetition rate. Also referred to as *phantom*.

Grass: See **Hash**.

Hash: Numerous, small indications appearing on the display screen of the ultrasonic instrument indicative of many small inhomogeneities in the material or background noise; also referred to as *grass*.

Hertz (Hz): One cycle per second.

Horizontal linearity: A measure of the proportionality between the positions of the indications appearing on the horizontal trace and the positions of their sources.

Immersion testing: A method of testing using a liquid as an ultrasonic couplant in which the test object and the transducer face are immersed in the couplant, and the transducer is not in contact with the test object.

Impedance (acoustic): Resistance to flow of ultrasonic energy in a medium. Impedance is a product of particle velocity and material density.

Indication (ultrasonics): The signal displayed on the ultrasonic screen display.

Initial pulse: The first indication that may appear on the screen. This indication represents the emission of ultrasonic energy from the crystal face, sometimes called the *main bang*.

Interface: The physical boundary between two adjacent surfaces.

Lamb wave: A type of ultrasonic vibration capable of propagation at specific angles dependent on the product of the test frequency and the test object thickness. Also referred to as *plate wave*.

Linearity (area): A system response in which a linear relationship exists between amplitude of response and the discontinuity sizes being evaluated (necessarily limited by the size of the ultrasonic beam).

Linearity (depth): A system response where a linear relationship exists with varying depth for a constant size discontinuity.

Longitudinal wave: See **Compression wave**.

Longitudinal-wave velocity: The unit speed of propagation of a longitudinal (compressional) wave through a material.

Loss of back reflection: Absence of, or a significant reduction of, an indication from the back surface of the object being tested.

Main bang: See **Initial pulse**.

Manipulator: A device used to orient the transducer assembly. As applied to immersion techniques, it provides either angular or normal incidence as well as transducer-to-test-object distance.

Material noise: Extraneous signals caused by the structure of the test object.

Mode: The manner in which acoustic energy is propagated through a material as characterized by the particle motion of the wave.

Mode conversion: The characteristic of surfaces to change the mode of propagation of acoustic energy from one mode into another.

Multiple back reflections: Repetitive echoes from the far boundary of the material being tested.

Nanosecond (ns): One billionth (10^{-9}) of a second.

Near field: A distance immediately in front of a transducer composed of complex and changing wave front characteristics. Also known as *fresnel zone.*

Nonrelevant indication: An indication that has no direct relation to reflected pulses from relevant discontinuities in the materials being tested.

Orientation: The angular relationship of a surface, plane, discontinuity axis, and so on, to a reference plane or surface.

Penetration (ultrasonics): Propagation of ultrasonic energy through a test object. See **Effective penetration**.

Piezoelectric effect: The characteristic of certain materials to generate electrical charges when subjected to mechanical vibrations and, conversely, to generate mechanical vibrations when subjected to electrical pulses.

Pitch-catch: See **Two-crystal method**.

Plate wave: See **Lamb wave**.

Presentation: The method used to show ultrasonic wave information. This may include A-, B-, or C-scans displayed on various types of recorders or cathode-ray tube instruments.

Probe: Transducer or search unit.

Propagation: Advancement of a wave through a medium.

Pulse-echo method: A single-crystal ultrasonic test method that both generates ultrasonic pulses and receives the return echo.

Pulse length: Time duration of the pulse from the search unit.

Pulse method: An ultrasonic test method using equipment that transmits a series of pulses separated by a constant period of time; that is, energy is not sent out continuously.

Pulse rate: For the pulse method, the number of pulses transmitted in a unit of time. Also called *pulse repetition rate.*

Pulse repetition rate: See **Pulse rate**.

Radio-frequency display: The presentation of unrectified signals on a display. See also **Video presentation**.

Rarefaction: The thinning out or moving apart of the consistent particles in the propagating medium caused by the relaxation phase of an ultrasonic cycle. Opposite in its effect to compression. The sound wave is composed of alternate compressions and rarefactions of the material.

Rayleigh wave: A wave that travels on or close to the surface and readily follows the curvature of the test object. Reflections occur only at sharp changes of direction of the surface. Also referred to as *surface wave*.

Reference blocks: A block or series of blocks of material containing artificial or actual discontinuities of one or more reflecting areas at one or more distances from the test surface, which are used for reference in calibrating instruments and in defining the size and distance of discontinuities in materials.

Reflection: The characteristic of a surface to change the direction of propagating acoustic energy; the return of sound waves from surfaces.

Reflectograph: A recording or chart made of either the signals transmitted through a test object or reflected back from discontinuities within a test object, or both.

Refracted beam: A beam that has been changed both in velocity and direction as a result of its having crossed an interface between two different media and having initially been directed at an acute angle to that interface.

Refraction: The characteristic of a material to change the direction of acoustic energy as it passes through an interface into the refracting material. A change in the direction and velocity of acoustic energy after it has passed at an acute angle through an interface into the refracting material.

Refractive index: The ratio of the velocity of a wave in one medium to the velocity of the wave in a second medium is the refractive index of the second medium with respect to the first. It is a measure of the amount a wave will be refracted when it enters the second medium after leaving the first.

Repetition rate: The rate at which the individual pulses of acoustic energy are generated. Also called *pulse rate* or *pulse repetition rate*.

Resolving power (resolution): The measure of the capability of an ultrasonic system to separate in time two discontinuities at slightly different distances or to separate the multiple reflections from the back surface of flat plates.

Saturation (scope): A test indication of such a size as to reach full scope amplitude (100%). Beyond this point, there is no visual display to estimate the actual real height of the response signal unless the equipment is provided with a decibel readout.

Scanning (manual and automatic): The moving of the search unit or units along a test surface to obtain complete testing of a material.

Scattering: Dispersion of ultrasonic waves in a medium due to causes other than absorption. See also **Diffuse reflection** and **Dispersion, sound**.

Send-and-receive transducer: A transducer containing two crystals mounted side-by-side separated by an acoustic barrier; one generates the acoustic energy, the other receives it.

Sensitivity: The ability of a probe to detect small discontinuities. The level of amplification at which the receiving circuit in an ultrasonic instrument is set.

Shear wave: The wave in which the particles of the medium vibrate in a direction perpendicular to the direction of propagation. Also called *transverse wave*.

Signal-to-noise ratio: The ratio of amplitudes of indications from the smallest discontinuity considered significant and those caused by random factors, such as heterogeneity in grain size.

Specific acoustic impedance: A characteristic that acts to determine the amount of reflection that occurs at an interface and that represents the product of the wave velocity and the density of the medium in which the wave is propagating.

Surface wave: See **Rayleigh wave**.

Transverse wave: See **Shear wave**.

Through transmission: A test method using two transducers in which the ultrasonic vibrations are emitted by one and received by another on the opposite side of the test object. The ratio of the magnitudes of vibrations transmitted and received is used as the criterion of soundness.

Transducer (search unit): An assembly consisting of a housing, piezoelectric element, backing material, wear plate (optional), and electrical leads for converting electrical impulses into mechanical energy and vice versa.

Transmission angle: The incident angle of the transmitted ultrasonic beam. It is 0° when the ultrasonic beam is perpendicular to the test surface.

Two-crystal method: Use of two transducers for sending and receiving. May be either send-and-receive or through-transmission method. Also referred to as *pitch-catch*.

Ultrasonic absorption: A dampening of ultrasonic vibrations that occurs when the wave traverses a medium.

Ultrasonic spectrum: The frequency span of elastic waves greater than the highest audible frequency, generally regarded as being higher than 20 kHz to about 100 MHz.

Ultrasonic testing: A nondestructive method of testing materials by the use of high-frequency sound waves introduced into or through them.

Velocity: The speed at which sound waves travel through a medium.

Video presentation: A screen presentation in which radio-frequency signals have been rectified and usually filtered.

Water path: In immersion testing, the distance from the face of the search unit to the entry surface of the test object.

Wavelength: The distance in the direction of propagation of a wave for the wave to go through a complete cycle.

Index

Figures in this index are denoted by *f* and tables by *t*.

B

C

D

E

I

J

K

L

M

N

O

P

Q

R

S

T